S0-BIW-028

JAMES M. BARRIE

THOMAS PATRICK DILLON

NOLAN LEARY

BURGESS MEREDITH

SERAFÍN AND JOAQUÍN QUINTERO

THORNTON WILDER

ROBERT ARDREY

PAUL GREEN

DAN TOTHEROH

LORD DUNSANY

JACK STUART KNAPP

ROBERT FINCH AND BETTY SMITH

GEORGE KELLY

TOM POWERS

ROBERT LOUIS STEVENSON

NORMAN CORWIN

LOUIS MacNEICE

MODERN ONE-ACT PLAYS

EDITED BY

FRANCIS GRIFFITH,

Principal, Richmond Hill High School, Richmond Hill, New York

and JOSEPH MERSAND,

Head of the Department of English, Jamaica High School, New York, New York

HARCOURT, BRACE & WORLD, INC.

New York Chicago San Francisco Atlanta Dallas

PRINTED IN THE UNITED STATES OF AMERICA

Contents

An Open Letter from the Editors

Dear Readers:

We're writing this letter to answer some of the questions that may occur to you as you begin this book. Our answers are going to be short because we know you don't like long-winded discussions. Neither do we.

Who selected these plays?

You did.

Every play was chosen with you in mind. We read about two thousand plays before deciding on the sixteen which follow, and in the course of our reading we took into consideration your likes and dislikes, your ages, and your backgrounds. We ruled out any play that wasn't good entertainment. We included only plays that were exciting, funny, unusual, or had a special appeal for young people. We've been working with high-school girls and boys for many years and have a good idea of what you like.

What's a one-act play?

That's a very good question – which is another way of saying that it's a hard question to answer.

A one-act play is a short play which can be read in one sitting; or to put it in another way, it is a short play which can be seen together with several other short plays during an evening in the theater. Sometimes a one-act play serves as a curtain raiser to a full-length play.

There is nothing mysterious about the word "act." Long plays are usually divided into acts so that the audience can catch a breath once or twice during the performance. In some cases a play is interrupted so that the scenery can be shifted, or so that a lapse of time in the action can be indicated. A one-act play usually has continuous action; hence it has only one act.

Perhaps we can best explain what a one-act play is by making a comparison. A one-act play has the same relationship to a full-length play that a short story has to a novel. Have you ever read "The Gold Bug" or *Treasure Island?* Both are tales of a search for buried treasure, but the former is called a short story and the latter a novel. "The Gold Bug" tells the story of a man who discovers a pirate treasure by solving the code of a map showing where it is buried. The story begins when the man thinks he is on the track of the discovery and ends after he has found the treasure. The story has only one main character and one main incident. A one-act play, like "The Gold Bug" or almost any other short story, is brief and uncomplicated.

On the other hand, *Treasure Island* has many characters, incidents, and high points or climaxes. It really tells several stories at one time, the stories of Jim Hawkins, Long John Silver, Blind Pew, Dr. Livesey, and many others. A full-length play, like *Treasure Island* or almost any other novel, is long and complex.

We've told you that a one-act play is a short play, but now let us say that brevity is not the only requirement. A one-act play, like a short story, attempts to show a single episode or to present a single problem in the lives of a few characters. The author tries to make a single vivid impression on his audience. He can't drag out an episode, or take time to explain some things in detail. If he does, he may weaken the effect on the reader or spectator. This is essentially why the one-act play is short.

Before starting to write, a playwright decides upon the main impression he wants to create. This usually means that he has a purpose in mind; he has an idea he wants to put across, or a question he wants to raise, or an emotion he wants his audience to feel. He expresses his purpose or *theme* by means of characters, dialogue, and plot. The theme, then, is the basic idea underlying a play; the theme is what the play is all about.

For example, one of the plays in this book concerns a woman who doesn't want to return some money she found. Still another is about a Jew who is depressed because of the persecution his race has suffered. In each of these plays the author states a viewpoint or theme. In the first play he wants to tell you that refusing to return a lost article to its owner is stealing, and in the second play that the answer to racial prejudice is love.

A radio program or a vaudeville skit consisting of a series of jokes between a comedian and his stooge usually has no theme, no underlying purpose that makes the fun grow out of a well-developed character or out of a consistent story. That's one reason why such sketches can't be called one-act plays.

So you see that *a one-act play is a short play in one act which tells a story involving only a few characters and creates a single impression arising out of a central purpose or theme.*

What kinds of one-act plays are there?

Let's answer this question by mentioning some examples. We'll begin with a *comedy.*

A typical comedy is *The Florist Shop* by Winifred Hawkridge. Maude is a young and sentimental cashier in a florist shop. She has watched many a love affair "grow from a fifty-cent bunch of violets to a fifty-dollar shower of roses and orange blossoms." She notices that Miss Wells, a timid spinster, sends an Easter lily each year to Mr. Jackson, the man to whom she has been engaged for fifteen years. But Mr. Jackson is slow, cautious, tightfisted, and altogether an unromantic suitor. Only once during the long engagement has he ever sent his fiancée flowers – cheap carnations at that.

Maude rashly sends Miss Wells some orchids at her employer's expense, pretending they were ordered by an unknown admirer. What happens? The boss fires Maude; Miss Wells is so flattered that she's all a-dither; and Mr. Jackson is so jealous that he demands that the marriage take place immediately, a church wedding with roses and Southern smilax, all bought at the florist shop. The fifteen-year courtship is thus brought to a happy end, and Maude gets back her job.

A comedy is a play in which the central character triumphs over all obstacles. Because Maude's plan succeeded and brought her satisfaction, *A Florist Shop* is called a comedy even though it contains few laughs and absolutely no gags or quips. A comedy need not excite laughter or be full of wisecracks and jokes. The movie you saw last week was probably a comedy. Most movies are. because movie audiences apparently like happy endings in which right wins over evil and the hero accomplishes what he set out to do.

The writers of comedies sometimes delight in ridiculing human faults. For example, in a famous comedy, *The Man Who Married a Dumb Wife* by Anatole France, a judge marries a woman who is as beautiful as the finest carved statue but who is as speechless as a fish. Although he is happy with her, he feels that he would be even happier if she could talk. At his request a doctor restores his wife's power of speech. She begins to talk and talk and talk. She rarely stops talking – as every man and boy might have guessed. The poor judge is driven almost mad by her long-windedness and begs the doctor to make him deaf. The doctor does so and the judge is happy again.

The humor of *The Man Who Married a Dumb Wife* is extravagant. It is caused by an incident that would not be likely to happen in real life. *When a comedy is improbable and emphasizes some ridiculous things that happen to people instead of emphasizing their characters, it is called a farce.*

So much for comedy and farce, both of which end happily. In contrast to these there is a type of play that ends unhappily, in which misfortune or grief befalls the main character. Such a play is called a *tragedy.*

One of the best-known modern tragedies is *Riders to the Sea* by J. M. Synge. The setting is an island off the west coast of Ireland where, as the play opens, an old woman waits for news of her son Michael, who was lost at sea nine days before. Bartley, the one remaining son, insists on making a trip to the mainland even though his mother wants him to remain with her. A few minutes after he leaves she hurries after him to give him a loaf of bread he had forgotten. Soon she returns moaning, telling of a fearful vision she has seen in which both her sons appeared before her as dead. She rightly fears that this strange sight means that Bartley has been drowned and that at the same time Michael's body has been discovered upon the rocky coast. Neighbors come in bearing the body of Bartley. They tell how he had fallen from his pony and had drowned in a great surf at the bottom of a cliff. The old woman mourns her dead and laments the tragic fate of her sons.

"Riders to the Sea" *is called a tragedy because the principal character is defeated by forces greater than herself.* But a tragedy doesn't have to end in death. Public disgrace, mental torture, and loss of worldly possessions are sufficient personal disasters to give the name of tragedy to plays in which they occur.

In addition to comedy and farce, which end happily, and tragedy, which results in the defeat of the chief person of the drama, there is a fourth type of play called *melodrama,* in which emphasis is on action rather than on character. A good example of melodrama is *The Drums of Oude* by Austin Strong, for it depends on the excessive use of violent physical movement.

The Drums of Oude tells of a British garrison in India menaced by an uprising of the populace. The commander decides to blow up the storeroom containing forty tons of gunpowder rather than let it fall into the hands of the insurgents. As the raging mob swarms over the walls he lights the fuse leading to the powder. Just as the flame is about to reach it, he hears the skirl of bagpipes in the distance. A Scots regiment is on its way to rescue the defenders! He swiftly quenches the fuse by striking it with his open hand, and as the curtain falls the stage is lit by red smoke and resounds with drums, bagpipes, and British cheers.

A melodrama is a thrilling, sensational drama which ends happily and emphasizes action instead of character portrayal. Wild West movies are generally melodramas, as are most murder mysteries and detective stories.

There's another type of play you ought to know about, a type often heard on the radio. Its plot is highly imaginative, almost like a fairy tale, and the play can be comical, farcical, tragical, or melodramatic. Its setting is fanciful, its characters are not quite true to life, and its style is poetic. Such a play is called a *fantasy.*

A good example of a fantasy is *The Odyssey of Runyon Jones,* a radio play by Norman Corwin. Runyon is a boy who wants to get the soul of his dead dog Pootzy into Heaven. But Pootzy was not a good dog in his lifetime — in fact, he used to chase autos, nip tires, bite dog catchers, and occasionally stay out at night — so Pootzy went to "Curgatory" instead of Heaven. Runyon goes to see Father Time, who sends him to Mother Nature, who in turn refers him to someone else. He travels from one supernatural person to another until he reaches Curgatory, where he pleads with the Board of Directors to release Pootzy, but in vain. Just as Runyon is about to leave, one of the directors discovers that Runyon himself is dead; he was killed trying to prevent Pootzy from being run over. That changes everything. Pootzy is released in custody of his owner, and both are admitted into Heaven.

As you see from this example, a fantasy goes beyond the limits of possibility. *A fantasy is a play resembling a fairy tale, written in a poetic style, depicting improbable or sometimes supernatural circumstances, and characters who are not intended to be realistic.*

How can I get the most enjoyment out of reading one-act plays?

Before photography became a popular hobby, a certain camera company advertised its products with the slogan "Picture as you go." That's good advice for play readers. *You must picture as you go* if you want to get the most out of a play. As a reader you're a one-man audience. You must set the stage in your own imagination, visualize the characters and their actions, and hear them talk.

Reading a play requires just a little more effort on the part of the reader than reading a short story or a novel. When you read a novel the author helps you visualize a scene by telling you how each character feels and acts, and by explaining — directly or indirectly — the reasons for each action. A playwright hasn't the same advantages. Because in a play there is usually no narrator, the playwright depends on action and dialogue alone to tell his story, and he must omit explanations and descriptions.

If the dramatist indicates that the scene is "the New York test studio of a large motion-picture company," he expects you to complete the scene in your own imagination. He wants you to visualize a large room containing a table around which are gathered a few chairs. Near by are a couple of movie cameras, several floodlights, and a director's chair and megaphone. Through a large window in the rear can be seen the outlines of tall buildings. A picture of the great Saul Goldbin hangs in a prominent place on the wall. A door leads into a corridor. Details such as these are not always mentioned; your imagination must supply them, or at least elaborate on them.

What you as the reader of a play must do is to put yourself in the author's place, creating each character in your mind's eye, giving him individuality and voice, costuming him, and placing him within a dramatic situation.

In addition to picturing each scene and the appearance of each character in your own imagination, you'll get more enjoyment out of reading one-act plays if you know something about their general structure, just as you can get more pleasure out of watching a football game if you know something about T-formations, single and double wing backs, defensive tactics, and the like.

Most plays, including those mentioned below which occur in this book, follow the same general pattern. It's rewarding to look for these four parts in every plot: the *exposition, rising action, climax,* and *denouement.*

The *exposition* occurs at the beginning of a play. It tells you who's who and what's what. Just as an artist always fills in the background of a painting before he works on the foreground details, so a playwright fills in the background of his characters before he involves them in any important action. For example, during the exposition of *The Adventures of Mr. Bean* we learn that a casting director has arranged for Mr. Bean, the celebrated actor, to play opposite a new starlet during her screen test. By mistake the wrong Mr. Bean arrives, a nervous little man without any stage experience. As you read the first part of a play, that is, the exposition, notice how unobtrusively the author acquaints you with this background information, introduces the characters, and at the same time keeps the plot moving forward.

During the *rising action* a conflict arises. It may consist of a clash of ideas, as in the case of the husband and wife in *Finders Keepers,* or in a conflict of personalities, as between the reporter and the executioner in *The Other Side,* or in a struggle between an individual and public opinion, as in *The Doctor from Dunmore.* But whatever its nature, there must be a struggle if there is to be a play. After showing us the opposing forces at work, the playwright builds up suspense. How is the conflict going to be resolved?

The moment in the play when the suspense is greatest is called the *climax,* a word derived from the Greek word meaning "ladder."

For instance, in *My Client Curley* the climax is the discovery that Curley has been lost and the subsequent search for him.

Just after the climax comes the ending. In technical language the ending is called the *denouement,* a word which means "untying." Since we can't give you an example of a denouement without robbing a plot of much of its interest, you'll have to find an example for yourself as you read.

To summarize, then: Two ways of increasing your enjoyment of one-act plays are: first, to visualize the play in your own imagination, and second, to observe the design or structure of the play – the exposition, the rising action, the climax, and the denouement.

Since you must fully understand a play before you can get the most pleasure from it, in this book there are AFTER READING sections presenting questions which will enable you to test your comprehension. Some of these questions ought to excite lively discussions between you and your classmates.

For those of you who have active imaginations we have included a series of CHALLENGES, which we think you'll find stimulating, especially if you have an interest in writing effectively.

Everyone wants to be able to choose and judge plays or movies intelligently. Perhaps some of you enjoy staging and acting in school plays. For both the audience and the participants we have included a section after each play called DRAMA WORKSHOP which contains practical hints on playgoing and acting.

At the end of each play we have also included a brief list of one-act plays similar in type or theme to the one just read, and we have indicated in one or two sentences what each of the recommended plays is about. (The numbers in parentheses following each play refer to the BIBLIOGRAPHY at the back of the book.)

At the end of the book is a very brief historical survey called A NOTE ON THE DEVELOPMENT OF THE ONE-ACT PLAY. Since you are becoming acquainted with a number of one-act plays, you may be curious to know how this form of drama developed both as literature and as theater entertainment.

It's curtain time!

Sincerely,

THE EDITORS

fully balancing an office ruler on his nose. He is recently from Oxford —

If you show him in Hyde Park, lawk, how they will stare,
Tho' a very smart figure in Bloomsbury Square.

Perhaps JUNIOR *is a smarter figure in the office (among the clerks) than he was at Oxford, but this is one of the few things about him that his shrewd father does not know.*

There moves to them by the only door into the room a middle-aged clerk called SURTEES, *who is perhaps worth looking at, though his manner is that of one who has long ceased to think of himself as of any importance to either God or man. Look at him again, however (which few would do), and you may guess that he has lately had a shock — touched a living wire — and is a little dazed by it. He brings a card to* MR. DEVIZES, SENIOR, *who looks at it and shakes his head.*

MR. DEVIZES. "Mr. Philip Ross." Don't know him.

SURTEES (*who has an expressionless voice*). He says he wrote you two days ago, sir, explaining his business.

MR. DEVIZES. I have had no letter from a Philip Ross.

ROBERT. Nor I.

[*He is more interested in his feat with the ruler than in a possible client, but* SURTEES *looks at him oddly.*]

MR. DEVIZES. Surtees looks as if he thought you had.

[ROBERT *obliges by reflecting in the light of* SURTEES's *countenance.*]

ROBERT. Ah, you think it may have been that one, Surty?

MR. DEVIZES (*sharply*). What one?

ROBERT. It was the day before yesterday. You were out, Father, and Surtees brought me in some letters. His mouth was wide open. (*Thoughtfully.*) I suppose that was why I did it.

MR. DEVIZES. What did you do?

ROBERT. I must have suddenly recalled a game we used to play at Oxford. You try to fling cards one by one into a hat. It requires great skill. So I cast one of the letters at Surtees's open mouth, and it missed him and went into the fire. It may have been Philip Ross's letter.

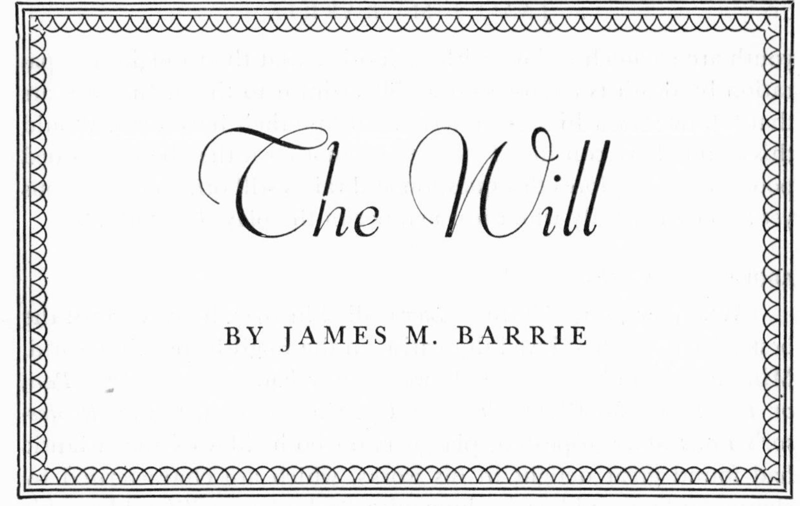

ABOUT THE PLAY

The Will displays many of the characteristics for which Barrie's plays are well known. The play's emphasis on preserving romance between man and wife, its scoffing at pompous greed, and its essential wholesomeness are all typical Barrie qualities. The characters in *The Will* are easy to grasp and the play as a whole shows a commendable compression. One critic has said that there is enough in it to make a full-length play.

Romance fades quickly: this is a theme that has occupied the minds of poets, dramatists, and novelists throughout the ages. If romance does not last long between two persons, then how can marital happiness be made to last? Today's popular song hits and movies would have us believe that "love" is all that is necessary to make a marriage happy. Yet every issue of the daily newspaper reminds us that what begins as a perfect romance ends much too often in bitter unhappiness. In *The Will* Barrie presents a couple who in their

---

youth are so much in love with each other that the thought of separation by death is almost unbearably painful to them. In the years that follow they achieve prosperity, but lose their happiness. Would this couple have continued to love one another if they had remained poor? Barrie explores this question and raises still others in a serious yet also delightfully whimsical manner in the play that follows.

ABOUT THE AUTHOR

When Sir James Matthew Barrie died in 1937, he was one of the best-known and best-loved dramatists in the English-speaking world. Millions of children the whole world over had seen his *Peter Pan, or The Boy Who Wouldn't Grow Up.* Since 1892, when his *Professor's Love Story* appeared, playgoers on both sides of the Atlantic had found great delight in his works, which are characterized by charm, fantasy, and love for humanity. Such plays as *The Admirable Crichton, Quality Street,* and *What Every Woman Knows* have been revived time after time to win new admirers for the quiet little Scotsman.

Barrie wrote about a dozen one-act plays, several of which, including *The Twelve-Pound Look* and *The Old Lady Shows Her Medals,* are today recognized as classics. Barrie's plays have been successful on the screen as well as over the radio. Katherine Hepburn starred in *Quality Street,* Bing Crosby in *The Admirable Crichton,* and Helen Hayes in *What Every Woman Knows.*

Barrie's plays appeal to the emotions rather than to the intellect. He idolizes woman as mother and household manager, and children are always dear to him. Indeed, his imagination is childlike at times, which is perhaps why he appeals so strongly to children as well as to the child in every adult. Romance pervades all his writing, including his excellent novels: *The Little Minister, Sentimental Tommy, Tommy and Grizel.*

THE WILL

Characters

MR. DEVIZES, SENIOR

MR. DEVIZES, JUNIOR

SURTEES, *a clerk*

PHILIP ROSS

EMILY ROSS, *Philip's wife*

SENNET, *a clerk*

CREED, *a clerk*

The scene is any lawyer's office. It may be, and no doubt will be, the minute reproduction of some actual office, with all the characteristic appurtenances thereof, every blot of ink in its proper place; but for the purpose in hand any bare room would do just as well. The only thing essential to the room, save the two men sitting in it, is a framed engraving on the wall of Queen Victoria, which dates sufficiently the opening scene, and will be changed presently to King Edward, afterward to King George, to indicate the passing of time. No other alteration is called for. Doubtless different furniture came in, and the tiling of the fireplace was renewed, and at last someone discovered that the flowers in the window box were dead, but all that is as immaterial to the action as the new bluebottles; the succession of monarchs will convey allegorically the one thing necessary, that time is passing, but that the office of Devizes, Devizes, & Devizes goes on.

The two men are DEVIZES SENIOR *and* JUNIOR. SENIOR, *who is middle-aged, succeeded to a good thing years ago, and as the curtain rises we see him bent over his table making it a better thing. It is pleasant to think that before he speaks he adds another thirteen and fourpence, say, to the fortune of the firm.*

JUNIOR *is quite a gay dog, twenty-three, and we catch him skill-*

MR. DEVIZES (*wrinkling his brows*). Too bad, Robert.

ROBERT (*blandly*). Yes, you see I am out of practice.

SURTEES. He seemed a very nervous person, sir, and quite young. Not a gentleman of much consequence.

ROBERT (*airily*). Why not tell him to write again?

MR. DEVIZES. Not fair.

SURTEES. But she –

ROBERT. She? Who?

SURTEES. There is a young lady with him, sir. She is crying.

ROBERT. Pretty?

SURTEES. I should say she is pretty, sir, in a quite inoffensive way.

ROBERT (*for his own gratification*). Ha!

MR. DEVIZES. Well, when I ring show them in.

ROBERT (*with roguish finger*). And let this be a lesson to you, Surty, not to go about your business with your mouth open. (SURTEES *tries to smile as requested, but with poor success.*) Nothing the matter, Surty? You seem to have lost your sense of humor.

SURTEES (*humbly enough*). I'm afraid I have, sir. I never had very much, Mr. Robert.

[*He goes quietly. There has been a suppressed emotion about him that makes the incident poignant.*]

ROBERT. Anything wrong with Surtees, Father?

MR. DEVIZES. Never mind him. I am very angry with you, Robert.

ROBERT (*like one conceding a point in a debating society*). And justly.

MR. DEVIZES (*frowning*). All we can do is to tell this Mr. Ross that we have not read his letter.

ROBERT (*bringing his knowledge of the world to bear*). Is that necessary?

MR. DEVIZES. We must admit that we don't know what he has come about.

ROBERT (*tolerant of his father's limitations*). But don't we?

MR. DEVIZES. Do you?

ROBERT. I rather think I can put two and two together.

MR. DEVIZES. Clever boy! Well, I shall leave them to you.

ROBERT. Right.

MR. DEVIZES. Your first case, Robert.

ROBERT (*undismayed*). It will be as good as a play to you to sit there and watch me discovering before they have been two minutes in the room what is the naughty thing that brings them here.

MR. DEVIZES (*dryly*). I am always ready to take a lesson from the new generation. But of course we old fogies could do that also.

ROBERT. How?

MR. DEVIZES. By asking them.

ROBERT. Pooh. What did I go to Oxford for?

MR. DEVIZES. God knows. Are you ready?

ROBERT. Quite.

[MR. DEVIZES *rings.*]

MR. DEVIZES. By the way, we don't know the lady's name.

ROBERT. Observe me finding it out.

MR. DEVIZES. Is she married or single?

ROBERT. I'll know at a glance. And mark me, if she is married, it is our nervous gentleman who has come between her and her husband; but if she is single, it is little Wet Face who has come between him and his wife.

MR. DEVIZES. A Daniel!

[*A young man and woman are shown in: very devoted to each other, though* ROBERT *does not know it. Yet it is the one thing obvious about them; more obvious than his cheap suit, which she presses so carefully beneath the mattress every night, or than the strength of his boyish face. Thinking of him as he then was by the light of subsequent events one wonders whether if he had come alone something disquieting could have been read in that face which was not there while she was by. Probably not; it was certainly already there, but had not yet reached the surface. With her, too, though she is to be what is called changed before we see them again, all seems serene; no warning signals; nothing in the way of their happiness in each other but this alarming visit to a lawyer's office. The stage direction might be "Enter two lovers." He is scarcely the less nervous of the two, but he enters stoutly in front of her as if to receive the first charge. She has probably nodded valiantly to him outside the door, where she let go his hand.*]

ROBERT (*master of the situation*). Come in, Mr. Ross (*and he bows reassuringly to the lady*). My partner — indeed my father.

[MR. DEVIZES *bows but remains in the background.*]

PHILIP (*with a gulp*). You got my letter?

ROBERT. Yes — yes.

PHILIP. I gave you the details in it.

ROBERT. Yes, I have them all in my head. (*Cleverly.*) You will sit down, Miss — I don't think I caught the name.

[*As much as to say, "You see, Father, I spotted that she was single at once."*]

MR. DEVIZES (*who has also formed his opinion*). You didn't ask for it, Robert.

ROBERT (*airily*). Miss — ?

PHILIP. This is Mrs. Ross, my wife.

[ROBERT *is a little taken aback, and has a conviction that his father is smiling.*]

ROBERT. Ah yes, of course. Sit down, please, Mrs. Ross.

[*She sits as if this made matters rather worse.*]

PHILIP (*standing guard by her side*). My wife is a little agitated.

ROBERT. Naturally. (*He tries a "feeler."*) These affairs — very painful at the time — but one gradually forgets.

EMILY (*with large eyes*). That is what Mr. Ross says, but somehow I can't help — (*The eyes fill.*) You see, we have been married only four months.

ROBERT. Ah — that does make it — yes, certainly. (*He becomes the wife's champion, and frowns on* PHILIP.)

PHILIP. I suppose the sum seems very small to you?

ROBERT (*serenely*). I confess that is the impression it makes on me.

PHILIP. I wish it was more.

ROBERT (*at a venture*). You are sure you can't make it more?

PHILIP. How can I?

ROBERT. Ha!

EMILY (*with sudden spirit*). I think it's a great deal.

PHILIP. Mrs Ross is so nice about it.

ROBERT (*taking a strong line*). I think so. But she must not be taken advantage of. And of course we shall have something to say as to the amount.

PHILIP (*blankly*). In what way? There it is.

ROBERT (*guardedly*). Hum. Yes, in a sense.

EMILY (*breaking down*). Oh dear!

ROBERT (*more determined than ever to do his best for this wronged woman*). I am very sorry, Mrs. Ross. (*Sternly.*) I hope, sir, you realize that the mere publicity to a sensitive woman –

PHILIP. Publicity?

ROBERT (*feeling that he has got him on the run*). Of course for her sake we shall try to arrange things so that the names do not appear. Still –

PHILIP. The names?

[*By this time* EMILY *is in tears.*]

EMILY. I can't help it. I love him so.

ROBERT (*still benighted*). Enough to forgive him? (*Seeing himself suddenly as a mediator.*) Mrs. Ross, is it too late to patch things up?

PHILIP (*now in flame*). What do you mean, sir?

MR. DEVIZES (*who has been quietly enjoying himself*). Yes, Robert, what do you mean precisely?

ROBERT. Really I – (*He tries browbeating.*) I must tell you at once, Mr. Ross, that unless a client gives us his fullest confidence we cannot undertake a case of this kind.

PHILIP. A case of what kind, sir? If you are implying anything against my good name –

ROBERT. On your honor, sir, is there nothing against it?

PHILIP. I know of nothing, sir.

EMILY. Anything against my husband, Mr. Devizes! He is an angel.

ROBERT (*suddenly seeing that little Wet Face must be the culprit*). Then it is you.

EMILY. Oh, sir, what is me?

PHILIP. Answer that, sir.

ROBERT. Yes, Mr. Ross, I will. (*But he finds he cannot.*) On second thoughts I decline. I cannot believe it has been all this lady's fault, and I decline to have anything to do with such a painful case.

MR. DEVIZES (*promptly*). Then I will take it up.

PHILIP (*not to be placated*). I think your son has insulted me.

EMILY. Philip, come away.

MR. DEVIZES. One moment, please. As *I* did not see your letter, may I ask Mr. Ross what is your business with us?

PHILIP. I called to ask whether you would be so good as to draw up my will.

ROBERT (*blankly*). Your will! Is that all?

PHILIP. Certainly.

MR. DEVIZES. Now we know, Robert.

ROBERT. But Mrs. Ross's agitation?

PHILIP (*taking her hand*). She feels that to make my will brings my death nearer.

ROBERT. So that's it.

PHILIP. It was all in the letter.

MR. DEVIZES (*coyly*). Anything to say, Robert?

ROBERT. Most – ah – extremely – (*He has an inspiration.*) But even now I'm puzzled. You are Edgar Charles Ross?

PHILIP. No, Philip Ross.

ROBERT (*brazenly*). Philip Ross? We have made an odd mistake, Father. (*There is a twinkle in* MR. DEVIZES's *eye. He watches interestedly to see how his son is to emerge from the mess.*) The fact is, Mrs. Ross, we are expecting today a Mr. Edgar Charles Ross on a matter – well – of a kind – Ah me. (*With fitting gravity.*) His wife, in short.

EMILY (*who has not read the newspapers in vain*). How awful. How sad.

ROBERT. Sad indeed. You will quite understand that professional etiquette prevents my saying one word more.

PHILIP. Yes, of course – we have no desire – But I did write.

ROBERT. Assuredly. But about a will. That is my father's department. No doubt you recall the letter now, Father?

MR. DEVIZES (*who if he won't hinder won't help*). I can't say I do.

ROBERT (*unabashed*). Odd. You must have overlooked it.

MR. DEVIZES. Ha. At all events, Mr. Ross, I am quite at your service now.

PHILIP. Thank you.

ROBERT (*still ready to sacrifice himself on the call of duty*). You don't need me any more, Father?

MR. DEVIZES. No, Robert; many thanks. You run off to your club now and have a bit of lunch. You must be tired. Send Surtees in to me. (*To his clients.*) My son had his first case today.

PHILIP (*politely*). I hope successfully.

MR. DEVIZES. Not so bad. He rather bungled it at first, but he got out of a hole rather cleverly. I think you'll make a lawyer yet, Robert.

ROBERT. Thank you, Father. (*He goes jauntily, with a flower in his buttonhole.*)

MR. DEVIZES. Now, Mr. Ross.

[*The young wife's hand goes out for comfort and finds* PHILIP'S *waiting for it.*]

PHILIP. What I want myself is that the will should all go into one sentence, "I leave everything of which I die possessed to my beloved wife."

MR. DEVIZES (*thawing to the romance of this young couple*). Well, there have been many worse wills than that, sir.

[EMILY *is emotional.*]

PHILIP. Don't give way, Emily.

EMILY. It was those words, "of which I die possessed." (*Imploringly.*) Surely he doesn't need to say that – please, Mr. Devizes?

MR. DEVIZES. Certainly not. I am confident I can draw up the will without mentioning death at all.

EMILY (*huskily*). Oh, thank you.

MR. DEVIZES. At the same time, of course, in a legal document in which the widow is the sole –

[EMILY *again needs attention.*]

PHILIP (*reproachfully*). What was the need of saying "widow"?

MR. DEVIZES. I beg your pardon, Mrs. Ross. I unreservedly withdraw the word "widow." Forgive a stupid old solicitor. (*She smiles gratefully through her tears.* SURTEES *comes in.*) Surtees, just take a few notes, please. (SURTEES *sits in the background and takes notes.*) The facts of the case, as I understand, Mrs. Ross, are these: Your husband (*Quickly.*) – who is in the prime of health – but knows life to be uncertain –

EMILY. Oh!

MR. DEVIZES. – though usually, as we learn from Holy Script itself, it lasts seven times ten years — and believing that he will in all probability live the allotted span, nevertheless, because of his love of you thinks it judicious to go through the form — it is a mere form — of making a will.

EMILY (*fervently*). Oh, thank you.

MR. DEVIZES. Any details, Mr. Ross?

PHILIP. I am an orphan. I live at Belvedere, 14 Tulphin Road, Hammersmith.

EMILY (*to whom the address has a seductive sound*). We live there.

PHILIP. And I am a clerk in the employ of Curar and Gow, the foreign coaling agents.

MR. DEVIZES. Yes, yes. Any private income?

[*They cannot help sniggering a little at the quaint question.*]

PHILIP. Oh no!

MR. DEVIZES. I see it will be quite a brief will.

PHILIP (*to whom the remark sounds scarcely worthy of a great occasion*). My income is a biggish one.

MR. DEVIZES. Yes?

EMILY (*important*). He has a hundred and seventy pounds a year.

MR. DEVIZES. Ah.

PHILIP. I began at sixty pounds. But it is going up, Mr. Devizes, by leaps and bounds. Another fifteen pounds this year.

MR. DEVIZES. Good.

PHILIP (*darkly*). I have a certain ambition.

EMILY (*eagerly*). Tell him, Philip.

PHILIP (*with a big breath*). We have made up our minds to come to three hundred and sixty-five pounds a year before I — retire.

EMILY. That is a pound a day.

MR. DEVIZES (*smiling sympathetically on them*). So it is. My best wishes.

PHILIP. Thank you. Of course the furnishing took a good deal.

MR. DEVIZES. It would.

EMILY. He insisted on my having the very best. (*She ceases. She is probably thinking of her superb spare bedroom.*)

PHILIP. But we are not a penny in debt, and I have two hundred pounds saved.

MR. DEVIZES. I think you have made a brave beginning.

EMILY. They have the highest opinion of him in the office.

PHILIP. Then I am insured for five hundred pounds.

MR. DEVIZES. I am glad to hear that.

PHILIP. Of course I would like to leave her a house in Kensington and a carriage and pair.

MR. DEVIZES. Who knows, perhaps you will.

EMILY. Oh!

MR. DEVIZES. Forgive me.

EMILY. What would houses and horses be to me without him!

MR. DEVIZES (*soothingly*). Quite so. What I take Mr. Ross to mean is that when he dies — if he ever should die — everything is to go to his — his spouse.

PHILIP (*dogged*). Yes.

EMILY (*dogged*). No.

PHILIP (*sighing*). This is the only difference we have ever had. Mrs. Ross insists on certain bequests. You see, I have two cousins, ladies, not well off, whom I have been in the way of helping a little. But in my will, how can I?

MR. DEVIZES. You must think first of your wife.

PHILIP. But she insists on my leaving fifty pounds to each of them. (*He looks appealingly to his wife.*)

EMILY (*grandly*). A hundred pounds.

PHILIP. Fifty pounds.

EMILY. Dear, a hundred pounds.

MR. DEVIZES. Let us say seventy-five pounds.

PHILIP (*reluctantly*). Very well.

EMILY. No, a hundred pounds.

PHILIP. She'll have to get her way. Here are their names and addresses.

MR. DEVIZES. Anything else?

PHILIP (*hurriedly*). No.

EMILY. The convalescent home, dear. He was in it a year ago, and they were so kind.

PHILIP. Yes, but —

EMILY. Ten pounds. (*He has to yield, with a reproachful, admiring look.*)

MR. DEVIZES. Then if that is all, I won't detain you. If you look in tomorrow, Mr. Ross, about this time, we shall have everything ready for you.

[*Their faces fall.*]

EMILY. Oh, Mr. Devizes, if only it could all be drawn up now, and done with.

PHILIP. You see, sir, we are screwed up to it today.

[*"Our fate is in your hands," they might be saying, and the lawyer smiles to find himself such a power.*]

MR. DEVIZES (*looking at his watch*). Well, it certainly need not take long. You go out and have lunch somewhere, and then come back.

EMILY. Oh, don't ask me to eat.

PHILIP. We are too excited.

EMILY. Please may we just walk about the street?

MR. DEVIZES (*smiling*). Of course you may, you ridiculous young wife.

EMILY. I know it's ridiculous of me, but I am so fond of him.

MR. DEVIZES. Yes, it is ridiculous. But don't change, especially if you get on in the world, Mr. Ross.

PHILIP. No fear!

EMILY (*backing from the will, which may now be said to be in existence*). And please don't give us a copy of it to keep. I would rather not have it in the house.

MR. DEVIZES (*nodding reassuringly*). In an hour's time. (*They go, and the lawyer has his lunch, which is simpler than* ROBERT'S: *a sandwich and a glass of wine. He speaks as he eats.*) You will get that ready, Surtees. Here are the names and addresses he left. (*Cheerily.*) A nice couple.

SURTEES (*who is hearing another voice*). Yes, sir.

MR. DEVIZES (*unbending*). Little romance of its kind. Makes one feel quite gay.

SURTEES. Yes, sir.

MR. DEVIZES (*struck perhaps by the deadness of his voice*). You don't look very gay, Surtees.

SURTEES. I'm sorry, sir. We can't all be gay. (*He is going out without looking at his employer.*) I'll see to this, sir.

MR. DEVIZES. Stop a minute. Is there anything wrong? (SURTEES *has difficulty in answering, and* MR. DEVIZES *goes to him kindly.*) Not worrying over that matter we spoke about? (SURTEES *inclines his head.*) Is the pain worse?

SURTEES. It's no great pain, sir.

MR. DEVIZES (*uncomfortably*). I'm sure it's not – what you fear. Any specialist would tell you so.

SURTEES (*without looking up*). I have been to one, sir – yesterday.

MR. DEVIZES. Well?

SURTEES. It's – that, sir.

MR. DEVIZES. He couldn't be sure.

SURTEES. Yes, sir.

MR. DEVIZES. An operation –

SURTEES. Too late, he said, for that. If I had been operated on long ago there might have been a chance.

MR. DEVIZES. But you didn't have it long ago.

SURTEES. Not to my knowledge, sir; but he says it was there all the same, always in me, a black spot, not so big as a pin's head, but waiting to spread and destroy me in the fullness of time. All the rest of me as sound as a bell. (*That is the voice that* SURTEES *has been hearing.*)

MR. DEVIZES (*helpless*). It seems damnably unfair.

SURTEES (*humbly*). I don't know, sir. He says there's a spot of that kind in pretty nigh all of us, and if we don't look out it does for us in the end.

MR. DEVIZES (*hurriedly*). No, no, no.

SURTEES. He called it the accursed thing. I think he meant we should know of it and be on the watch. (*He pulls himself together.*) I'll see to this at once, sir.

[*He goes out.* MR. DEVIZES *continues his lunch.*]

The curtain falls here for a moment only, to indicate the passing of a number of years. When it rises we see that the engraving of Queen Victoria has given way to one of King Edward.

ROBERT *is discovered, immersed in affairs. He is now a middle-aged man who has long forgotten how to fling cards into a hat. To him comes* SENNET, *a brisk clerk.*

SENNET. Mrs. Philip Ross to see you, sir.

ROBERT. Mr. Ross, don't you mean, Sennet?

SENNET. No, sir.

ROBERT. Ha. It was Mr. Ross I was expecting. Show her in. (*Frowning.*) And, Sennet, less row in the office, if you please.

SENNET (*glibly*). It was these young clerks, sir —

ROBERT. They mustn't be young here, or they go. Tell them that.

SENNET (*glad to be gone*). Yes, sir.

[*He shows in* MRS. ROSS. *We have not seen her for twenty years and would certainly not recognize her in the street. So shrinking her first entrance into this room, but she sails in now a galleon. She is not so much dressed as richly upholstered. She is very sure of herself. Yet she is not a different woman from the* EMILY *we remember; the pity of it is that somehow this is the same woman.*]

ROBERT (*who makes much of his important visitor and is also wondering why she has come*). This is a delightful surprise, Mrs. Ross. Allow me. (*He removes her fine cloak with proper solicitude, and* EMILY *walks out of it in the manner that makes it worth possessing.*) This chair, alas, is the best I can offer you.

EMILY (*who is still a good-natured woman if you attempt no nonsense with her*). It will do quite well.

ROBERT (*gallantly*). Honored to see you in it.

EMILY (*smartly*). Not you. You were saying to yourself, "Now what brings the woman here?"

ROBERT. Honestly, I —

EMILY. And I'll tell you. You are expecting Mr. Ross, I think?

ROBERT (*cautiously*). Well — ah —

EMILY. Pooh. The cunning of you lawyers. I know he has an appointment with you, and that is why I've come.

ROBERT. He arranged with you to meet him here?

EMILY (*preening herself*). I wouldn't say that. I don't know that he will be specially pleased to find me here when he comes.

ROBERT (*guardedly*). Oh?

EMILY (*who is now a woman that goes straight to her goal*). I know what he is coming about. To make a new will.

ROBERT (*admitting it*). After all, not the first he has made with us, Mrs. Ross.

EMILY (*promptly*). No, the fourth.

ROBERT (*warming his hands at the thought*). Such a wonderful career. He goes from success to success.

EMILY (*complacently*). Yes, we're big folk.

ROBERT. You are indeed.

EMILY (*sharply*). But the last will covered everything.

ROBERT (*on guard again*). Of course it is a matter I cannot well discuss even with you. And I know nothing of his intentions.

EMILY. Well, I suspect some of them.

ROBERT. Ah.

EMILY. And that's why I'm here. Just to see that he does nothing foolish.

[*She settles herself more comfortably as* MR. ROSS *is announced. A city magnate walks in. You know he is that before you see that he is* PHILIP ROSS.]

PHILIP (*speaking as he enters*). How do, Devizes, how do. Well, let us get at this thing at once. Time is money, you know, time is money. (*Then he sees his wife.*) Hello, Emily.

EMILY (*unperturbed*). You didn't ask me to come, Philip, but I thought I might as well.

PHILIP. That's all right.

[*His brow had lowered at first sight of her, but now he gives her cleverness a grin of respect.*]

EMILY. It is the first will you have made without taking me into your confidence.

PHILIP. No important changes. I just thought to save you the – unpleasantness of the thing.

EMILY. How do you mean?

PHILIP (*fidgeting*). Well, one can't draw up a will without feeling for the moment that he is bringing his end nearer. Is that not so, Devizes?

ROBERT (*who will quite possibly die intestate*). Some do have that feeling.

EMILY. But what nonsense. How can it have any effect of that kind one way or the other?

ROBERT. Quite so.

EMILY (*reprovingly*). Just silly sentiment, Philip. I would have thought it would be a pleasure to you handling such a big sum.

PHILIP (*wincing*). Not handling it, giving it up.

EMILY. To those you love.

PHILIP (*rather shortly*). I'm not giving it up yet. You talk as if I was on my last legs.

EMILY (*imperturbably*). Not at all. It's you that are doing that.

ROBERT (*to the rescue*). Here is my copy of the last will. I don't know if you would like me to read it out?

PHILIP. It's hardly necessary.

EMILY. We have our own copy at home and we know it well.

PHILIP (*sitting back in his chair*). What do you think I'm worth to-day, Devizes?

[*Everyone smiles. It is as if the sun had peeped in at the window.*]

ROBERT. I daren't guess.

PHILIP. An easy seventy thou.

EMILY. And that's not counting the house and the country cottage. We call it a cottage. You should see it!

ROBERT. I have heard of it.

EMILY (*more sharply, though the sun still shines*). Well, go on, Philip. I suppose you are not thinking of cutting me out of anything.

PHILIP (*heartily*). Of course not. There will be more to you than ever.

EMILY (*coolly*). There's more to leave.

PHILIP (*hesitating*). At the same time —

EMILY. Well? It's to be mine absolutely of course. Not just a life interest.

PHILIP (*doggedly*). That is a change I was thinking of.

EMILY. Just what I have suspected for days. Will you please to say why?

ROBERT (*whose client after all is the man*). Of course it is quite common.

EMILY. I didn't think my husband was quite common.

ROBERT. I only mean that as there are children —

PHILIP. That's what I mean too.

EMILY. And I can't be trusted to leave my money to my own children! In what way have I ever failed them before?

PHILIP (*believing it, too*). Never, Emily, never. A more devoted mother — If you have one failing it is that you spoil them.

EMILY. Then what's your reason?

PHILIP (*less sincerely*). Just to save you worry when I'm gone.

EMILY. It's no worry to me to look after my money.

PHILIP (*bridling*). After all, it's my money.

EMILY. I knew that was what was at the back of your mind.

PHILIP (*reverently*). It's such a great sum.

EMILY. One would think you were afraid I would marry again.

PHILIP (*snapping*). One would think you looked to my dying next week.

EMILY. Tuts.

[PHILIP *is unable to sit still.*]

PHILIP. My money. If you were to invest it badly and lose it . . . I tell you, Devizes, I couldn't lie quiet in my grave if I thought my money was lost by injudicious investments.

EMILY (*coldly*). You are thinking of yourself, Philip, rather than of the children.

PHILIP. Not at all.

ROBERT (*hastily*). How are the two children?

EMILY. Though I say it myself, there never were better. Harry is at Eton, you know, the most fashionable school in the country.

ROBERT. Doing well, I hope.

PHILIP (*chuckling*). We have the most gratifying letters from him. Last Saturday he was caught smoking cigarettes with a lord. (*With pardonable pride.*) They were sick together.

ROBERT. And Miss Gwendolen? She must be almost grown-up now.

[*The parents exchange important glances.*]

EMILY. Should we tell him?

PHILIP. Under the rose, you know, Devizes.

ROBERT. Am I to congratulate her?

EMILY. No names, Philip.

PHILIP. No, no names — but she won't be a plain Mrs., no sir.

ROBERT. Well done, Miss Gwendolen. (*With fitting jocularity.*) Now I see why you want a new will.

PHILIP. Yes, that's my main reason, Emily.

EMILY. But none of your life interests for me, Philip.

PHILIP (*shying*). We'll talk that over presently.

ROBERT. Will you keep the legacies as they are?

PHILIP. Well, there's that five hundred pounds for the hospitals.

EMILY. Yes, with so many claims on us, is that necessary?

PHILIP (*becoming stouter*). I'm going to make it a thousand pounds.

EMILY. Philip!

PHILIP. My mind is made up. I want to make a splash with the hospitals.

ROBERT (*hurrying to the next item*). There is fifty pounds a year each to two cousins, ladies.

PHILIP. I suppose we'll keep that as it is, Emily?

EMILY. It was just gifts to them of a hundred pounds each at first.

PHILIP. I was poor at that time myself.

EMILY. Do you think it's wise to load them with so much money? They'll not know what to do with it.

PHILIP. They're old.

EMILY. But they're wiry. Seventy-five pounds a year between them would surely be enough.

PHILIP. It would be if they lived together, but you see they don't. They hate each other like cat and dog.

EMILY. That's not nice between relatives. You could leave it to them on condition that they do live together. That would be a Christian action.

PHILIP. There's something in that.

ROBERT. Then the chief matter is whether Mrs. Ross —

EMILY. Oh, I thought that was settled.

PHILIP (*with a sigh*). I'll have to give in to her, sir.

ROBERT. Very well. I suppose my father will want to draw up the will. I'm sorry he had to be in the country today.

EMILY (*affable now that she has gained her point*). I hope he is wearing well?

ROBERT. Wonderfully. He is away playing golf.

PHILIP (*grinning*). Golf. I have no time for games. (*Considerately.*) But he must get the drawing-up of my will. I couldn't deprive the old man of that.

ROBERT. He will be proud to do it again.

PHILIP (*well satisfied*). Ah! There's many a one would like to look over your father's shoulder when he's drawing up my will. I wonder what I'll cut up for in the end. But I must be going.

EMILY. Can I drop you anywhere? I have the grays out.

PHILIP. Yes, at the club. (*Now* MRS. ROSS *walks into her cloak.*) Good-day, Devizes. I won't have time to look in again, so tell the old man to come to me.

ROBERT (*deferentially*). Whatever suits you best. (*Ringing.*) He will be delighted. I remember his saying to me on the day you made your first will –

PHILIP (*chuckling*). A poor little affair that.

ROBERT. He said to me you were a couple whose life looked like being a romance.

PHILIP. And he was right – eh, Emily? – though he little thought what a romance.

[*They make a happy departure, and* ROBERT *is left reflecting.*]

The curtain again falls, and rises immediately, as the engraving shows, on the same office in the reign of King George. It is a foggy morning and a fire burns briskly. MR. DEVIZES, SENIOR, *arrives for the day's work just as he came daily for over half a century. But he has no right to be here now. A year or two ago they got him to retire, as he was grown feeble; and there is an understanding that he does not go out of his house alone. He has, as it were, escaped today, and his feet have carried him to the old office that is the home of his mind. He was almost portly when we saw him first, but he has become little again and as light as the schoolboy whose deeds are nearer to him than many of the events of later years. He arrives at the office, thinking it is old times, and a clerk surveys him uncomfortably from the door.*

CREED (*not quite knowing what to do*). Mr. Devizes has not come in yet, sir.

MR. DEVIZES (*considering*). Yes I have. Do you mean Mr. Robert?

CREED. Yes, sir.

MR. DEVIZES (*querulously*). Always late. Can't get that boy to settle down. (*Leniently.*) Well, well, boys will be boys — eh, Surtees?

CREED (*wishing* MR. ROBERT *would come*). My name is Creed, sir.

MR. DEVIZES (*sharply*). Creed? Don't know you. Where is Surtees?

CREED. There is no one of that name in the office, sir.

MR. DEVIZES (*growing timid*). No? I remember now. Poor Surtees! (*But his mind cannot grapple with troubles.*) Tell him I want him when he comes in. (*He is changing, after his old custom, into an office coat.*)

CREED. That is Mr. Dev— Mr. Robert's coat, sir.

MR. DEVIZES. He has no business to hang it there. That is my nail.

CREED. He has hung it there for years, sir.

MR. DEVIZES. Not at all. I must have it. Why does Surtees let him do it? Help me into my office coat, boy.

[CREED *helps him into the coat he has taken off, and the old man is content.*]

CREED (*seeing him lift up the correspondence*). I don't think Mr. Devizes would like you to open the office letters, sir.

MR. DEVIZES (*pettishly*). What's that? Go away, boy. Send Surtees.

[*To the relief of* CREED, ROBERT *arrives, and, taking in the situation, signs to the clerk to go. He has a more youthful manner than when last we saw him, has* ROBERT, *but his hair is iron-gray. He is kindly to his father.*]

ROBERT. You here, Father?

MR. DEVIZES (*after staring at him*). Yes, you are Robert. (*A little frightened.*) You are an old man, Robert.

ROBERT (*without wincing*). Getting on, Father. But why did they let you come? You haven't been here for years.

MR. DEVIZES (*puzzled*). Years? I think I just came in the old way, Robert, without thinking.

ROBERT. Yes, yes. I'll get someone to go home with you.

MR. DEVIZES (*rather abject*). Let me stay, Robert. I like being here. I won't disturb you. I like the smell of the office, Robert.

ROBERT. Of course you may stay. Come over to the fire. (*He settles his father by the fire in the one armchair.*) There, you can have a doze by the fire.

MR. DEVIZES. A doze by the fire. That is all I'm good for now. Once —

but my son hangs his coat there now. (*Presently he looks up fearfully.*) Robert, tell me something in a whisper: Is Surtees dead?

ROBERT (*who has forgotten the name*). Surtees?

MR. DEVIZES. My clerk, you know.

ROBERT. Oh. Why, he has been dead this thirty years, Father.

MR. DEVIZES. So long! Seems like yesterday.

ROBERT. It is just far-back times that seem clear to you now.

MR. DEVIZES (*meekly*). Is it?

[ROBERT *opens his letters, and his father falls asleep.* CREED *comes.*]

CREED. Sir Philip Ross.

[*The great* SIR PHILIP *enters, nearly sixty now, strong of frame still, but a lost man. He is in mourning, and carries the broken pieces of his life with an air of braggadocio. It should be understood that he is not a "sympathetic" part, and any actor who plays him as such will be rolling the play in the gutter.*]

ROBERT (*on his feet at once to greet such a client*). You, Sir Philip.

PHILIP (*head erect*). Here I am.

ROBERT (*because it will out*). How are you?

PHILIP (*as if challenged*). I'm all right – great. (*With defiant jocularity.*) Called on the old business.

ROBERT. To make another will?

PHILIP. You've guessed it – the very first time. (*He sees the figure by the fire.*)

ROBERT. Yes, it's my father. He's dozing. Shouldn't be here at all. He forgets things. It's just age.

PHILIP (*grimly*). Forgets things. That must be fine.

ROBERT (*conventionally*). I should like, Sir Philip, to offer you my sincere condolences. In the midst of life we are – How true that is. I attended the funeral.

PHILIP. I saw you.

ROBERT. A much-esteemed lady. I had a great respect for her.

PHILIP (*almost with relish*). Do you mind, when we used to come here about the will, somehow she – we – always took for granted I should be the first to go.

ROBERT (*devoutly*). These things are hid from mortal eyes.

PHILIP (*with conviction*). There's a lot hid. We needn't have worried so much about the will if – Well, let us get at it. (*Fiercely.*) I haven't given in, you know.

ROBERT. We must bow our heads –

PHILIP. Must we? Am I bowing mine?

ROBERT (*uncomfortably*). Such courage in the great hour – yes – and I am sure Lady Ross –

PHILIP (*with the ugly humor that has come to him*). She wasn't that.

ROBERT. The honor came so soon afterward – I feel she would like to be thought of as Lady Ross. I shall always remember her as a fine lady richly dressed who used –

PHILIP (*harshly*). Stop it. That's not how I think of her. There was a time before that – she wasn't richly dressed – (*He stamps upon his memories.*) Things went wrong, I don't know how. It's a beast of a world. I didn't come here to talk about that. Let us get to work.

ROBERT (*turning with relief from the cemetery*). Yes, yes, and after all life has its compensations. You have your son who –

PHILIP (*snapping*). No I haven't. (*This startles the lawyer.*) I'm done with him.

ROBERT. If he has been foolish –

PHILIP. Foolish! (*Some dignity comes into the man.*) Sir, I have come to a pass when "foolish" as applied to my own son would seem to me a very pretty word.

ROBERT. Is it as bad as that?

PHILIP. He's a rotter.

ROBERT. It is very painful to me to hear you say that.

PHILIP. More painful, think you, than for me to say it? (*Clenching his fists.*) But I've shipped him off. The law had to wink at it, or I couldn't have done it. Why don't you say I pampered him and it serves me right? It's what they are all saying behind my back. Why don't you ask me about my girl? That's another way to rub it in.

ROBERT. Don't, Sir Philip. I knew her. My sympathy –

PHILIP. A chauffeur, that is what he was. The man who drove her own car.

ROBERT. I was deeply concerned –

PHILIP. I want nobody's pity. I've done with both of them, and if you think I'm a broken man you're much mistaken. I'll show them. Have you your papers there? Then take down my last will. I have everything in my head. I'll show them.

ROBERT. Would it not be better to wait till a calmer –

PHILIP. Will you do it now, or am I to go across the street?

ROBERT. If I must.

PHILIP. Then down with it. (*He wets his lips.*) I, Philip Ross, of 77 Bath Street, W., do hereby revoke all former wills and testaments, and I leave everything of which I die possessed –

ROBERT. Yes?

PHILIP. Everything of which I die possessed –

ROBERT. Yes?

PHILIP. I leave it – I leave it – (*The game is up.*) My God, Devizes, I don't know what to do with it.

ROBERT. I – I – really – come –

PHILIP (*cynically*). Can't you make any suggestions?

ROBERT. Those cousins are dead, I think?

PHILIP. Years ago.

ROBERT (*troubled*). In the case of such a large sum –

PHILIP (*letting all his hoarded gold run through his fingers*). The money I've won with my blood. God in heaven! (*Showing his teeth.*) Would that old man like it to play with? If I bring it to you in sacks, will you fling it out of the window for me?

ROBERT. Sir Philip!

PHILIP (*taking a paper from his pocket*). Here, take this. It has the names and addresses of the half-dozen men I've fought with most for gold; and I've beaten them. Draw up a will leaving all my money to be divided between them, with my respectful curses, and bring it to my house and I'll sign it.

ROBERT (*properly shocked*). But really I can't possibly –

PHILIP. Either you or another. Is it to be you?

ROBERT. Very well.

PHILIP. Then that's settled. (*He rises with a laugh. He regards* MR. DEVIZES *quizzically.*) So you weren't in at the last will after all, old Sleep-by-the-Fire.

[*To their surprise the old man stirs.*]

MR. DEVIZES. What's that about a will?

ROBERT. You are awake, Father?

MR. DEVIZES (*whose eyes have opened on* PHILIP'S *face*). I don't know you, sir.

ROBERT. Yes, yes, Father, you remember Mr. Ross. He is Sir Philip now.

MR. DEVIZES (*courteously*). Sir Philip? I wish you joy, sir, but I don't know you.

ROBERT (*encouragingly*). Ross, father.

MR. DEVIZES. I knew a Mr. Ross long ago.

ROBERT. This is the same.

MR. DEVIZES (*annoyed*). No, no. A bright young fellow he was, with such a dear, pretty wife. They came to make a will. (*He chuckles.*) And bless me, they had only twopence halfpenny. I took a fancy to them, such a happy pair.

ROBERT (*apologetically*). The past is clearer to him than the present nowadays. That will do, Father.

PHILIP (*brusquely*). Let him go on.

MR. DEVIZES. Poor souls, it all ended unhappily, you know.

PHILIP (*who is not brusque to him*). Yes, I know. Why did things go wrong, sir? I sit and wonder, and I can't find the beginning.

MR. DEVIZES. That's the sad part of it. There was never a beginning. It was always there. He told me all about it.

ROBERT. He is thinking of something else, I don't know what.

PHILIP. Quiet. What was it that was always there?

MR. DEVIZES. It was always in them — a spot no bigger than a pin's head, but waiting to spread and destroy them in the fullness of time.

ROBERT. I don't know what he has got hold of.

PHILIP. He knows. Could they have done anything to prevent it, sir?

MR. DEVIZES. If they had been on the watch. But they didn't know, so they weren't on the watch. Poor souls.

PHILIP. Poor souls.

MR. DEVIZES. It's called the accursed thing. It gets nearly everybody in the end, if they don't look out. (*He sinks back into his chair and forgets them.*)

ROBERT. He is just wandering.

PHILIP. The old man knows. (*He slowly tears up the paper he had given* ROBERT.)

ROBERT (*relieved*). I am glad to see you do that.

PHILIP. A spot no bigger than a pin's head. (*A wish wells up in him, too late perhaps.*) I wish I could help some young things before that spot has time to spread and destroy them as it has destroyed me and mine.

ROBERT (*brightly*). With such a large fortune –

PHILIP (*summing up his life*). It can't be done with money, sir.

[*He goes away, God knows where.*]

AFTER READING

1. One critic has said that there was enough material in *The Will* for a full-length play. What is your opinion?

2. How can you account for the change in attitude between Philip and Emily Ross? Would their personalities have changed had they remained poor, or would they in any circumstances have shown the traits they do?

3. Why did Sir Philip's children turn out as they did? Apparently they went to the most exclusive schools. Do you think that character can be developed best in school or at home?

4. What change in attitude did Philip Ross adopt toward the lawyers?

5. What do you think Sir Philip finally did with his money?

6. What examples of humor do you see in this play?

7. In *Courage,* his inaugural address as rector of St. Andrew's University, Barrie referred to his plays as "inoffensive." Would you agree with him? Death and romance are rather sacred topics. How has Barrie touched on them with good taste and judgment?

CHALLENGES

1. Sir Philip decides to leave his wealth for some worthy cause. Write the letter in which he states his conditions.

2. The older Devizes reminisces about the past. Philip Ross appears in the reverie. How would he appear?

3. Sir Philip's son repents and writes to his father asking his forgiveness. What would the letter contain?

4. What changes have gone on in the office of the Devizes since Queen Victoria's picture was placed on the wall?

DRAMA WORKSHOP

A hint for playgoers: Reflect on each play.

You have often heard people remark, "It's easy to criticize." Superficial criticism is easy, but discerning criticism is difficult. If you want to be a sound critic, you must do three things: listen receptively, observe attentively, and reflect carefully.

Here are some things to reflect upon after you have read or seen a play. Consider the dramatic conflict in the play and decide whether it was important or trivial. Notice whether the characters were true to life or artificial. Were they dynamic or static — that is, did they change during the course of the play or were they the same at the end as in the beginning? Recall whether the dialogue was appropriate to the characters or whether it was stilted and padded. Reflect on the theme, judging its sincerity and soundness. Ask yourself, finally, why the play succeeded or failed in holding your interest.

Begin now to improve your critical judgment by applying these suggestions to *The Will.*

A hint for actors: Acting is also reacting.

In a professional production an actor remains in character every moment he is on the stage. He does much — if not most — of his acting when he is not speaking. He is constantly reacting to what is going on even when he is not the center of attention.

If you want to give your acting a professional touch, keep in character even when you are not involved in the action. Don't slip back into your normal manner while some other actor is speaking. Get into character before you step in front of the audience, play your part every moment you are before the footlights, and maintain your role until after the curtain falls.

OTHER DRAMAS YOU WILL LIKE TO READ

Allison's Lad by Beulah M. Dix (26). When put to the test, and under the inspiration of a fellow prisoner who had once loved his mother, a young Cavalier soldier goes nobly to his death at the hands of the Roundheads.

Beauty and the Jacobin by Booth Tarkington (7). French aristocrats manage to escape to England when an agent of the French Republic succumbs to the charm of one of them.

The Boy Comes Home by A. A. Milne (21). A boy returned from World War I is not inclined to listen to his uncle's orders to go into his business. A dream changes everything.

The Brink of Silence by E. E. Galbraith (26). An English explorer has been considered lost for ten years. He meets his son, now an explorer in his own right, but is strong enough to conceal his identity to avoid embarrassments.

The Good and Obedient Young Man by Betty Barr and Gould Stevens (29). A mirror brings trouble to a married couple who do not understand that the images they see in the glass are their own reflections.

In the Zone by Eugene O'Neill (30). A United States soldier is suspected of being a spy because of a tin box which his buddies mistake for an infernal machine.

Just Neighborly by Alexander Dean (42). After an absence of thirty years a wayward son returns to his New England parents to find suspicions of his identity.

The Old Lady Shows Her Medals by James M. Barrie (1). An old charwoman pretends to have a heroic son and is surprised to find that a fine soldier of the Black Watch is willing to pretend with her.

The Twelve-Pound Look by J. M. Barrie (2). Twelve pounds to buy a typewriter is enough to free the wife of a pompous self-made man.

THE DOCTOR FROM DUNMORE

BY THOMAS PATRICK DILLON

AND NOLAN LEARY

ABOUT THE PLAY

Occasionally we hear about an entire community banding together to procure expensive medical treatment for one of its members. In *The Doctor from Dunmore* the entire population of an island contributes to a fund to bring a physician from the mainland to treat an injured inhabitant. Trouble comes when the doctor's fee of £10 can't be raised, and other complications arise.

In this comedy of Irish life you will discover that the people have some customs quite different from your own. Basically, how-

---

ever, they are not unlike people you know: they are warmhearted, eager to help a neighbor in distress, hard-working, and resentful of unfairness. Innisheen, the setting of the play, seems far away from our modern world of radios and airplanes and fast motorboats. Perhaps that is why the characters appear so genuine.

The meaning and pronunciation of Gaelic words used in the play appear at the end.

ABOUT THE AUTHORS

Thomas Patrick Dillon has had a varied career as actor and dramatist. He was born in County Roscommon, Ireland. In 1911 he came to America, where he acquired an education while working at many jobs. As an actor he has toured in the United States, Canada, and Mexico. All kinds of drama — legitimate stage, radio, screen, and television — are familiar to him. On Broadway he has played important roles in such successes as *Juno and the Paycock, Father Malachy's Miracle,* and *My Sister Eileen.* He has written two other one-act plays besides the one included here: *Ten Gallons of Gas* and *Broadway Prelude.*

Nolan Leary comes from the Middle West. He was born in Rock Island, Illinois, and educated in Iowa. As a boy he became interested in the theater almost from the time he saw his first play on a Mississippi River showboat. He has had a long and successful career as actor and as playwright, many of his one-act plays having been headliners in the Keith and Orpheum circuits when vaudeville was in its heyday. He has also written several full-length plays.

THE DOCTOR FROM DUNMORE

Characters

MAGGIE RAFFERTY, *a neighbor*

LIZZIE FUREY, *another neighbor*

NORA O'MALLEY, *a bonesetter*

KATIE CLAFFEY, *a neighbor*

DENNIS O'CONNOR, *Mollie's son*

FATHER TIM WHALEN, *a priest*

MAUREEN O'FLAHERTY, *an Island girl*

DR. FITZWILLIAMS, *a physician*

MICAL DUV, PADRIC KEARNY, SHAMUS O'LOUGHLIN, *curraghmen*

SHAUN MOR O'MALLEY, *"The King"*

PLACE. Interior of Mollie O'Connor's cottage, on the Island of Innisheen, off the west coast of Ireland.

TIME. The present. An afternoon in summer.

The interior of an Irish cottage. The cottage is situated on a cliff, overlooking the sea. Its plain, whitewashed walls are discolored from the smoke of a peat fire. It is poor, but clean. The entrance door (with iron latch), downstage right, opens outward. A little vessel of holy water hangs on the wall just inside the door; over the door, a Sacred Heart medallion. BACK WALL: *a small window right, a door center opens into a bedroom.* LEFT WALL: *a large turf-burning fireplace where cooking is done on the hearth. Iron kettle and pot hang from hooks. The furniture is of the plainest kind.*

DISCOVERED AT RISE: MAGGIE RAFFERTY *is looking out through the window up right, anxiously watching for something.* LIZZIE FUREY *sits on a three-legged stool above the fireplace left, smoking an old clay pipe and looking into the turf fire. A slight pause after the rise of the curtain. Then the door of the sickroom up left center opens and* NORA *enters carrying an empty water glass. Goes to the cupboard center and fills the glass with milk from a crock on the shelf. Through the open bedroom door is seen the foot of the bed and disarranged bedclothes. Kneeling beside the bed is an old woman saying her beads. At the foot of it kneels* DENNIS. *Also seen is a small table holding a crucifix and an unlighted candle.*

LIZZIE. Is she any better, Nora?

NORA (*pouring milk*). Ah, she's only middlin', God help her. (*To* MAGGIE.) Any sign of them yet?

MAGGIE. No. The divil a sign.

NORA. Now don't be worryin'. Sure it takes three hours' good rowin' in a curragh to come from the mainland even in daycent weather. (*She exits into the sickroom with the milk, quietly closing the door.*)

MAGGIE. Them waves 'ud put terror in yer heart at the sight o' them. (*Turns from the window making the sign of the cross.*)

LIZZIE. Yerra, Maggie, I don't see why they had to send to the mainland for a doctor when Nora in there is better than any doctor that ever set foot on dry land.

MAGGIE (*crossing left to* LIZZIE). But didn't the priest say the poor woman might die if she didn't get a doctor? Faith if *you* fell off a rock that high, you'd be a corpse for the rest o' yer life.

LIZZIE. Well, ten thousand curses on that ould Dr. Fitzwilliams for askin' ten pounds to come. An' him round-shouldered with the weight o' the gold he does be carryin' in his pockets.

MAGGIE (*sitting on a chair left*). Musha, Lizzie, it's a fearful thing to have to depend on any doctor.

LIZZIE. An' wasn't the doctor the blackhearted ould scoundrel to make us raise the ten pounds before he'd come. The curse o' Cromwell on him! (*Spits in the fire.*)

MAGGIE. Now don't be cursin' him, Lizzie. . . . (*Rises.*) Not till

. But sure the priest says the dowry doesn't matter.

Musha, woman, an' what would the priest, God bless him, knowin' about it? Sure, *he* doesn't have to worry about :tin' married!

EN (*coming out of the sickroom and closing the door*). Is the y wet?

: (*looking into the teapot*). 'Tis, Maureen, an' it's nice an' rong.

EN (*going to the cupboard and gettin a cup and saucer*). I'll ke a little sup in to Katie Claffey. Sure, the poor woman's iees must be wore out prayin'.

E. Aye. It takes a long time to get around them seven-decade eads . . . (*Pours tea into the cup held by* MAUREEN.) . . . an' atie's such a terrible slow pray-er.

s (*entering right in great excitement*). I'm just after seein' the urragh! It's landin' now in the cove.

E. Thanks be to God!

women bestir themselves. MAUREEN *puts the cup on the table enter. Runs to the window to look out.*]

: (*rising and lifting a shawl over her head*). I'll run over to haun Scanlan's an' get a drop o' poteen to warm the men. (*She tarts across the room right.*)

IE. Do in the name o' God. Sure they'll be kilt with the cold. (LIZZIE *exits right.* MAGGIE, *tidying up the room, takes a clean towel from a locker under the cupboard and hangs it above the bench left.*) Dennis dear, will ye put some water in the kettle? The doctor'll be needin' it. (DENNIS *puts water from a bucket into the kettle on the fire.*) I'll take Katie's tay in.

REEN. I'll do it, Maggie.

GIE (*at the door of the sickroom*). I want to go in anyway an' say a few prayers. An' while I'm at it, I'll say one for the doctor. Sure he must be a terrible heathen entirely. (*Exits, closing the door.*)

NIS (*going to* MAUREEN). Maureen darlin' . . . there's somethin' I must say to ye.

JREEN. What's troublin' ye, Dennie?

NIS. Suppose something happens to my mother?

after he gets here anyhow. (*Crosses back to the window right.*) God send he makes a safe crossin'.

LIZZIE. An' why wouldn't he? Hasn't he got the three best curragh-men in the west of Ireland rowin' him across?

MAGGIE (*at the window*). The divil himself must be kickin' up the ocean the way that west wind is blowin'. An' the dark clouds black'nin' the width of the sea.

LIZZIE. Arrah, you're a terrible woman for worryin', Maggie Rafferty. Sure they'll be all right. Hasn't every one of them got the St. Christopher medal tied 'round their necks?

MAGGIE (*crossing back to left*). Did they take a medal for the doctor?

LIZZIE. They did indeed . . . an extra big one. An' sure he'll need it, bad luck to him! (DENNIS O'CONNOR *comes tiptoeing out of his mother's room, closing the door softly.*) Is yer mother asleep, Dennis?

DENNIS. She is, thank God. (*Getting his tam o' shanter from a hook on the wall above the door right.*) I'll go up on the cliff and look . . . maybe I can see them from there.

LIZZIE. Do that. An' put yer coat on, avic, or it's destroyed you'll be with the sharp blasts o' that west wind cuttin' through yer bones. (*He takes his coat and puts it on.*) I'll have a nice cup of tay waitin' for ye when ye get back.

[*The door right opens.* FATHER TIM *enters. The priest dips his forefinger and thumb in the holy-water basin on the wall just inside the door and makes a small sign of the cross on his forehead with his thumb. The two women rise and make an awkward curtsy.* DENNIS *removes his tam o' shanter.*]

FATHER TIM. God bless the house.

ALL. You too, Father.

FATHER TIM (*patting the boy's shoulder*). Ah, stop frettin', Dennie avic. Sure yer face is as long as a Palm Sunday gospel. (DENNIS *smiles, puts his tam o' shanter on, and exits right, closing the door behind him. The priest starts toward the sickroom.*) An' how's Mollie?

MAGGIE. She just went to sleep, Father.

FATHER TIM. Thank God for that. I won't disturb her. (*Crosses down left.*) Have ye e'er a bit o' snuff on ye, Maggie?

MAUREEN. Aw it won't, Dennie.

DENNIS. It's a terrible thing to talk about, but if – if anything happened to her, God forbid, 'twould – 'twould mean a whole year before we could get married an' . . . well . . . 'twouldn't be fair to ask ye to wait.

MAUREEN. Ye *do* want to marry me, don't ye, Dennie?

DENNIS. More than anythin' else in the world. I'll never love anyone else.

MAUREEN. Then what's a year, Dennie avic? Sure, I'd wait if it took a thousand years. Haven't I waited for ye all me life?

DENNIS (*patting* MAUREEN'S *arm, simply*). God bless ye, Maureen. (*He starts pacing the floor, worried.*)

MAUREEN. Now sit down, Dennie dear, an' don't be walkin' around like a slippery eel on a fryin' pan. (*She takes his pipe down from the mantelpiece and hands it to him.*) Here. Take a blast out o' yer pipe and I'll give ye a nice cup of tay.

DENNIS (*impatiently*). No. I'll go out an' meet the doctor. (*Exits right.*)

[MAUREEN *gets five cups, saucers, spoons, from the cupboard and places them on table center. A sugar bowl and a small milk pitcher are added.*]

LIZZIE (*entering right, with a package of tea and a bottle of poteen*). God bless ye, Maureen. You'll make a grand woman o' the house. (*She uncorks the poteen bottle and pours some into four of the cups.*) I saw ould Dr. Fitzwilliams comin' up the cliff road with the men . . . streelin' along behind like an ould cow's tail he was. . . . I never liked a bone in that fella's skin. May the divil roast him for ten thousand years!

MAUREEN (*over her shoulder from the fireplace left*). Musha, Lizzie, you're a terrible cursin' woman.

[*As she finishes filling the fourth cup,* LIZZIE, *noting that* MAUREEN *is not looking, takes a quick drink from the poteen bottle, wipes her lips, and puts the bottle on the cupboard shelf.* DENNIS *enters right, followed by the* DOCTOR, *who does not dip his fingers in the holy water.*)

DENNIS (*starting immediately toward the sickroom*). She's in here, Doctor.

DR. FITZWILLIAMS. Take your time, my boy, take your time. (*He lays his satchel on the table center.*)

[*Three* CURRAGHMEN *enter. They all dip their fingers in the holy-water basin, unobtrusively cross their foreheads, and mumble the traditional greetings simultaneously.*]

MICAL DUV and SHAMUS O'LOUGHLIN. God bless the house.

PADRIC KEARNY. An' all that's in it.

LIZZIE. You too. (*She takes a pipe from her dress pocket and puts it in her mouth.*)

MAUREEN. And welcome back. (*The* DOCTOR *removes his overcoat as the three* CURRAGHMEN *up right stand about awkwardly. The* DOCTOR *hands his coat and hat to the nearest* CURRAGHMAN, *who, puzzled as to what to do with them, tosses them over his shoulder onto the bench up right. They probably land on the floor and stay there.* MAUREEN *hands each man a cup from the table.*) Good health to ye!

CURRAGHMEN (*raising their cups in a toast*). God's blessin' on this house.

LIZZIE (*seated at the fireplace, takes the pipe from her mouth*). More power to yer elbows!

[*The men drink their poteen in one gulp. The* DOCTOR, *now seated in a chair, pays no attention to anyone, but is busy grunting as he removes his sea boots.* DENNIS *is impatiently standing at the sickroom door.*]

MAUREEN (*coming to* DOCTOR *with a cup*). Just a drop to warm ye, Doctor.

DOCTOR (*looking up*). What is it?

MAUREEN. Poteen, sir.

DOCTOR (*waving it away gruffly*). I'll take a cup of tea.

[MAUREEN *replaces the cup on the table and pours a cup of tea.*]

DENNIS (*anxiously*). But Doctor . . . me mother is . . .

DOCTOR. Yes, yes . . . I know. . . .

MAUREEN (*coming over with tea, milk, and sugar*). We just made the tay an' it's nice and strong.

[*He takes it, adds milk and sugar, tastes it as if critical of its quality. He is indifferent to the stern looks of the* CURRAGHMEN.]

DOCTOR. Now then . . . who's been attending the patient?

MAUREEN. Nora O'Malley, sir — Shaun Mor's sister. She's inside.

DOCTOR (*rising and removing his other coat and hanging it over the back of the armchair*). Bring her out!

MAUREEN (*exiting into the sickroom*). Yes sir.

DOCTOR (*to* LIZZIE). Let me have some hot water and soap! And a clean towel — if you have one. (*Rolls up his sleeves.*)

[DENNIS *takes a towel and soap and gets a washbasin off a hook on the wall up left, and places them on the chair down left.*]

LIZZIE (*filling the basin with hot water from the kettle*). Dennie avic, run over and tell Father Tim that the doctor is here.

[DENNIS *gets his cap and exits right.* NORA *and* MAUREEN *come out of the sickroom, closing the door.*]

NORA. Ye wanted to see me, Doctor?

DOCTOR (*washing his hands*). Yes. Now — eh — tell me, just what have you done for the patient?

NORA. Well, sir . . . when I got here the men were after carryin' her up from the black rocks, where she went to cut seaweed for kelp . . .

DOCTOR (*impatiently*). All right, all right, what did you do for her? (*He takes the towel from the back of the chair and carefully dries his hands.*)

NORA. Well, sir . . . I could see her leg was broke an' the collarbone was hurted, so I straightened them out an' tied a piece o' wood to her leg. Then I sprinkled it with the blessed water from St. Colum's well. It has great curin' powers in it, an' it's better than any doctor. (*The* DOCTOR *gives her a quick glance.*) I remember the time when ould Mick Corrigan, God rest his soul, slipped an' . . .

DOCTOR (*cutting her off and tossing the towel on a chair*). All right. Bring my bag. We'll have a look at her. (NORA *takes the bag from the table. He leads the way into the sickroom, opens the door, and sees two women kneeling in prayer at the bedside.*) Get these women out of here! (*Goes into the room, followed by* NORA.)

[MAGGIE *and* KATIE *rise quickly and humbly leave the room.* MAGGIE *closes the door after them.* KATIE *goes to the bench up left, and sits there, resuming her prayers on the rosary.* MAUREEN *hangs up the* DOCTOR'S *coat and hat.*]

MICAL DUV (*moving down behind the table*). Wouldn't that ould fella provoke a saint?

MAGGIE (*taking the basin the* DOCTOR *used and crossing right*). He's enough to provoke the whole *twelve* Apostles. (*Exits at the door right.*)

LIZZIE (*to two* CURRAGHMEN *standing up right*). Will ye stop standin' there gawkin' an' drag that bench over, an' I'll give ye some tay to warm yer insides.

[PADRIC *and* SHAMUS *bring the bench from up right, down to back of the table center.*]

MAUREEN (*looking out the window up right*). There's a great surf tearin' at the black rocks below. 'Twas a terrible bad crossin' ye had, Mical Duv.

MICAL DUV. It was. But we got here with God's help.

[*The* CURRAGHMEN *are seated at the table now,* PADRIC *right,* SHAMUS *center, and* MICAL DUV *left.*]

SHAMUS. If the sea keeps runnin' like this, 'twill be terrible hard on the fishin'. There's a heavy feel to that north wind.

[MAGGIE *enters with an empty basin, crosses up left, wipes the basin, and hangs it on the wall.*]

PADRIC. Sure, 'tisn't like summer at all. Divil a sight o' the sun we've seen in weeks.

[*A man passes the window up right.*]

MAUREEN. Here's Shaun Mor comin' with the collection money for the doctor.

LIZZIE (*pouring tea*). Hope he got enough to pay the pernicious ould pagan.

NORA (*opening the door of the sickroom*). Maggie, will ye come in an' give me a hand?

[MAGGIE *exits into the sickroom, closing the door.*]

SHAUN MOR (*entering right; holy-water business*). God save all here.

ALL. You too.

SHAMUS. An' how are ye, Shaun?

SHAUN MOR. I m finely, thank God. (*Indicating the sickroom.*) An' how's herself?

LIZZIE (*putting the teapot on the table*). The doctor's in there with her now. Did ye get the money?

SHAUN MOR (*coming to the right of the table*). It's distressed I am to tell ye, it was only a little over five pounds I was able to get. (*Taking the money from his pockets and placing it on the table.*) An' I scoured the Island clean. A fearful scarce thing is money nowadays.

MAUREEN. God help us.

SHAUN MOR. Will ye count it, Maureen? I never was much of a hand at the countin' o' money or sheep. (*He pulls out a ten-shilling note and a half-crown piece from another pocket as* MAUREEN *counts silently.*) An' here's twelve and sixpence from Father Tim, God bless him. He had it saved up to buy a pair o' shoes.

PADRIC. He's a daycent man.

LIZZIE (*back of the table*). Isn't ten pounds a power o' money to be chargin'?

MICAL DUV. It is. If Dr. O'Sullivan wasn't up in Dublin he'd have wanted to come over for nothin'. Wait till he hears about this.

LIZZIE. But why in the name o' God did ye agree to pay it?

SHAMUS. We had to. He was the only doctor in Dunmore, an' he didn't want to come at all on account o' the storm.

PADRIC. Musha, he's a terrible ould coward.

SHAMUS. Sure, he only attends the rich people, an' he's got bags o' money.

MICAL DUV. You should see the grand house he lives in, Lizzie. Like a king's palace it is, with carpets that ye'd sink up to yer knees in, an' fine, soft chairs to sit on.

[SHAUN MOR *sits in the chair right of the table.*]

SHAMUS (*with boyish delight*). An' on his table is the queerest sort o' bell. Faith, ye can pick it up and shake it, an' divil a ring. But when it stood on the table, an' ye'd hit it on the top . . . just a small wallop . . . on the button . . . (*He demonstrates.*) . . . it makes a sweet, silvery music sound.

MICAL DUV. Aye, an' then a skinny woman 'ud come runnin' in an' get terrible cross every time we hit it.

LIZZIE. Tsk, tsk, tsk! It must be a great wonder entirely.

SHAMUS. I had a good chance to steal it when the ould fella's back was turned, but I didn't, God forgive me.

[MAUREEN *has finished counting, and the money is carefully stacked on the table.*]

SHAUN MOR (*rising*). How much is it, Maureen?

MAUREEN. Five pounds two an' ninepence ha'penny.

MICAL DUV. Sure, that's only a little more than half it.

LIZZIE. It's enough for him, the cross-tempered ould weasel.

SHAUN MOR. It's more than enough, but we gave him our word, an' if we can't pay it, what'll the big world outside think of us?

MAUREEN. What are we goin' to do?

SHAUN MOR. I don't know, God help us. . . . (*Crossing left, pondering the situation.*) I don't know.

SHAMUS. It's goin' to be a fearful disgrace.

[MAUREEN *wanders up right, and gazes out the window.*]

PADRIC. I could write to me Uncle Matt in Australia.

SHAUN MOR. Maybe the doctor wouldn't wait.

[*The sickroom door opens.* NORA *enters with a drinking glass, goes to the water bucket on the bench left. She leaves the door open.*]

NORA. Give us a spoon, Lizzie.

[*During this action,* MAUREEN *unobtrusively slips out the door at the right.*]

LIZZIE (*handing* NORA *a spoon*). What does the doctor say?

NORA (*hurrying back into the sickroom*). I'll tell ye later. (*Exits, closing the door.*)

SHAUN MOR (*going up to the bucket*). I'll have a drop o' that water meself. (*He raises a dipper to his lips.* LIZZIE *stops him.*)

LIZZIE (*going to the cupboard*). Oh, I forgot! I have a grand bottle of poteen that Shaun Scanlan sent over. (*Picking up the bottle.*) Sure, a toothful of it 'ud make ye feel like the Sultan o' Turkey.

SHAUN MOR (*regretfully*). Ah no, Lizzie. . . . I – I took the pledge.

LIZZIE (*sympathetically*). Tsk, tsk! Well, God help ye.

[*All laugh, including* SHAUN.]

SHAUN MOR (*lifting the cup in a toast*). Slauncha! (*Drinks the water.*)

PADRIC *(laughing and pointing to the bench left)*. Will ye look at the Widow Claffey there! She went to sleep with the angels, sayin' the rosary.

LIZZIE. Ah, the poor woman's wore out from bein' up with Mollie all night.

[KATIE, *as if hearing them, wakes and resumes her beads. The* DOCTOR *enters from the sickroom carrying his satchel, followed by* NORA. *All stare at him expectantly.*]

DOCTOR. She'll be all right in a couple of weeks. *(The* DOCTOR *goes to the chair at the right of the table, where he sits and pulls on his sea boots.* KATIE CLAFFEY *rises and exits into the sickroom.)* I made a careful examination. No internal injuries, but a broken leg and a bruised collarbone. They're setting nicely, though. *(To* NORA, *who stands near the door.)* You're a very good bone-setter, Nora. See that you follow my instructions and everything will be all right.

NORA. Yes, sir.

[MAUREEN *enters the door at the right quietly, and stands listening.*]

DOCTOR. And give her plenty of milk and a bit of meat . . . if you can get it.

NORA. I will, Doctor. *(Exits into the sickroom, closing the door.)*

DOCTOR *(rising, and putting on his first coat)*. I won't need to come back. *(Noticing the money piled on the table.)* And now – eh . . . *(Coughs.)* You know we doctors have to live, too. *(With a little forced laugh the* DOCTOR *goes up right to get his overcoat and hat.* MAUREEN *slides out of his way, going to the back of the table at the center.)* Unfortunately, we have to charge what may sometimes seem like an exorbitant fee . . . but of course . . . that's all a matter of opinion. After all, the trip here entails a long and dangerous crossing, and eh . . . my time is valuable. *(He puts on his overcoat and returns to the chair at the right of the table. He looks at everybody as he waits for some response, but there is only an embarrassing silence.)* It's too bad that society hasn't seen its way clear to adopt a more charitable attitude toward you Islanders and provide you with adequate medical attention.

SHAUN MOR *(rising and coming to the chair at left center)*. Doctor

. . . it's distressed I am to tell ye . . . but we weren't able to get the ten pounds to pay ye.

DOCTOR. *What!*

SHAUN MOR (*indicating the money*). We were only able to collect five pounds two an' ninepence ha'penny, sir.

DOCTOR. Have you the effrontery to suggest that I cut my fee?

SHAUN MOR. 'Tisn't that at all, Doctor . . . but, ye see, we . . .

DOCTOR (*sarcastically*). Yes! I'm beginning to see. Now that you know the patient is out of danger, it's obvious that you don't intend to live up to your obligations. Isn't that it?

[*A second's pause as* SHAUN *attempts to control himself.*]

MAUREEN (*going to* SHAUN *quietly and holding out five gold pounds in her hand*). Shaun . . .

SHAUN MOR (*putting his hands behind his back and shaking his head*). Blessin's o' God on ye, child . . . I couldn't!

MAUREEN (*simply, but determined*). Take it, Shaun, or I'll pitch it into the sea!

SHAUN MOR. 'Twould be an unlucky thing to give up yer dowry, an' you only goin' to be wed.

MAUREEN. It's for Mollie I'm doin' it. I'd never forgive meself if I didn't. (*Deliberately places her gold on the table with the rest of the money.*) There! It's done now. (*Steps back and looks appealingly at the men.*) And don't any of ye tell Dennie.

LIZZIE. Maureen alana . . . it's bad luck to fly in the face of God and tamper with the ould customs.

MAUREEN. I know. "Ne'er a fortune, ne'er a child." 'Tis the will o' God! (*She goes up left and sits on the bench.*)

SHAUN MOR (*picking up the money, leaving several small coins, and crossing in front of the table*). We gave ye our word, Doctor. Here's yer money!

DOCTOR (*taking it, and counting*). Thank you. . . . It isn't exactly the money . . . eight, nine, ten. . . . (*Putting it in his fat wallet.*) It's the principle of the thing. (*Places his wallet in his pocket, picks up his satchel, starts right toward the door.*) Well! Come on, you men! I'm ready to go back to the mainland. (*Turns to see if they are coming.*)

PADRIC (*quietly, after an ominous pause*). Can ye swim, Doctor?

DOCTOR. Why?

MICAL DUV (*deliberately*). Because we're not takin' ye back!

DOCTOR (*looks from one to the other, steps forward*). What do you mean? You agreed . . .

MICAL DUV. We only agreed to bring ye over. There was no word said about takin' ye back!

SHAMUS. Ye made a hard bargain, Doctor. We kept our end of it. We took ye here . . . ye got yer money. Now get back the best way ye can.

DOCTOR. But it's nine miles to the mainland. How am I going to get there? (*The men smile at each other. The* DOCTOR *starts again to the door.*) All right! I'll get three other curraghmen to do it.

[*The men laugh.*]

SHAMUS. There's not a curraghman on the Island of Innisheen would row ye back.

MICAL DUV (*poking* SHAMUS). Now why did ye tell him, Shamus! 'Twould be no harm for him to go round and find out for himself.

SHAMUS. Ah, sure, wouldn't it be a sin now, to have the doctor wastin' his valuable time.

LIZZIE (*adjusting the armchair cushion*). Arrah, sit down, Doctor darlin', and make yerself at home. (*She pours tea and puts milk in it.*) Sure, ye'll need the rest. It's a long trip back . . . even if ye don't make it. There's nothin' like a daycent cup o' tay to calm yer nerves. How much sugar do ye take?

DOCTOR. I don't want any tea.

LIZZIE (*shaking her head*). Isn't that strange now, an' when ye first came here ye were so fond of it. Tsk, tsk, tsk! Musha, the poor man's losin' his appetite.

[*The men shake their heads in mock sympathy, stir and drink their tea noisily as the* DOCTOR *paces up and down.* LIZZIE *offers a cup to* SHAUN, *who is seated on a chair at left center.*]

SHAUN MOR. No, thank ye kindly.

[LIZZIE *sits on the stool below the fire and drinks the tea herself, enjoying the following scene.*]

DOCTOR (*stops pacing*). You can't do this to me. I'll have the law on you.

SHAUN MOR *(quietly, removing his pipe)*. *What* law?

DOCTOR. I'll have you all thrown into jail for this.

SHAUN MOR *(rising and taking a step to center)*. Ah, it's nonsense yer talkin', Doctor. There's only one law here and we need nayther police nor jails to enforce it. 'Tis the law o' God. Maybe ye never heard of it? The law of this Island is Christian charity . . . to visit the sick, help the poor, and love yer fella man for the love o' God.

DOCTOR. I didn't come here to listen to any of your ignorant Island sermons.

SHAUN MOR. No! Ye came here for ten pounds that we could ill afford. An' you knowin' that the money among us is as scarce as the potatoes we eat. An' it's distressed we are to get the price of a daycent pair o' britches to wear to Mass on Sunday.

DOCTOR. I'm not concerned with your economic circumstances. I had a right to exact what I consider a reasonable fee for my services.

SHAUN MOR *(turning back to the chair at left center, sitting)*. An' so did Judas!

[*The* DOCTOR *looks at the men. All ignore him and eat their bread and drink their tea with relish. The* DOCTOR *paces the floor, sits in the armchair, drumming the wood with nervous fingers. No sound is heard except the ticking of the large clock.*]

DOCTOR *(looking at the clock, then at his watch, rising)*. This is nothing short of kidnaping. Every minute you keep me here you make it harder for yourselves.

MICAL DUV *(to* SHAMUS*)*. Couldn't we let the doctor have that ould boat that was wrecked on Slieve Head? You know . . . the one with the big hole in the bottom?

SHAMUS. Ah, now, sure ye wouldn't want the doctor to be gettin' his feet wet. Besides he might fall through the hole and be drownded with the weight of all that gold in his pockets.

[*The men grin.*]

PADRIC. A grand idea just came into me mind. Do ye remember the story of Jonah in the whale's belly?

MICAL DUV. Faith, I do indeed.

PADRIC. Well, I was just wonderin'. Maybe if we talked to one o' them whales lyin' off the Cliffs o' Mohill, he might be willin' to swally the doctor and spit him out in Dunmore?

MICAL DUV. It's a darlin' idea. We could toss the gentleman to the whales from the end o' the cliff . . .

SHAMUS. Ah no, boys. I'm afeared that wouldn't work at all. Them whales has terrible sensitive stomachs.

DOCTOR. Will you please stop this buffoonery? I'll . . . I'll pay you to take me back.

[*The men laugh hilariously.*]

SHAUN MOR (*rising, crossing to the left of the table*). Stop yer jokin' now, boys. The doctor made a bargain with us to come here, so why shouldn't we make a bargain with him to take him back?

DOCTOR (*taking out his wallet*). All right. How much do you want?

SHAUN MOR (*hitting the table a thump*). The price is ten pounds!

[*The men rock with laughter.*]

DOCTOR. Ten pounds? It's ridiculous . . . absurd! I can't *afford* it!

SHAUN MOR. "We're not concerned with yer economic circumstances."

DOCTOR. But the price is unreasonable.

SHAUN MOR. These men "have a right to exact what they consider a reasonable fee for their services."

DOCTOR. I'm willing to offer you a pound for the trip. That's eh . . . six shillings and eightpence a piece. Take it or leave it. (*He turns away right.*)

[FATHER TIM *and* DENNIS *enter at the right. The priest uses the holy water.*]

FATHER TIM. God save all here, and take it or leave what?

[DENNIS *goes into the sickroom.*]

DOCTOR. Father . . . these men have refused to take me back to the mainland. I even offered to pay them. I made them a very generous offer.

SHAUN MOR (*left center, on a chair*). Father, he said that a man had a right to charge what he thinks a job is worth. So *I* set a price of ten pounds for the trip back . . . an' cheap at that.

FATHER TIM. Ten pounds? (*He thinks, then laughs.*) Shaun, you're a king and a poet. (*To the* DOCTOR.) I'm afraid ye've put your foot in it, Doctor.

DOCTOR. But what am I going to do, Father?

FATHER TIM. Well, if it was for me to say . . . I might meet ye halfway on the price. (*He looks at the men.*) But it's not for me to decide. That's Shaun Mor's job. He's the elected King of this Island and a fair man. (*The priest goes into the sickroom, closing the door behind him.*)

DOCTOR (*taking out his wallet again*). What's your lowest price?

SHAUN MOR. All right . . . like Father Tim said . . . I'll meet ye halfway on it.

PADRIC. Hey, Shaun! Come here. There's somethin' else we want.

SHAUN MOR. Excuse me, Doctor.

[*He goes to the men. They whisper and laugh while the* DOCTOR *paces up and down.* SHAUN MOR *leaves them and goes left to the fireplace, where he fills and lights his pipe, using a folded paper from a can on the mantel, which he lights from the fire, replacing the unburnt portion in the can afterward.*]

SHAMUS (*during the above business*). We're willin' to take ye, Doctor . . . if ye'll give us that little bell we saw on the table in yer house.

DOCTOR. What bell?

SHAMUS. The queer-lookin' bell with the knob on top that makes the silvery music sound.

DOCTOR. The servant's call bell?

PADRIC. That's the one.

DOCTOR (*relieved*). Oh! Yes . . . yes, of course. (*Puts his wallet back in his pocket, speaks magnanimously.*) Yes. I'll make you a present of it.

SHAMUS (*rising*). Well, that's real daycent of ye. Come on, lads, we'll get the boat ready. (*Getting his coat.* MICAL DUV *has risen and is putting on his coat.*)

MICAL DUV. We'd better take an extra pair of long oars. I'll run across to the house and get them. (*Goes to the door at the right.*)

SHAMUS. Do that. We might need them. And make haste, will ye? The tide'll be turnin' soon.

MACAL DUV. I will. (*Exits at the right.*)

[SHAMUS *returns to the bench, sits. The* DOCTOR *paces the floor.* DENNIS *and* FATHER TIM *come out of the sickroom.* FATHER TIM *sits on the bench up left, with* MAUREEN. DENNIS *stands near by.*]

SHAUN MOR. Ye might as well sit down, Doctor, an' keep yerself warm while yer waitin'. There's a sharp wind blowin' outside. Mick won't be long.

DOCTOR (*sitting in the armchair*). I'm glad that's all settled.

SHAUN MOR. An' so am I. Well, eh – if ye don't mind, Doctor, we'd like ye to pay us that five pounds . . . now.

DOCTOR (*jumping to his feet*). *Five pounds?* For what?

SHAUN MOR. Don't ye remember? I agreed to meet ye halfway on the price.

DOCTOR. But . . . eh . . . I must have misunderstood you?

SHAUN MOR. I'm sorry if ye did, Doctor. But that was the bargain. Sure, we only want the return of Maureen's dowry money.

DENNIS (*looking toward* MAUREEN). Maureen . . .

DOCTOR. I won't pay it! (*The* DOCTOR *sits down stubbornly.*)

[SHAUN MOR *shrugs his shoulders, turns to the left, and sits.*]

PADRIC. Looks like the doctor's thinkin' o' settlin' down here, Shamus.

SHAMUS (*taking off his coat*). Well, now . . . 'twill be a great blessin' havin' a doctor handy.

DOCTOR (*arises, goes to* SHAMUS *and* PADRIC). I'm willing to make a private deal with you fellows, if you'll only listen to reason.

PADRIC (*to* DOCTOR). *Nee hig-um thu un Bearla.*[1]

SHAMUS (*to* PADRIC). *Kade thaw shea a-raw, ah Fhawdrick?*[2]

DOCTOR (*to the priest*). What are they talking about?

FATHER TIM. They say they don't understand English.

DOCTOR. B-but they were just speaking . . .

FATHER TIM. If ye'll take my advice, ye'll deal with Shaun Mor.

DOCTOR (*taking out his wallet, going to* SHAUN MOR). All right. I'm willing to pay you two pounds. (SHAUN MOR *turns his back.*) Very well then, *three* pounds. (*Places three pound notes on the table.*)

SHAUN MOR. I think the men might be willin' to row ye back . . . about *halfway* . . . four an' a half miles . . . for that. Sure, ye could swim the rest o' the way.

DOCTOR (*putting down another pound note*). Four pounds, then?

---

[1] I don't understand English.

[2] What is it he's saying, Padric?

SHAUN MOR. Ah, ye're gettin' closer to shore now. But it's still five pounds, an' *in gold,* Doctor, to land ye *safe an' sound* in Dunmore.

DOCTOR. It's an outrage! That's what it is. (*Picks up the pound notes and grudgingly lays down five pounds in gold.*) There!

PADRIC. An' the bell?

DOCTOR (*turning, thoroughly exasperated*). *Yes, you can have it.*

SHAUN MOR (*rising*). Maureen . . . come here, alana. (MAUREEN *rises from the bench up left, crosses down to* SHAUN MOR. *He picks up the money, takes her hand, and puts the gold in it.*) And may God bless ye, Maureen, with a grand houseful o' children.

MAUREEN. Thank ye kindly, Shaun. (*She returns to the bench at the left.*)

[*The priest smiles, rises, and nods to* DENNIS. DENNIS *sits on the bench with* MAUREEN, *and takes her hand. She smiles up at him happily.* MICAL DUV *enters at the right. He looks worried. He has trouble closing the door against the wind. The* DOCTOR *rises, picking up his satchel.*]

MICAL DUV. There's a big flock o' sea birds after flyin' in from the northwest.

[*All but the* DOCTOR *cross themselves. The men look at each other fearfully.*]

FATHER TIM. How does it look, Mick?

MICAL DUV. There's a bad sea risin'. I'm afeared it looks like a nor'wester.

[SHAUN *and the priest cross to the window up right and look out.*]

DOCTOR (*almost beside himself*). What does all this mean?

FATHER TIM. It means, Doctor, that no boat can leave or land here in the teeth of a northwest gale.

SHAUN MOR. St. Christopher himself couldn't get through *that* sea.

FATHER TIM (*getting his hat*). I'd better go over to the chapel and ring the storm signal. I'm afraid ye'll have to wait till it blows over, Doctor. (*He exits hurriedly right, having the same difficulty as* MICAL DUV *with the door.*)

DOCTOR (*crossing anxiously to* SHAUN MOR). How long will this storm last?

SHAUN MOR. Oh, sometimes only a few days . . . sometimes a month. . . .

DOCTOR. *A month!*

SHAUN MOR. We can't control the weather, Doctor.

[MICAL DUV *and* SHAMUS *hang up their coats and sit at the table.*]

DOCTOR (*worried*). But I just paid you five pounds to take me back.

SHAUN MOR (*calmly, as he lights his pipe at the fireplace*). An' so we will . . . when the storm blows over.

DOCTOR. When the storm blows over?

SHAUN MOR. Amn't I after tellin' ye, Doctor, that the men'll land ye safe and sound?

[*A low rumble of thunder is heard.*]

DOCTOR. Yes, but . . .

SHAUN MOR. 'Twouldn't be honest now, would it, if ye got drownded before the men could keep their word?

DOCTOR. But you said . . .

SHAUN MOR. We said we'd take ye back, but sure we didn't say *when*, did we?

[LIZZIE *has risen from the stool near the fireplace and is pouring tea for* DENNIS *and* MAUREEN. *She notices the* DOCTOR *pacing impatiently and looking out the window up right.*]

LIZZIE. Arrah, Doctor, ye'll be gettin' yerself seasick lookin' out there. Come on over by the fire and make yerself comfortable.

DOCTOR (*irritably cynical*). Don't worry about me. I'm *quite comfortable.*

[*A louder rumble of thunder.*]

LIZZIE (*to* SHAUN MOR *in a loud whisper*). Ah, the poor man is homesick. (*Sincerely solicitous.*) Arrah, sit down, Doctor darlin', an' give yer ould carcass a rest, an' while yer waitin' for the storm to blow over, maybe we can coax Shaun to tell us some of his grand stories.

[*All but the* DOCTOR *are delighted. The* CURRAGHMEN *rise and pull their bench to place at a parallel angle facing the fireplace.*]

ALL (*like children*). Yes, come on, Shaun, tell us one.

PADRIC. Aye, tell the one ye told the night o' Matt O'Brien's wake.

MAUREEN. Shaun, tell us about the time the Devil went through Athlone.

SHAMUS. Ah, that's a darlin' story.

[*They have all seated themselves around the fireplace, their backs to the* DOCTOR. *The* DOCTOR, *thoroughly disgusted, slumps in the armchair at the right of the table.*]

SHAUN MOR (*holding up his hand for silence*). Sh! I'll tell ye one now, if ye'll all keep still. (*Notices the* DOCTOR. *Hospitably.*) Wouldn't ye like to come over an' join us, Doctor?

DOCTOR (*sourly*). No thanks.

[SHAUN MOR *shrugs in disappointment, then deliberately lights his pipe from the fire while all wait expectantly. A louder rumble of thunder.* DENNIS *slips an arm around* MAUREEN'S *waist.* SHAUN MOR *clears his throat and narrates in the measured tones of the native storyteller. He pays no further attention to the* DOCTOR. *During the recital, the* DOCTOR *coughs, looks impatiently at his watch, and nervously fingers his heavy gold watch chain.*]

SHAUN MOR. Well, here's a story was told me by a sailorman who sailed the seven seas o' the world. . . . Once upon a time, there was an ould king, an' he lived in a grand golden palace in a lovely land across the sea. This ould king was a terrible heathen entirely. He had bags an' bags o' gold which he loved better than anything else in the world . . .

MICAL DUV. What was his name, Shaun?

SHAUN MOR. Oh, heh-heh, I forgot to tell ye. Sure his name was King Midas. Now, besides his gold, the king had a lot o' learnin' from grand books. But in spite of his learnin', he had no wisdom at all. He spent all his time thinkin' of the gold, an' wishin' he had more of it. But, heh-heh . . . sure the divil a bit o' good the gold did him either, for he was so busy thinkin' of it that he never had time to get a little fun out o' life! (*They all laugh. The* DOCTOR *sits staring at his gold chain wound round his hand. A very loud thunder crash, followed by the distant tolling of a church bell. All listen.*) There's the storm bell ringin'. (*They listen. Intermittent bell to the curtain.*)

SHAMUS. Isn't a bell a grand sound! (*Sighs.*) I wish we had that little bell the Doctor promised us. 'Twas a darlin' sound.

MICAL DUV. Faith it was that. And a lovely lookin' object it was, too. Ah, 'twould be a real joy to have it.

PADRIC (*fishing in his downstage pocket, he pulls forth the little bell, holds it proudly in the palm of his hand, and grins at* MICAL DUV). Well, here it is, me boys! Sure I couldn't resist it. . . . I said a little prayer when I was takin' it.

MICAL DUV (*shocked*). But sure, that's *stealin'*, Padric, an' stealin's a *terrible* sin!

PADRIC. Aw, what're ye talkin' about, man? Didn't the Doctor *give* it to us for takin' him *back?*

[*The* DOCTOR *throws up his hands in complete resignation. Intermittent sound of the church bell heard through the storm until the curtain. "Bing!"* PADRIC *taps the bell. He holds out his hand with the bell on it. Laughing and vastly amused, they all start taking turns at striking the bell, as*]

THE CURTAIN FALLS.

GLOSSARY OF ISLAND AND GAELIC WORDS

	Definition	*Pronunciation*
alana	my beauty	as spelled
arrah	indeed	ar'ra
avic	my son	a-vick'
Bannock live	a blessing (to a group)	ban'nock; live, as in "to live"
Bannock Dia lath	God's blessing	dia sounds like jee-a
fortune	a dowry	as spelled
ha'penny	halfpenny (one cent)	hayp'ny
curragh	native rowboat	kur'rah
Innisheen	Little Innish	Innisheen'
Mical Duv	Dark Michael	as spelled
musha	indeed	"u" as in "put"
O', o'	of	uh (not "oh")
Padric	Patrick	pahdrick
poteen	a native beverage	putch'een
St. Christopher medal	a religious medal for a safe voyage or journey	as spelled

	Definition	*Pronunciation*
Shaun Mor (Gaelic spelling "Sean")	Big John	shaun
slauncha	good luck	slawn'cha
slieve	mountain	sleeve
streelin'	trailing	sthreelin
turf (sod)	peat for fire	as spelled
whisht	sh!	as spelled
ye	you (singular)	yuh (not "yee")
yerra	verily	as spelled

AFTER READING

1. Can Dr. Fitzwilliams' fee be justified? What is his defense?

2. What do you think of Maureen's surrendering her dowry?

3. Are people in small communities necessarily better neighbors than people in large cities? Give instances to defend your answer.

4. What is the author's theme in this play? Refer to the "Open Letter" at the beginning of the book for an explanation of "theme."

5. Suppose this play were written about an island off the Massachusetts coast or the Florida coast. What differences would there be?

6. How can you account for Dr. Fitzwilliams' attitude toward money? Do you think he always had this attitude? What effect do you think this experience will have on him?

7. How would you defend the curraghmen for their refusal to take the doctor home? Did Dr. Fitzwilliams deserve his treatment? Give your reasons.

8. Lizzie says, "It's bad luck to fly in the face of God and tamper with the ould customs." Have you ever read of the dire results that followed when old customs were broken?

CHALLENGES

1. What do you think Maggie said when she was told of Maureen's offer?

2. Imagine that Dr. Fitzwilliams writes a diary. After he has arrived on the mainland, he makes an entry concerning his experience on the island. Write his entry.

3. When Dr. Fitzwilliams arrives home, his housekeeper asks him where he has been. Write the ensuing conversation.

4. Five years after their marriage, Maureen and Dennis reminisce about this experience. Write their conversation.

DRAMA WORKSHOP

A hint for playgoers: Reading widens your experience.

A radio program entitled *You Are There* recently became popular overnight. Such historic events as the assassination of Julius Caesar and the trial of Aaron Burr were dramatized and depicted on this program as if they were happening here and now. Through the magic of radio, listeners were able to catch the excitement of great incidents in the distant centuries as if they were actual witnesses.

Through the magic of literature, also, you can live in other times and other places and learn to understand all kinds of people. This is true of all literature, but particularly of dramatic literature. When you read or see a play, *you are there.* You identify yourself with the characters and you experience their emotions, thoughts, and actions. In the play you have just read, you were in Ireland; in another play you will be in the famous Alamo. Still other plays in this book will widen your experience.

A hint for actors: Recognize that the director is supreme.

When a group is putting on a play, there can be no divided authority. The director must be in supreme control. He should be ready to accept suggestions when they are offered in the right spirit, but if he rejects your advice for reasons of his own, abide by his decisions willingly and cheerfully.

A director needs assistants, all of whom are important. He needs a *prompter,* who helps the actors when they "run up" on their lines; a *property man,* who gathers together all the movable things needed in the play (for example, clay pipes, water glasses, and a darning basket in *The Doctor from Dunmore*); and a *stage manager,* who is responsible for setting the stage and for all activities behind the footlights. These persons are important to producing a play, as important in their own way as the actors are.

OTHER COMEDIES YOU WILL LIKE TO READ

The Grand Cham's Diamond by Allan Monkhouse (36). The dull routine of an English family is jarred suddenly by a valuable diamond thrown into the parlor.

A Husband for Breakfast by Ronald Elwy Mitchell (23). A stingy man who has bought the wife of a neighbor for half a crown has to pay much more to get rid of her.

Jazz and Minuet by Ruth Giorloff (43). A dream about the contents of her aunt's diary teaches a modern young girl a lesson in patience with her fiancé.

The Kelly Kid by Kathleen Norris and Dan Totheroh (4). The Kelly Kid is saved from the police by assuming the disguise of an old lady.

Lonesome-Like by Harold Brighouse (3). Two lonesome people, one an old lady and the other a rejected suitor, are given a new lease on life when the young man adopts her.

A Marriage Has Been Arranged by Alfred Sutro (41). An impoverished daughter of the British aristocracy finally consents to marry a wealthy, though self-educated, American.

The Lost Silk Hat by Lord Dunsany (12). A romantic young man has left his sweetheart after a quarrel and has forgotten his hat. His attempts to recover it are fateful.

Modesty by Paul Hervieu (20). Although she boasts of her ability to hear the truth about herself, Henriette has difficulties with a suitor who is frank.

The Noble Lord by Percival Wilde (15). A money-hunting American girl gets what she deserves from the English lord when he discovers she is after his money.

The Adventures of Mr. Bean

BY BURGESS MEREDITH

ABOUT THE PLAY

Mistaken identity is a favorite topic for dramatists. In the Greek play *Amphitryon* and Shakespeare's *Comedy of Errors,* among many others, laughter is created from the embarrassments of people mistaken for others. Life is actually full of situations like these; the newspapers tell about them almost daily. All of us have, at one time or other, been mistaken for somebody else, though rarely with such eventful consequences as befall Mr. Bean. Mr. Bean is one of those "little men" in this world who don't win any battles or make any startling discoveries, but who work hard, who are honest and law-abiding citizens, and who really carry most of the burdens of the world. As a hero, he is not very striking, but after all neither are most of us. To such a humble person may come one moment when

---

the spotlight is on him. Mr. Bean's moment comes when he is mistaken for someone else.

ABOUT THE AUTHOR

Burgess Meredith began his acting career as an apprentice in Eva Le Gallienne's famous Civic Repertory Company in the part of the Duck in *Alice in Wonderland.* Since this unusual debut he has played leading roles in Maxwell Anderson's *Winterset, High Tor,* and *The Star-Wagon,* in the revival of J. M. Synge's *The Playboy of the Western World,* and in many other plays. He has enjoyed an equally prominent career in Hollywood, where he re-created his role in *Winterset.* During World War II he served with distinction in the Air Corps.

THE ADVENTURES OF MR. BEAN

Characters

JULIE DRESSLER

OLIVER BEAN

GOMPERS

SAUL GOLDBIN

HARRY

CREW

Our scene is the New York test studio of a large motion-picture company where young discoveries are first photographed to determine their screen possibilities. Cameras, lights, and scenery litter the large room, which is deserted except for a little man who sits stiffly on a chair in one of the corners. He is obviously nervous, for his eyes flit uneasily about the tangle of movie equipment, and when the door opens to admit a lovely young girl, he scrambles awkwardly to his feet. She approaches him, smiling.

JULIE. Excuse me. Are you Mr. Bean?

OLIVER. Oh . . . er . . . no. I mean *Yes!* I'm Mr. Bean.

JULIE. I'm Julie Dressler. I believe we're going to do a scene together. (*Pause.*) Am I right?

OLIVER. I'm sorry . . . I mean I get confused here. How do you do!

JULIE. How do you do. I don't blame you for getting upset. It is a frightening place. Has Mr. Gompers been here yet?

OLIVER. Mr. Gompers? Now let me see . . . Gompers . . . Gompers. Who . . . ?

JULIE. He's casting head – stocky man, small mustache – in charge of tests for Saul Goldbin.

OLIVER. Yes, of course. How slow of me – he's the one I saw. Yes, of course. Very sorry.

JULIE. Well, has he been here?

OLIVER. Who? Mr. Gompers? Oh no – I haven't seen him.

JULIE. Well, I suppose he'll be late. But this will be a good chance to run over our scene a few times.

OLIVER. Our scene?

JULIE. Yes.

OLIVER. Oh, yes. Our scene . . . of course. That would be splendid.

JULIE. You see this is my first test and I want to be very sure of the lines, because once those cameras begin to turn and those lights go on, I'm afraid I'll get nervous and forget everything.

OLIVER. Oh! I'm so happy to hear you say that, Miss . . . ?

JULIE. Dressler. Julie Dressler.

OLIVER. Of course, excuse me. But I'm so happy to hear that someone else feels the same way. I've been nervous for days – ever since last week when I got that call – and now I'm worse than ever. Look at my hand – my fingers. See? They're jumping. And just feel my forehead.

JULIE. . . . It's burning.

OLIVER. Yes, it's dreadful. I wonder Miss . . . er . . . Miss . . . ?

JULIE. Dressler.

OLIVER. Miss Dressler. I wonder if we could call this off and do it some other time. Sometime when I'm feeling better. Tomorrow perhaps. Do you think we could?

JULIE. Sssssh! Be quiet! Here comes Gompers. No, don't postpone it. We'll never get another test.

[*Enter* GOMPERS]

GOMPERS. Hello there, Julie my girl. Sorry to be late, but I got some great news for you. Guess who's here?

JULIE. Why . . . I don't know, I'm sure, Mr. Gompers.

GOMPERS. None other than the great Saul Goldbin himself. Just flew in from the Coast. Those still pictures of yours got him all steamed up. He wants to see you make this test.

JULIE. Saul Goldbin!! Here to see me . . . !!

GOMPERS. Yes sirree, baby. I told him you were good. Now he can see for himself. Hey, by the way, where's Bean? Someone said he was here already.

JULIE. This is Mr. Bean.

GOMPERS. What!

OLIVER. H'd j' do?

GOMPERS. *What!!*

OLIVER. H'do?

GOMPERS. Say, what's goin' on here? I told my secretary to ask George Bean to do me the favor of helping you out on this test. And look what shows up. He ain't George Bean. Say, who are you, buddy?

OLIVER. I'm . . . er . . . I'm . . .

JULIE. Listen, Mr. Gompers. He's frightened to death. His name is Bean, too. He told me a little while ago.

GOMPERS. Can't he talk?

JULIE. Certainly he can talk. We were just talking before you came in.

GOMPERS. Well, how did he get here?

JULIE. I don't know . . . I . . . I suppose your secretary made a mistake.

GOMPERS. Mistake? . . . Sure! That's what happened. That dumb dame! She called the wrong Bean. Now what are we going to do? Goldbin here from the Coast. . . . The crew comes on in fifteen minutes. . . . Honest that dame has pulled some bad ones, but this wins prizes. Whatta mess, whatta mess!

JULIE. Could we postpone it, Mr. Gompers, until you get ahold of the real George Bean?

GOMPERS. Postpone it! With the big boss here waiting to see you! He'd fire me like a skyrocket. And George Bean lives way out in the country – couldn't get him here for hours. I swear I don't know what I'm gonna do.

JULIE. Mr. Gompers. Maybe this chap can do it. You've rehearsed it, haven't you, Mr. Bean?

OLIVER. Rehearsed . . . ? Well, er . . .

JULIE. Yes. See, he's rehearsed it.

GOMPERS. What's he gonna do it in – pantomine?

JULIE. He can act it. I'm sure he can, Mr. Gompers. We must try it. There's nothing else to do.

GOMPERS. I guess you're right at that, Julie. We gotta do something. Have you had any experience, Mr. Bean?

OLIVER. Experience?

GOMPERS. Yeah. What experience have you had?

OLIVER. I work at present for A. F. Blowheim.

GOMPERS. Blowheim?

OLIVER. In Jersey. It's a dye works.

GOMPERS (*groaning*). Oh my Lord!! Julie, we'll have to cancel the test.

JULIE. Please, Mr. Gompers. He's got to do this test with me. It's not fair.

GOMPERS. I'm sorry Julie, really . . . but this man's never been on the stage.

OLIVER. Pardon me. You will forgive me for speaking . . . but I have been.

GOMPERS. Been what?

OLIVER. On the stage.

GOMPERS. Well, well. Suppose you tell us about it.

OLIVER. Well, it's quite a story. You see, three years ago last month I had a vacation – ten days summer vacation. Now we get two weeks – but at that time it was only ten days.

GOMPERS. Very kind of Mr. Blowheim . . . to give you the time.

OLIVER. Yes, wasn't it. Well, anyway, I went to visit an aunt of mine – my mother's sister – whom my mother loved very much and asked me before she died to be kind to. Aunt Susie herself died last year . . . but as I was saying . . . I'm sorry to be so rambling, but I suppose it's because I'm nervous.

JULIE. You're lots better now.

OLIVER. Oh, I am. Indeed I am. But to go on, Aunt Susie lived in Carlton, New York, beyond Albany, and while I was there I went to a fair the village firemen were holding. In one tent there was a magician. There were two or three hundred people there, but regardless of that he picked *me* out – the magician did – and asked me to stand on the stage and help him with his tricks.

GOMPERS. I see.

OLIVER. Now all my life I've been shy in meeting people and it's very difficult, *very* difficult, for me to talk to strangers. But that night I saw the lights and heard the excitement of the crowd and was allowed to hold the big silk handkerchief the magician gave me . . . and . . . and I began to feel all excited in my stomach and I could feel the hair on my head stiffen like when you step under an ice shower.

JULIE. Yes, I know exactly how you felt.

OLIVER. You won't believe it, but I wasn't nervous! I was very excited but very *free*. That's the only way I can say it – I was free. When he talked I answered him right back . . . and very loud . . . and what I said was very funny because the people laughed . . .

GOMPERS. I'll bet they did.

OLIVER. No. It's not what you think. They didn't laugh at me. It was what I said that amused them. That made my head tingle more and my stomach got warm and happy and then when he turned away to do a trick I winked at the audience and did a dance step . . . and they laughed some more and the poor magician . . .

GOMPERS. You'll pardon this interruption, Mr. Bean. But the time is getting short. Is that the extent of your experience?

OLIVER. That was the end of my professional experience. But I must tell you that from then on I never gave up acting. I organized the Blowheim Dramatic Club.

GOMPERS. I knew it – I knew it!

OLIVER. Yes, and we've been very earnest about our rehearsals and three times a year for the last two years we have performed before the friends and employees of the company.

JULIE. Mr. Gompers, don't you think we ought to start? We should get through it at least once.

GOMPERS. O.K. But first let me tell you, Mr. Bean. . . . By the way, what's your first name?

OLIVER. Oliver.

GOMPERS. It would be. Well, listen, Oliver. I am praying deeply and sincerely that you are good. Not for the sake of the test itself, but because this is one of those situations – one of those storybook things – that never happens. But it's here and let's hope it works out.

OLIVER. Thank you.

GOMPERS. All right. Now let's walk through it. You stand there, Oliver, behind that chair. You're kinda short for her . . . but . . . oh, well, let's go. You start, Julie.

JULIE.

"When we first came to this island
I felt a comfort at being alone,
Just you and I – but now –
Well, now – the articulate moon haunts me,
And when you play your fiddle
The music makes me uneasy of my surroundings.
Why is it?"

GOMPERS. That's your cue, Mr. Bean.

OLIVER. My cue? Oh yes. Oh . . . I'm . . . er . . . gosh, I can hardly speak . . .

JULIE. You must try. Please, Mr Bean.

GOMPERS. Come on, Oliver. You can do it. Give him the last three lines, Julie. "And when . . ."

JULIE.

"And when you play your fiddle
The music makes me uneasy of my surroundings.
Why is it?"

OLIVER.

"Oh, time alters even here – here where the sands
Seemed ageless before . . . before . . ."

GOMPERS. That's right. Go on. Go on.

OLIVER.

" – here where the sands
Seemed ageless before our coming."

[*Mumbling of voices in the background.*]

GOMPERS. Oh good Lord! Here's the crew. We'll have to start in a minute. Go on, Oliver. Go on.

OLIVER.

"So I'll confess that we were . . . we were wrong
And the fate we thought we'd lost in the escaping wake
And the . . . and the . . . the . . .

GOMPERS. "And the varied sand . . ."

OLIVER.

"And the varied sand has reappeared
And we are lonely again and sad again
With the same misery."

[GOLDBIN *hurries in.*]

GOLDBIN. Well, well, Gompers. All ready to shoot? Let's start. Time's worth money. Let's go!

GOMPERS. Oh . . . yes, Mr. Goldbin. We're all set. Harry, your crew ready for a take?

HARRY. All set, Mr. Gompers.

GOMPERS. O.K. We don't waste any time around here, Mr. Goldbin.

GOLDBIN. That's good, Gompers.

GOMPERS. Start the arcs! Light up! Turn 'em over! That's the girl, Mr. Goldbin. Think she looks as good as the stills?

GOLDBIN. Looks plenty good. But can she act?

GOMPERS. Just watch her on this take. O.K. Shoot. Don't know who the mug is with her. Got let in by mistake.

GOLDBIN. That's O.K. Not interested. Just want to watch her.

VOICE. Quiet! Camera! Sticks! Action!

JULIE.

"When we first came to this island
I felt a comfort at being alone,
Just you and I – but now, –
Well, now – the articulate moon haunts me,
And when you play your fiddle
The music makes me uneasy of my surroundings.
Why is it?"

[*Pause.*]

OLIVER.

"Oh, time alters even here – here where the sands
Seemed ageless before our coming.
So I'll confess that we were wrong.
And the fate we thought we'd lost in the escaping wake
And the varied sand has reappeared
And we are lonely again and sad again
With the same misery."

JULIE.

"And yet though we've encountered
A new unhappiness — with no ship
To take us away this time — no land
Farther toward the horizon to bend to —
Still my love for you makes me bear it happily!
Oh, my darling, come to me . . . closer . . ."

OLIVER.

"No ship, you say, and no horizon?
No escapement. There's my kisses . . . (*Pause.*)
. . . my kisses and . . . and . . ."

GOMPERS. *Cut!* Kill the lights! Retake!

[*Voices off mumbling.*]

GOLDBIN. No. Wait on that. Hold it.

GOMPERS. Wait!!! Hold it!

GOLDBIN. Don't shoot any more. Save it. We've got those two speeches of hers. Just print those and I'll fly them right back to the Coast. She's a great bet. Why waste more film? Come on, let's get back to your office, Gompers.

GOMPERS. O.K., Mr. Goldbin. Be right with you. Kill everything! Break! We're all through.

[*Voices off mumbling.*]

JULIE. Oh, Mr. Bean. Could I talk to you before you go?

OLIVER. Yes. Pardon me. (*Sniffs.*) Bad cold. You know. Very bad. (*Sniffs.*) Pardon me.

JULIE. Listen, Oliver. No, look at me. That's right. You mustn't feel badly. They just weren't interested in trying to get anything of you this time. You'll have another chance.

OLIVER. No I won't . . . ever.

JULIE. Yes you will. You will. And if I'm ever in a position to help you, I will. I promise you that.

OLIVER. I'm afraid I spoiled it for you. That's what really worries me.

JULIE. Don't worry about me. You didn't spoil it. Just the other way round. It's hard to describe, but — in some way — you made me say those speeches better than I would have with someone else. I forgot about myself; I wasn't nervous. It's hard to explain what I mean exactly.

OLIVER. I could never forgive myself if I had ruined it for you. Because — well . . . because . . .

JULIE. Yes, Oliver . . . ?

OLIVER. Well . . . it's only this. This is as far as I should go. Here doing this test, I mean. Perhaps it was too far — but I braved it out, and in a way I'm glad. It's a terrible thing this . . . well, this excitement of the theater. I braved it this once, and really, honestly — this was enough. My way of life is quiet. Nothing could ever change that. Quiet and . . . well, if you knew how much fun it is at Blowheim's, you would realize that my way of life is sufficient.

JULIE. That's fine, Oliver, it is really.

OLIVER. Because I'm not . . . well, I'm not hardy enough, I don't think, ever to try this again; this real professional business, I mean. I don't think I am.

JULIE. No. Perhaps not, Oliver.

OLIVER. But it will be kind of fun to go back to the club again, now that I've done all this, and tell them about it. They're waiting to hear. There's going to be a special meeting tonight. You see, I got today off to come here.

JULIE. I see.

OLIVER. As a matter of fact, even if they offered me a job here I couldn't take it, because my boss said he'd let me off today, but it was the last time. See what I mean?

JULIE. Yes . . . You mean . . .

OLIVER. I mean I couldn't afford to give up my position at Blowheim's permanently. And anyway I'm too involved with the club now. I'm president.

JULIE. That . . . that's fine . . . Oliver.

OLIVER. By the way Miss . . . er . . . Miss . . . ?

JULIE. Dressler.

OLIVER. Dressler. I'll never forget your name again as long as I live.

JULIE. Why?

OLIVER. Because I'll be watching for you always — from now on. I'll hope and watch and pray for you. Then someday I'll take my club to our local theater and we will sit all along in a row and there will be a lot of announcements and music and then —

suddenly — your name will flash up — Julie Dressler — and then . . . then you yourself will come out. There on the screen. And I will sit a little straighter and smile in a familiar way and all the members of the club will stop breathing because they will know that you and I worked together once upon a time. (*Pause.*) Well . . . good-by . . . Miss Dressler . . .

JULIE. Good-by . . . Oliver . . .

AFTER READING

1. When the play first appeared in print it was called *The Adventures of Mr. Bean.* Later, in a magazine, the title was changed to *Screen Test.* Which title do you prefer? Why?

2. Have you ever turned up in the wrong place? How did you meet the situation?

3. Can you make a case for saying that Julie is the typical young movie star? Do you know enough about Julie to prophesy about her career?

4. Is the author poking fun at Mr. Bean or sympathizing with him? Defend your answer.

5. What were Oliver's hopes when he received the message to take a screen test?

6. Are the characters of Mr. Gompers and Mr. Goldbin clearly delineated, or do they appear to be types?

7. What kind of life do you think Mr. Bean leads in his home town in New Jersey? What qualities led to his election as president of the Dramatic Society?

8. What motion-picture actor would you cast for the part of Mr. Bean? Mr. Gompers?

CHALLENGES

1. Imagine that you are Mr. Bean on the evening of his return to his home. How will he tell his fellow members of the Dramatic Society of his experience that day?

2. Julie Dressler is in Hollywood making her first picture. She thinks of Oliver and writes him a letter. Write her letter and Oliver's answer. Make both *in character.*

3. The local newspaper in Mr. Bean's home town hears of his

screen test and sends a reporter over. Write the newspaper account – humorous or serious – for the paper.

4. Oliver Bean passes a movie house a year later and sees a picture of Julie starring in her first production. He decides to see the movie and then send her a note of congratulation. What would he say in the letter? How would Julie reply?

DRAMA WORKSHOP

A hint for playgoers: Know why people laugh.

Walt Disney once drew an animated cartoon about a dog that swallowed a magnet. As Pluto, the dog, walked through the kitchen, knives leaped from the drawers and began to pursue him. Although audiences howled with laughter at this scene, Disney declared they were also glad that Pluto finally suffered no serious harm.

This illustration helps us to understand two things about laughter. First, we laugh at things that are inappropriate. For example, we laugh when a pompous man wearing a silk hat slips on a banana peel because we recognize the disparity between his view of his own importance and our view of him landing on the pavement with a sudden thud. We laugh when a pupil gives a silly answer to a serious question because we perceive a lack of harmony between two ideas or actions. Laughter arises when we recognize incongruity or, to use a less learned term, inappropriateness in a person or a situation.

Second, the best type of laughter is touched with sympathy. We enjoy seeing a slapstick comedian hit with a custard pie, but at the same time we feel a little sorry for him. In the same way we laugh at Oliver Bean but we also feel sympathetic toward him. The best laughter is kindly and understanding, never derisive and malicious.

A hint for actors: Enter and exit on time and in character.

Amateurs sometimes fail to realize the importance of an actor's first entrance. When a new character enters, the audience immediately forms an impression of him and his relation to the other characters in the play; hence the actor must be in character from the first moment he steps upon the stage.

Start your entrance at least a dozen paces from the door, so that you will be properly in character by the time you come upon the stage. Entrances must be properly timed; to arrive too early or too late may spoil the illusion. Have two cues: one to start your entrance and the other to speak.

Exits must also be carefully rehearsed. Generally a character should deliver his last two lines while near an exit. Thus he can make a smooth exit and the scene can progress with little interruption. Exits, like entrances, must be made on time and in character.

OTHER COMEDIES YOU WILL LIKE TO READ

The Man in the Bowler Hat by A. A. Milne (29). What seems to be a performance of a play turns out to be a rehearsal.

Over the Hills by John Palmer (16). A wife proves wiser than her husband who has the wanderlust at an age when it is more appropriate to enjoy the comforts of home.

The Philosopher of Butterbiggins by Harold Chapin (18). By startling means a grandfather wins the right to tell his nightly bedtime story to his eager grandson.

The Rising of the Moon by Lady Gregory (16). An appeal to early memories and love for Ireland saves a rebel.

The Romancers by Edmond Rostand (12). To introduce romance into the match of their children, two fathers feign a feud.

Saved by John W. Rogers, Jr. (4). One of two old-maid sisters saves her niece from their fate by assisting in her elopement.

Sham by Frank Tompkins (12). A young couple upon returning to their home meet a burglar who tries to convince them he can brighten their social reputation.

Thursday Evening by Christopher Morley (36). Two mothers-in-law bring their children closer together at a time when their quarrel is becoming serious.

A SUNNY MORNING

BY SERAFÍN AND JOAQUÍN ALVAREZ QUINTERO

Translated from the Spanish by LUCRETIA XAVIER FLOYD

ABOUT THE PLAY

Richard Watts, Jr., a dramatic critic of national reputation, has said about *A Sunny Morning:* "There is in this story of ancient sweethearts a true sunniness of heart, a gay spirit, a romantic graciousness and a gently ironic humor that make it thoroughly enchanting." This opinion must be shared by many thousands, for *A Sunny Morning* has delighted audiences for almost half a century and its popularity shows no sign of waning.

The audience seeing *A Sunny Morning* is in a favored position. Each of the two main characters discovers that the other is a former sweetheart but each keeps the discovery to himself. The audience, however, makes this discovery before the characters do and thus enjoys watching their attempts at deception.

ABOUT THE AUTHORS

The brothers Serafín Alvarez and Joaquín Alvarez Quintero were only fifteen and seventeen years old respectively when their

---

first play was produced. During their lifetimes they collaborated in writing more than fifty plays, their most successful and brilliant being comedies set in their native Andalusia, a section of Spain which borders on the Atlantic Ocean and the Mediterranean Sea. The London *Times* once called them "the Spanish equivalent of J. M. Barrie." Their best-known successes include *Lady from Alfaqueque, One Hundred Years Ago, Fortunato,* and *The Women Have Their Way*. Both brothers maintained a steady output of plays over the first thirty years of this century.

A SUNNY MORNING

Characters

DOÑA LAURA

PETRA, *a maid*

DON GONZALO

JUANITO, *an attendant*

SCENE. *A sunny morning in a retired corner of a park in Madrid. Autumn. A bench at the right.*

DOÑA LAURA, *a handsome, white-haired old lady of about seventy, refined in appearance, her bright eyes and entire manner giving evidence that despite her age her mental faculities are unimpaired, enters leaning upon the arm of her maid,* PETRA. *In her free hand she carries a parasol, which serves also as a cane.*

DOÑA LAURA. I am so glad to be here. I feared my seat would be occupied. What a beautiful morning!

PETRA. The sun is hot.

DOÑA LAURA. Yes, you are only twenty. (*She sits down on the bench.*) Oh, I feel more tired today than usual. (*Noticing* PETRA, *who seems impatient.*) Go, if you wish to chat with your guard.

PETRA. He is not mine, señora; he belongs to the park.

DOÑA LAURA. He belongs more to you than he does to the park. Go find him, but remain within calling distance.

PETRA. I see him over there waiting for me.

DOÑA LAURA. Do not remain more than ten minutes.

PETRA. Very well, señora. (*Walks toward the right.*)

DOÑA LAURA. Wait a moment.

PETRA. What does the señora wish?

DOÑA LAURA. Give me the bread crumbs.

PETRA. I don't know what is the matter with me.

DOÑA LAURA (*smiling*). I do. Your head is where your heart is — with the guard.

PETRA. Here, señora. (*She hands* DOÑA LAURA *a small bag. Exit* PETRA *by the right.*)

DOÑA LAURA. Adiós. (*Glances toward the trees at the right.*) Here they come! They know just when to expect me. (*She rises, walks toward the right, and throws three handfuls of bread crumbs.*) These are for the spryest, these for the gluttons, and these for the little ones which are the most persistent. (*Laughs. She returns to her seat and watches, with a pleased expression, the pigeons feeding.*) There, that big one is always first! I know him by his big head. Now one, now another, now two, now three — that little fellow is the least timid. I believe he would eat from my hand. That one takes his piece and flies up to that branch alone. He is a philosopher. But where do they all come from? It seems as if the news had spread. Ha, ha! Don't quarrel. There is enough for all. I'll bring more tomorrow.

[*Enter* DON GONZALO *and* JUANITO *from the left center.* DON GONZALO *is an old gentleman of seventy, gouty and impatient. He leans upon* JUANITO's *arm and drags his feet somewhat as he walks.*]

DON GONZALO. Idling their time away! They should be saying Mass.

JUANITO. You can sit here, señor. There is only a lady. (DOÑA LAURA *turns her head and listens.*)

DON GONZALO. I won't, Juanito. I want a bench to myself.

JUANITO. But there is none.

DON GONZALO. That one over there is mine.

JUANITO. There are three priests sitting there.

DON GONZALO. Rout them out. Have they gone?

JUANITO. No indeed. They are talking.

DON GONZALO. Just as if they were glued to the seat. No hope of their leaving. Come this way, Juanito. (*They walk toward the birds, right.*)

DOÑA LAURA (*indignantly*). Look out!

DON GONZALO. Are you speaking to me, señora?

DOÑA LAURA. Yes, to you.

DON GONZALO. What do you wish?

DOÑA LAURA. You have scared away the birds who were feeding on my crumbs.

DON GONZALO. What do I care about the birds?

DOÑA LAURA. But I do.

DON GONZALO. This is a public park.

DOÑA LAURA. Then why do you complain that the priests have taken your bench?

DON GONZALO. Señora, we have not met. I cannot imagine why you take the liberty of addressing me. Come, Juanito. (*Both go out by the right.*)

DOÑA LAURA. What an ill-natured old man! Why must people get so fussy and cross when they reach a certain age? (*Looking toward the right.*) I am glad. He lost that bench, too. Serves him right for scaring the birds. He is furious. Yes, yes, find a seat if you can. Poor man! He is wiping the perspiration from his face. Here he comes. A carriage would not raise more dust than his feet.

[*Enter* DON GONZALO *and* JUANITO *by the right, and walk toward the left.*]

JUANITO. No indeed, señor. They are still there.

DON GONZALO. The authorities should place more benches here for these sunny mornings. Well, I suppose I must resign myself and sit on the bench with the old lady. (*Muttering to himself, he sits at the extreme end of* DOÑA LAURA's *bench and looks at her indignantly. He touches his hat as he greets her.*) Good morning.

DOÑA LAURA. What, you here again?

DON GONZALO. I repeat that we have not met.

DOÑA LAURA. I was responding to your salute.

DON GONZALO. "Good morning" should be answered by "Good morning," and that is all you should have said.

DOÑA LAURA. You should have asked permission to sit on this bench, which is mine.

DON GONZALO. The benches here are public property.

DOÑA LAURA. Why, you said the one the priests have was yours.

DON GONZALO. Very well, very well. I have nothing more to say. (*Be-*

tween his teeth.) Senile old lady! She ought to be at home knitting and counting her beads.

DOÑA LAURA. Don't grumble any more. I'm not going to leave just to please you.

DON GONZALO (*brushing the dust from his shoes with his handkerchief*). If the ground were sprinkled a little it would be an improvement.

DOÑA LAURA. Do you use your handkerchief as a shoebrush?

DON GONZALO. Why not?

DOÑA LAURA. Do you use a shoebrush as a handkerchief?

DON GONZALO. What right have you to criticize my actions?

DOÑA LAURA. A neighbor's right.

DON GONZALO. Juanito, my book. I do not care to listen to nonsense.

DOÑA LAURA. You are very polite.

DON GONZALO. Pardon me, señora, but never interfere with what does not concern you.

DOÑA LAURA. I generally say what I think.

DON GONZALO. And more to the same effect. Give me the book, Juanito.

JUANITO. Here, señor.

[JUANITO *takes a book from his pocket, hands it to* DON GONZALO, *then exits by the right.* DON GONZALO, *casting indignant glances at* DOÑA LAURA, *puts on an enormous pair of glasses, takes from his pocket a reading glass, adjusts both to suit him, and opens his book.*]

DOÑA LAURA. I thought you were taking out a telescope.

DON GONZALO. Was that you?

DOÑA LAURA. Your sight must be keen.

DON GONZALO. Keener than yours is.

DOÑA LAURA. Yes, evidently.

DON GONZALO. Ask the hares and partridges.

DOÑA LAURA. Ah! Do you hunt?

DON GONZALO. I did, and even now —

DOÑA LAURA. Oh yes, of course!

DON GONZALO. Yes, señora. Every Sunday I take my gun and dog, you understand, and go to one of my estates near Aravaca and kill time.

DOÑA LAURA. Yes, kill time. That is all you kill.

DON GONZALO. Do you think so? I could show you a wild boar's head in my study –

DOÑA LAURA. Yes, and I could show you a tiger's skin in my boudoir. What does that prove?

DON GONZALO. Very well, señora, please allow me to read. Enough conversation.

DOÑA LAURA. Well, you subside, then.

DON GONZALO. But first I shall take a pinch of snuff. (*Takes out a snuffbox.*) Will you have some? (*Offers the box to* DOÑA LAURA.)

DOÑA LAURA. If it is good.

DON GONZALO. It is of the finest. You will like it.

DOÑA LAURA (*taking a pinch of snuff*). It clears my head.

DON GONZALO. And mine.

DOÑA LAURA. Do you sneeze?

DON GONZALO. Yes, señora, three times.

DOÑA LAURA. And so do I. What a coincidence!

[*After taking the snuff, they await the sneezes, both anxiously, and sneeze alternately three times each.*]

DON GONZALO. There, I feel better.

DOÑA LAURA. So do I. (*Aside.*) The snuff has made peace between us.

DON GONZALO. You will excuse me if I read aloud?

DOÑA LAURA. Read as loud as you please; you will not disturb me.

DON GONZALO (*reading*).

"All love is sad, but sad as it is,
It is the best thing that we know."

That is from Campoamor.

DOÑA LAURA. Ah!

DON GONZALO (*reading*).

"The daughters of the mothers I once loved
Kiss me now as they would a graven image."

Those lines, I take it, are in a humorous vein.

DOÑA LAURA (*laughing*). I take them so, too.

DON GONZALO. There are some beautiful poems in this book. Here. "Twenty years pass. He returns."

DOÑA LAURA. You cannot imagine how it affects me to see you reading with all those glasses.

DON GONZALO. Can you read without any?

DOÑA LAURA. Certainly.

DON GONZALO. At your age? You're jesting.

DOÑA LAURA. Pass me the book, then. (*Takes the book, reads aloud.*)

"Twenty years pass. He returns.
And each, beholding the other, exclaims —
Can it be that this is he?
Heavens, is it she?"

[DOÑA LAURA *returns the book to* DON GONZALO.]

DON GONZALO. Indeed I envy you your wonderful eyesight.

DOÑA LAURA (*aside*). I know every word by heart.

DON GONZALO. I am very fond of good verses, very fond. I even composed some in my youth.

DOÑA LAURA. Good ones?

DON GONZALO. Of all kinds. I was a great friend of Espronceda, Zorrilla, Bécquer, and others. I first met Zorrilla in America.

DOÑA LAURA. Why, have you been in America?

DON GONZALO. Several times. The first time I went I was only six years old.

DOÑA LAURA. You must have gone with Columbus in one of his caravels!

DON GONZALO (*laughing*). Not quite as bad as that. I am old, I admit, but I did not know Ferdinand and Isabella. (*They both laugh.*) I was also a great friend of Campoamor. I met him in Valencia. I am a native of that city.

DOÑA LAURA. You are?

DON GONZALO. I was brought up there and there I spent my early youth. Have you ever visited that city?

DOÑA LAURA. Yes, señor. Not far from Valencia there was a villa that, if still there, should retain memories of me. I spent several seasons there. It was many, many years ago. It was near the sea, hidden away among lemon and orange trees. They called it — let me see, what did they call it? — Maricela.

DON GONZALO (*startled*). Maricela?

DOÑA LAURA. Maricela. Is the name familiar to you?

DON GONZALO. Yes, very familiar. If my memory serves me right, for we forget as we grow old, there lived in that villa the most beautiful woman I have ever seen, and I assure you I have seen many. Let me see — what was her name? Laura — Laura — Laura Llorente.

DOÑA LAURA (*startled*). Laura Llorente?

DON GONZALO. Yes. (*They look at each other intently.*)

DOÑA LAURA (*recovering herself*). Nothing. You reminded me of my best friend.

DON GONZALO. How strange!

DOÑA LAURA. It is strange. She was called "The Silver Maiden."

DON GONZALO. Precisely, "The Silver Maiden." By that name she was known in that locality. I seem to see her as if she were before me now, at that window with the red roses. Do you remember that window?

DOÑA LAURA. Yes, I remember. It was the window of her room.

DON GONZALO. She spent many hours there. I mean in my day.

DOÑA LAURA (*sighing*). And in mine, too.

DON GONZALO. She was ideal. Fair as a lily, jet-black hair and black eyes, with an uncommonly sweet expression. She seemed to cast a radiance wherever she was. Her figure was beautiful, perfect. "What forms of sovereign beauty God models in human clay!" She was a dream

DOÑA LAURA (*aside*). If you but knew that dream was now by your side, you would realize what dreams come to. (*Aloud.*) She was very unfortunate and had a sad love affair.

DON GONZALO. Very sad. (*They look at each other.*)

DOÑA LAURA. Did you hear of it?

DON GONZALO. Yes.

DOÑA LAURA. The ways of Providence are strange. (*Aside.*) Gonzalo!

DON GONZALO. The gallant lover, in the same affair —

DOÑA LAURA. Ah, the duel?

DON GONZALO. Precisely, the duel. The gallant lover was — my cousin, of whom I was very fond.

DOÑA LAURA. Oh yes, a cousin? My friend told me in one of her letters the story of that affair, which was truly romantic. He, your cousin, passed by on horseback every morning down the rose path under her window, and tossed up to her balcony a bouquet of flowers which she caught.

DON GONZALO. And later in the afternoon the gallant horseman would return by the same path, and catch the bouquet of flowers she would toss him. Am I right?

DOÑA LAURA. Yes. They wanted to marry her to a merchant whom she would not have.

DON GONZALO. And one night, when my cousin waited under her window to hear her sing, this other person presented himself unexpectedly.

DOÑA LAURA. And insulted your cousin.

DON GONZALO. There was a quarrel.

DOÑA LAURA. And later a duel.

DON GONZALO. Yes, at sunrise, on the beach, and the merchant was badly wounded. My cousin had to conceal himself for a few days and later to fly.

DOÑA LAURA. You seem to know the story well.

DON GONZALO. And so do you.

DOÑA LAURA. I have explained that a friend repeated it to me.

DON GONZALO. As my cousin did to me. (*Aside.*) This is Laura!

DOÑA LAURA (*aside*). Why tell him? He does not suspect.

DON GONZALO (*aside*). She is entirely innocent.

DOÑA LAURA. And was it you, by any chance, who advised your cousin to forget Laura?

DON GONZALO. Why, my cousin never forgot her!

DOÑA LAURA. How do you account, then, for his conduct?

DON GONZALO. I will tell you. The young man took refuge in my house, fearful of the consequences of a duel with a person highly regarded in that locality. From my home he went to Seville, then came to Madrid. He wrote Laura many letters, some of them in verse. But undoubtedly they were intercepted by her parents, for she never answered at all. Gonzalo then, in despair, believing his love lost to him forever, joined the army, went to Africa, and there, in a trench, met a glorious death, grasping the flag of Spain and whispering the name of his beloved Laura —

DOÑA LAURA (*aside*). What an atrocious lie!

DON GONZALO (*aside*). I could not have killed myself more gloriously.

DOÑA LAURA. You must have been prostrated by the calamity.

DON GONZALO. Yes, indeed, señora. As if he were my brother. I presume, though, on the contrary, that Laura in a short time was chasing butterflies in her garden, indifferent to regret.

DOÑA LAURA. No, señor, no!

DON GONZALO. It is woman's way.

DOÑA LAURA. Even if it were woman's way, "The Silver Maiden" was not of that disposition. My friend awaited news for days, months, a year, and no letter came. One afternoon, just at sunset, as the first stars were appearing, she was seen to leave the house, and with quickening steps wend her way toward the beach, the beach where her beloved had risked his life. She wrote his name on the sand, then sat down upon a rock, her gaze fixed upon the horizon. The waves murmured their eternal threnody and slowly crept up to the rock where the maiden sat. The tide rose with a boom and swept her out to sea.

DON GONZALO. Good heavens!

DOÑA LAURA. The fishermen of that shore, who often tell the story, affirm that it was a long time before the waves washed away that name written on the sand. (*Aside.*) You will not get ahead of me in decorating my own funeral.

DON GONZALO (*aside*). She lies worse than I do.

DOÑA LAURA. Poor Laura!

DON GONZALO. Poor Gonzalo!

DOÑA LAURA (*aside*). I will not tell him that I married two years later.

DON GONZALO (*aside*). In three months I ran off to Paris with a ballet dancer.

DOÑA LAURA. Fate is curious. Here are you and I, complete strangers, met by chance, discussing the romance of old friends of long ago! We have been conversing as if we were old friends.

DON GONZALO. Yes, it is curious, considering the ill-natured prelude to our conversation.

DOÑA LAURA. You scared away the birds.

DON GONZALO. I was unreasonable, perhaps.

DOÑA LAURA. Yes, that was evident. (*Sweetly.*) Are you coming again tomorrow?

DON GONZALO. Most certainly, if it is a sunny morning. And not only will I not scare away the birds, but I will bring a few crumbs.

DOÑA LAURA. Thank you very much. Birds are grateful and repay attention. I wonder where my maid is? Petra! (*Signals for her maid.*)

DON GONZALO (*aside, looking at* LAURA, *whose back is turned*). No, no, I will not reveal myself. I am grotesque now. Better that she recall the gallant horseman who passed daily beneath her window tossing flowers.

DOÑA LAURA. Here she comes.

DON GONZALO. That Juanito! He plays havoc with the nursemaids. (*Looks to the right and signals with his hand.*)

DOÑA LAURA (*aside, looking at* GONZALO, *whose back is turned*). No, I am too sadly changed. It is better he should remember me as the black-eyed girl tossing flowers as he passed among the roses in the garden.

[JUANITO *enters by the right,* PETRA *by the left. She has a bunch of violets in her hand.*]

DOÑA LAURA. Well, Petra! At last!

DON GONZALO. Juanito, you are late.

PETRA (*to* DOÑA LAURA). The guard gave me these violets for you, señora.

DOÑA LAURA. How very nice! Thank him for me. They are fragrant.

[*As she takes the violets from her maid a few loose ones fall to the ground.*]

DON GONZALO. My dear lady, this has been a great honor and a great pleasure.

DOÑA LAURA. It has also been a pleasure to me.

DON GONZALO. Good-by until tomorrow.

DOÑA LAURA. Until tomorrow.

DON GONZALO. If it is sunny.

DOÑA LAURA. A sunny morning. Will you go to your bench?

DON GONZALO. No, I will come to this — if you do not object?

DOÑA LAURA. This bench is at your disposal.

DON GONZALO. And I will surely bring the crumbs.

DOÑA LAURA. Tomorrow, then?

DON GONZALO. Tomorrow!

[LAURA *walks away toward the right, supported by her maid.* GONZALO, *before leaving with* JUANITO, *trembling and with a great effort, stoops to pick up the violets* LAURA *dropped. Just then* LAURA *turns her head and surprises him picking up the flowers.*]

JUANITO. What are you doing, señor?

DON GONZALO. Juanito, wait —

DOÑA LAURA (*aside*). Yes, it is he!

DON GONZALO (*aside*). It is she, and no mistake.

[DOÑA LAURA *and* DON GONZALO *wave farewell.*]

DOÑA LAURA. "Can it be that this is he?"

DON GONZALO. "Heavens, is it she?"

[*They smile once more, as if she were again at the window and he below in the rose garden, and then disappear upon the arms of their servants.*]

AFTER READING

1. At what point did you find out that Doña Laura and Don Gonzalo were once lovers?

2. When does Doña Laura discover that the man to whom she is speaking is her former sweetheart? Why doesn't she tell him who she is? How does she conceal her identity from him?

3. Does Don Gonzalo ever suspect that Doña Laura knows his identity? Justify your answer by referring to lines and incidents in the play.

4. Why does Don Gonzalo pick up the flowers Doña Laura dropped? What memories do they awaken?

5. In what way is the poem Doña Laura recites appropriate to the play?

6. Do you have any proof that Doña Laura and Don Gonzalo still love each other? If so, state it. How do they differ in character?

7. What purpose do the asides — comments heard by the audience but not by the other actors — serve?

CHALLENGES

1. Doña Laura and Don Gonzalo meet on the same bench the next day. Write the conversation between the two as if it were the second scene of the play.

2. Describe in writing the duel between young Don Gonzalo and the merchant on the beach.

3. Describe the changes the years have wrought in both Doña Laura and Don Gonzalo. Consider not merely physical changes but also changes in disposition.

DRAMA WORKSHOP

A hint for playgoers: Modern playwriting and acting are naturalistic in style.

As you read *A Sunny Morning* you noticed that several times Doña Laura and Don Gonzalo spoke in asides, that is, comments intended to be heard by the audience but not by anyone on the stage.

Such a device is called a convention; in other words, it is a practice which everyone agrees to observe even when, as in the case of the aside, it violates common sense. Obviously, if a remark is uttered loud enough to be heard by the audience it ought to be heard by the actors, but by tacit agreement it isn't.

Another dramatic convention is the soliloquy, a speech in which one of the characters of the drama voices his thoughts while alone on the stage. Prologues and epilogues — that is, speeches which precede and follow a play — are also dramatic conventions.

Modern dramatists do not usually employ these conventions. Asides, soliloquies, prologues, and epilogues were still used at the time the Quintero brothers wrote *A Sunny Morning,* but if the Quinteros were constructing plays today they might look for other means of conveying information to an audience. Naturalism in acting, and avoidance of actions that do not occur in everyday life, are the keynotes of today's stage. Conventions of the kind described here often appear stilted in the modern theater.

A hint for actors: Don't be like Bottom.

In Shakespeare's *A Midsummer-Night's Dream* a group of artisans prepare to present a play. One of the company, Bottom, is not content with the role assigned to him but wants to play other parts besides, especially those that seem more important. "Let me play the lion too," cries Bottom, but Quince, the director, won't let him. Bottom always wanted to be the center of attention. He didn't realize that every part in a play is important, no matter how few lines the actor has to utter.

A cast is a team. Everyone has a job to do and the success of the play depends upon the way the cast, the director, and the backstage assistants work together as a unit. Gladly take whatever role is assigned to you, and give it your honest and sincere effort. Petra and Juanito in *A Sunny Morning* haven't many lines to say, but these characters are essential to the success of the play and poor acting in these parts could easily spoil the effect. There is no such thing as a little part; there are only little actors.

OTHER COMEDIES YOU WILL LIKE TO READ

Hearts Enduring by John Erskine (7). Rather than show her returned sweetheart the ravages of the plague in her appearance, the lady practices a desperate deception.

A Minuet by Louis N. Parker (36). After years of estrangement, an aristocratic couple go bravely to their death.

The Beau of Bath by Constance D'Arcy Mackay (38). The Beau of Bath has a dream in which his former loved one comes out of her picture frame.

The Thrice Promised Bride by Cheng-Chin Hsuing (12). Of the three suitors for the hand of a lovely Chinese maiden, the scholar displays winning qualities.

The Florist Shop by Winifred Hawkridge (15). A long-delayed marriage proposal ensues when a romantic girl clerk in a florist shop sends flowers to the patient fiancée.

The Happy Journey to Trenton and Camden

BY THORNTON WILDER

ABOUT THE PLAY

Meet the Kirbys. There's nothing unusual about them, nothing exciting. They're just plain folks, like ourselves, who are doing the best they can, helping one another and living on good terms with their neighbors. They're a rather typical family: father and mother, two children of school age, and a married daughter. We forgot to mention the cat – but then the cat has no speaking part. The Kirbys have their little family disagreements, as we all do, but these are not really of any importance. No doubt they would be surprised if you told them that they are proud of one another, but they are, and even proud of their battered old Chevvie. When we meet them they are going on a trip in that very car.

Ever go on a trip with your folks in a car? Generally, you'll agree, you have a happy time together. Generally, too, nothing adventuresome or dramatic happens, at least not anything to write a play about. Well, let's see. *The Happy Journey* is the story of a trip, just such a trip as you would make with your family, uneventful but a lot of fun. There's no scenery used in the play and no furniture except a few chairs. But after all you won't need scenery or furniture in a play like this. The situations will all be familiar even without stage trappings.

ABOUT THE AUTHOR

Thornton Wilder was once a high-school teacher — but don't let that scare you. He's interested in ordinary people no matter where they live, whether in Greece, South America, or his own home town. One of his most successful plays, which was later made into a movie, is *Our Town,* a story of everyday people, their getting born, their growing up, their marrying, their performing daily jobs, and their dying.

Mr. Wilder is recognized as one of our foremost dramatists and novelists, a deviser of unusual plots, and a distinctive stylist. He has won two Pulitzer awards, one for the novel *The Bridge of San Luis Rey* and the other for the play *Our Town.* You'll find both entirely to your liking. In addition to his longer works he has written several one-act plays, which you'll find in a collection entitled *The Long Christmas Dinner.*

THE HAPPY JOURNEY TO TRENTON AND CAMDEN

Characters

THE STAGE MANAGER

MA KIRBY

ARTHUR KIRBY

CAROLINE KIRBY

ELMER KIRBY (PA)

BEULAH

No scenery is required for this play. Perhaps a few dusty flats may be seen leaning against the brick wall at the back of the stage.

The five members of the Kirby family and THE STAGE MANAGER *compose the cast.* THE STAGE MANAGER *not only moves forward and withdraws the few properties that are required, but he reads from a typescript the lines of all the minor characters. He reads them clearly, but with little attempt at characterization, scarcely troubling himself to alter his voice, even when he responds in the person of a child or a woman.*

As the curtain rises THE STAGE MANAGER *is leaning lazily against the proscenium pillar at the audience's left. He is smoking.*

ARTHUR *is playing marbles in the center of the stage.*

CAROLINE *is at the remote back, right, talking to some girls who are invisible to us.*

MA KIRBY *is anxiously putting on her hat before an imaginary mirror.*

MA. Where's your pa? Why isn't he here? I declare we'll never get started.

ARTHUR. Ma, where's my hat? I guess I don't go if I can't find my hat.

MA. Go out into the hall and see if it isn't there. Where's Caroline gone to now, the plagued child?

ARTHUR. She's out waitin' in the street talkin' to the Jones girls. — I just looked in the hall a thousand times, Ma, and it isn't there. (*He spits for good luck before a difficult shot and mutters.*) Come on, baby.

MA. Go and look again, I say. Look carefully.

[ARTHUR *rises, runs to the right, turns around swiftly, returns to his game, flinging himself on the floor with a terrible impact, and starts shooting an aggie.*]

ARTHUR. No. Ma, it's not there.

MA (*serenely*). Well, you don't leave Newark without that hat, make up your mind to that. I don't go no journeys with a hoodlum.

ARTHUR. Aw, Ma!

[MA *comes down to the footlights and talks toward the audience as through a window.*]

MA. Oh, Mrs. Schwartz!

THE STAGE MANAGER (*consulting his script*). Here I am, Mrs. Kirby. Are you going yet?

MA. I guess we're going in just a minute. How's the baby?

THE STAGE MANAGER. She's all right now. We slapped her on the back and she spat it up.

MA. Isn't that fine! — Well now, if you'll be good enough to give the cat a saucer of milk in the morning and the evening, Mrs. Schwartz, I'll be ever so grateful to you. — Oh, good afternoon, Mrs. Hobmeyer!

THE STAGE MANAGER. Good afternoon, Mrs. Kirby, I hear you're going away.

MA (*modest*). Oh, just for three days, Mrs. Hobmeyer, to see my married daughter Beulah, in Camden. Elmer's got his vacation week from the laundry early this year, and he's just the best driver in the world.

[CAROLINE *comes "into the house" and stands by her mother.*]

THE STAGE MANAGER. Is the whole family going?

MA. Yes, all four of us that's here. The change ought to be good for the children. My married daughter was downright sick a while ago —

THE STAGE MANAGER. Tchk — tchk — tchk! Yes. I remember you tellin' us.

MA. And I just want to go down and see the child. I ain't seen her since then. I just won't rest easy in my mind without I see her. (*To* CAROLINE.) Can't you say good afternoon to Mrs. Hobmeyer?

CAROLINE (*blushes and lowers her eyes and says woodenly*). Good afternoon, Mrs. Hobmeyer.

THE STAGE MANAGER. Good afternoon, dear. — Well, I'll wait and beat these rugs until after you're gone, because I don't want to choke you. I hope you have a good time and find everything all right.

MA. Thank you, Mrs. Hobmeyer, I hope I will. — Well, I guess that milk for the cat is all, Mrs. Schwartz, if you're sure you don't mind. If anything should come up, the key to the back door is hanging by the icebox.

ARTHUR and CAROLINE. Ma! Not so loud. Everybody can hear yuh.

MA. Stop pullin' my dress, children. (*In a loud whisper.*) The key to the back door I'll leave hangin' by the icebox and I'll leave the screen door unhooked.

THE STAGE MANAGER. Now have a good trip, dear, and give my love to Loolie.

MA. I will, and thank you a thousand times. (*She returns "into the room."*) What can be keeping your pa?

ARTHUR. I can't find my hat, Ma.

[*Enter* ELMER *holding a hat.*]

ELMER. Here's Arthur's hat. He musta left it in the car Sunday.

MA. That's a mercy. Now we can start. — Caroline Kirby, what you done to your cheeks?

CAROLINE (*defiant, abashed*). Nothin'.

MA. If you've put anything on 'em, I'll slap you.

CAROLINE. No, Ma, of course I haven't. (*Hanging her head.*) I just rubbed'm to make'm red. All the girls do that at high school when they're goin' places.

MA. Such silliness I never saw. Elmer, what kep' you?

ELMER (*always even-voiced and always looking out a little anxiously through his spectacles*). I just went to the garage and had Charlie give a last look at it, Kate.

MA. I'm glad you did. I wouldn't like to have no breakdown miles from anywhere. Now we can start. Arthur, put those marbles away. Anybody'd think you didn't want to go on a journey to look at yuh.

[*They go out through the "hall," take the short steps that denote going downstairs, and find themselves in the street.*]

ELMER. Here, you boys, you keep away from that car.

MA. Those Sullivan boys put their heads into everything.

[THE STAGE MANAGER *has moved forward four chairs and a low platform. This is the automobile. It is in the center of the stage and faces the audience. The platform slightly raises the two chairs in the rear.* PA's *hands hold an imaginary steering wheel and continually shift gears.* CAROLINE *sits beside him.* ARTHUR *is behind him and* MA *behind* CAROLINE.]

CAROLINE (*self-consciously*). Good-by, Mildred. Good-by, Helen.

THE STAGE MANAGER. Good-by, Caroline. Good-by, Mrs. Kirby. I hope y' have a good time.

MA. Good-by, girls.

THE STAGE MANAGER. Good-by, Kate. The car looks fine.

MA (*looking upward toward a window*). Oh, good-by, Emma! (*Modestly.*) We think it's the best little Chevrolet in the world. – Oh, good-by, Mrs. Adler!

THE STAGE MANAGER. What, are you going away, Mrs. Kirby?

MA. Just for three days, Mrs. Adler, to see my married daughter in Camden.

THE STAGE MANAGER. Have a good time.

[*Now* MA, CAROLINE, *and* THE STAGE MANAGER *break out into a tremendous chorus of good-bys. The whole street is saying good-by.* ARTHUR *takes out his peashooter and lets fly happily into the air. There is a lurch or two and they are off.*]

ARTHUR (*in sudden fright*). Pa! Pa! Don't go by the school. Mr. Biedenbach might see us!

MA. I don't care if he does see us. I guess I can take my children out of school for one day without having to hide down back streets about it. (ELMER *nods to a passer-by.* MA *asks without sharpness:*) Who was that you spoke to, Elmer?

ELMER. That was the fellow who arranges our banquets down to the Lodge, Kate.

MA. Is he the one who had to buy four hundred steaks? (PA *nods.*) I declare, I'm glad I'm not him.

ELMER. The air's getting better already. Take deep breaths, children.

[*They inhale noisily.*]

ARTHUR. Gee, it's almost open fields already. *"Weber and Heilbronner Suits for Well-dressed Men."* Ma, can I have one of them someday?

MA. If you graduate with good marks perhaps your father'll let you have one for graduation.

CAROLINE (*whining*). Oh, Pa! Do we have to wait while that whole funeral goes by?

[PA *takes off his hat.* MA *cranes forward with absorbed curiosity.*]

MA. Take off your hat, Arthur. Look at your father. – Why, Elmer, I do believe that's a lodge brother of yours. See the banner? I suppose this is the Elizabeth branch. (ELMER *nods.* MA *sighs: Tchk – tchk – tchk. They all lean forward and watch the funeral in silence, growing momentarily more solemnized. After a pause,* MA *continues almost dreamily:*) Well, we haven't forgotten the one that we went on, have we? We haven't forgotten our good Harold. He gave his life for his country, we mustn't forget that. (*She passes her finger from the corner of her eye across her cheek. There is another pause.*) Well, we'll all hold up the traffic for a few minutes someday.

THE CHILDREN (*very uncomfortable*). Ma!

MA (*without self-pity*). Well I'm "ready," children. I hope everybody in this car is "ready." (*She puts her hand on* PA*'s shoulder.*) And I pray to go first, Elmer. Yes. (PA *touches her hand.*)

THE CHILDREN. Ma, everybody's looking at you. Everybody's laughing at you.

MA. Oh, hold your tongues! I don't care what a lot of silly people in Elizabeth, New Jersey, think of me. – Now we can go on. That's the last. (*There is another lurch and the car goes on.*)

CAROLINE. *"Fit-Rite Suspenders. The Working Man's Choice."* Pa, why do they spell "Rite" that way?

ELMER. So that it'll make you stop and ask about it, missy.

CAROLINE. Papa, you're teasing me. — Ma, why do they say *"Three Hundred Rooms Three Hundred Baths"*?

ARTHUR. *"Miller's Spaghetti: The Family's Favorite Dish."* Ma, why don't you ever have spaghetti?

MA. Go along, you'd never eat it.

ARTHUR. Ma, I like it now.

CAROLINE (*with a gesture*). Yum-yum. It looks wonderful up there. Ma, make some when we get home?

MA (*dryly*). "The management is always happy to receive suggestions. We aim to please."

[*The whole family finds this exquisitely funny. The children scream with laughter. Even* ELMER *smiles.* MA *remains modest.*]

ELMER. Well, I guess no one's complaining, Kate. Everybody knows you're a good cook.

MA. I don't know whether I'm a good cook or not. but I know I've had practice. At least I've cooked three meals a day for twenty-five years.

ARTHUR. Aw, Ma, you went out to eat once in a while.

MA. Yes. That made it a leap year.

[*This joke is no less successful than its predecessor. When the laughter dies down,* CAROLINE *turns around in an ecstasy of well-being and kneeling on the cushions, says:*]

CAROLINE. Ma, I love going out in the country like this. Let's do it often, Ma.

MA. Goodness, smell that air, will you! It's got the whole ocean in it. — Elmer, drive careful over that bridge. This must be New Brunswick we're coming to.

ARTHUR (*jealous of his mother's successes*). Ma, when is the next comfort station?

MA (*unruffled*). You don't want one. You just said that to be awful

CAROLINE (*shrilly*). Yes, he did, Ma. He's terrible. He says that kind of thing right out in school and I want to sink through the floor, Ma. He's terrible.

MA. Oh, don't get so excited about nothing, Miss Proper! I guess we're all yewman beings in this car, at least as far as I know. And Arthur, you try and be a gentleman. – Elmer, don't run over that collie dog. (*She follows the dog with her eyes.*) Looked kinda peakèd to me. Needs a good honest bowl of leavings. Pretty dog, too. (*Her eyes fall on a billboard.*) That's a pretty advertisement for Chesterfield cigarettes, isn't it? Looks like Beulah, a little.

ARTHUR. Ma?

MA. Yes.

ARTHUR (*"route" rhymes with "out"*). Can't I take a paper route with the *Newark Daily Post?*

MA. No, you cannot. No, sir. I hear they make the paper boys get up at four-thirty in the morning. No son of mine is going to get up at four-thirty every morning, not if it's to make a million dollars. Your *Saturday Evening Post* route on Thursday mornings is enough.

ARTHUR. Aw, Ma.

MA. No, sir. No son of mine is going to get up at four-thirty and miss the sleep God meant him to have.

ARTHUR (*sullenly*). Hhm! Ma's always talking about God. I guess she got a letter from him this morning.

[MA *rises, outraged.*]

MA. Elmer, stop that automobile this minute. I don't go another step with anybody that says things like that. Arthur, you get out of this car. Elmer, you give him another dollar bill. He can go back to Newark by himself. I don't want him.

ARTHUR. What did I say? There wasn't anything terrible about that.

ELMER. I didn't hear what he said, Kate.

MA. God has done a lot of things for me and I won't have him made fun of by anybody. Go away. Go away from me.

CAROLINE. Aw, Ma – don't spoil the ride.

MA. No.

ELMER. We might as well go on, Kate, since we've got started. I'll talk to the boy tonight.

MA (*slowly conceding*). All right, if you say so, Elmer. But I won't sit beside him. Caroline, you come and sit by me.

ARTHUR (*frightened*). Aw, Ma, that wasn't so terrible.

MA. I don't want to talk about it. I hope your father washes your mouth out with soap and water. – Where'd we all be if I started talking about God like that, I'd like to know! We'd be in the speakeasies and night clubs and places like that, that's where we'd be. – All right, Elmer, you can go on now.

CAROLINE. What did he say, Ma? I didn't hear what he said.

MA. I don't want to talk about it.

[*They drive on in silence for a moment, the shocked silence after a scandal.*]

ELMER. I'm going to stop and give the car a little water, I guess.

MA. All right, Elmer. You know best.

ELMER (*to a garage hand*). Could I have a little water in the radiator – to make sure?

THE STAGE MANAGER (*in this scene alone he lays aside his script and enters into a rôle seriously*). You sure can. (*He punches the tires.*) Air all right? Do you need any oil or gas?

ELMER. No, I think not. I just got fixed up in Newark.

MA. We're on the right road for Camden, are we?

THE STAGE MANAGER. Yes, keep straight ahead. You can't miss it. You'll be in Trenton in a few minutes. (*He carefully pours some water into the hood.*) Camden's a great town, lady, believe me.

MA. My daughter likes it fine – my married daughter.

THE STAGE MANAGER. Ye'? It's a great burg all right. I guess I think so because I was born near there.

MA. Well, well. Your folks still live there?

THE STAGE MANAGER. No, my old man sold the farm and they built a factory on it. So the folks moved to Philadelphia.

MA. My married daughter Beulah lives there because her husband works in the telephone company. – Stop pokin' me, Caroline! – We're all going down to see her for a few days.

THE STAGE MANAGER. Ye'?

MA. She's been sick, you see, and I just felt I had to go and see her. My husband and my boy are going to stay at the Y.M.C.A. I hear they've got a dormitory on the top floor that's real clean and comfortable. Had you ever been there?

THE STAGE MANAGER. No. I'm Knights of Columbus myself.

MA. Oh.

THE STAGE MANAGER. I used to play basketball at the Y, though. It looked all right to me. (*He has been standing with one foot on the rung of* MA's *chair. They have taken a great fancy to one another. He reluctantly shakes himself out of it and pretends to examine the car again, whistling.*) Well, I guess you're all set now, lady. I hope you have a good trip; you can't miss it.

EVERYBODY. Thanks. Thanks a lot. Good luck to you.

[*Jolts and lurches.*]

MA (*with a sigh*). The world's full of nice people. — That's what I call a nice young man.

CAROLINE (*earnestly*). Ma, you oughtn't to tell 'm all everything about yourself.

MA. Well, Caroline, you do your way and I'll do mine. — He looked kinda thin to me. I'd like to feed him up for a few days. His mother lives in Philadelphia and I expect he eats at those dreadful Greek places.

CAROLINE. I'm hungry. Pa, there's a hot-dog stand. K'n I have one?

ELMER. We'll all have one, eh, Kate? We had such an early lunch.

MA. Just as you think best, Elmer.

ELMER. Arthur, here's half a dollar. — Run over and see what they have. Not too much mustard, either.

[ARTHUR *descends from the car and goes off stage right.* MA *and* CAROLINE *get out and walk a bit.*]

MA. What's that flower over there? — I'll take some of those to Beulah.

CAROLINE. It's just a weed, Ma.

MA. I like it. — My, look at the sky, wouldya! I'm glad I was born in New Jersey. I've always said it was the best state in the Union. Every state has something no other state has got.

[*They stroll about humming. Presently* ARTHUR *returns with his hands full of imaginary hot dogs, which he distributes. He is still very much cast down by the recent scandal. He finally approaches his mother and says falteringly:*]

ARTHUR. Ma, I'm sorry. I'm sorry for what I said. (*He bursts into tears and puts his forehead against her elbow.*)

MA. There. There. We all say wicked things at times. I know you didn't mean it like it sounded. (*He weeps still more violently than before.*) Why, now, now! I forgive you, Arthur, and tonight before you go to bed you . . . (*She whispers.*) You're a good boy at heart, Arthur, and we all know it. (CAROLINE *starts to cry too.* MA *is suddenly joyously alive and happy.*) Sakes alive, it's too nice a day for us all to be cryin'. Come now, get in. You go up in front with your father, Caroline. Ma wants to sit with her beau. I never saw such children. Your hot dogs are all getting wet. Now chew them fine, everybody. – All right, Elmer, forward march. – Caroline, whatever are you doing?

CAROLINE. I'm spitting out the leather, Ma.

MA. Then say "Excuse me."

CAROLINE. Excuse me, please.

MA. What's this place? Arthur, did you see the post office?

ARTHUR. It said Lawrenceville.

MA. Hhn. School kinda nice. I wonder what that big yellow house set back was. – Now it's beginning to be Trenton.

CAROLINE. Papa, it was near here that George Washington crossed the Delaware. It was near Trenton, Mamma. He was first in war and first in peace and first in the hearts of his countrymen.

MA (*surveying the passing world, serene and didactic*). Well, the thing I like about him best was that he never told a lie. (*The children are duly cast down. There is a pause.*) There's a sunset for you. There's nothing like a good sunset.

ARTHUR. There's an Ohio license in front of us. Ma, have you ever been to Ohio?

MA. No.

[*A dreamy silence descends upon them.* CAROLINE *sits closer to her father.* MA *puts her arm around* ARTHUR.]

ARTHUR. Ma, what a lotta people there are in the world, Ma. There must be thousands and thousands in the United States. Ma, how many are there?

MA. I don't know. Ask your father.

ARTHUR. Pa, how many are there?

ELMER. There are a hundred and twenty-six million, Kate.

MA (*giving a pressure about* ARTHUR'S *shoulder*). And they all like to drive out in the evening with their children beside'm.

(Another pause.) Why doesn't somebody sing something? Arthur, you're always singing something; what's the matter with you?

ARTHUR. All right. What'll we sing? *(He sketches:)*

"In the Blue Ridge mountains of Virginia,
On the trail of the lonesome pine . . ."

No, I don't like that any more. Let's do:

"I been workin' on de railroad
All de liblong day.
I been workin' on de railroad
Just to pass de time away."

[CAROLINE *joins in at once. Finally even* MA *is singing. Even* PA *is singing.* MA *suddenly jumps up with a wild cry.*]

MA. Elmer, that signpost said Camden, I saw it.

ELMER. All right, Kate, if you're sure.

[*Much shifting of gears, backing, and jolting.*]

MA. Yes, there it is. Camden – five miles. Dear old Beulah. – Now, children, you be good and quiet during dinner. She's just got out of bed after a big sorta operation, and we must all move around kinda quiet. First you drop me and Caroline at the door and just say hello, and then you menfolk go over to the Y.M.C.A. and come back for dinner in about an hour.

CAROLINE *(shutting her eyes and pressing her fists passionately against her nose)*. I see the first star. Everybody make a wish.

Star light, star bright,
First star I seen tonight.
I wish I may, I wish I might
Have the wish I wish tonight.

(Then solemnly.) Pins. Mamma, you say "needles." *(She interlocks little fingers with her mother.)*

MA. Needles.

CAROLINE. Shakespeare. Ma, you say "Longfellow."

MA. Longfellow.

CAROLINE. Now it's a secret and I can't tell it to anybody. Ma. you make a wish.

MA (*with almost grim humor*). No, I can make wishes without waiting for no star. And I can tell my wishes right out loud too. Do you want to hear them?

CAROLINE (*resignedly*). No, Ma, we know'm already. We've heard'm. (*She hangs her head affectedly on her left shoulder and says with unmalicious mimicry:*) You want me to be a good girl and you want Arthur to be honest-in-word-and-deed.

MA (*majestically*). Yes. So mind yourself.

ELMER. Caroline, take out that letter from Beulah in my coat pocket by you and read aloud the places I marked with red pencil.

CAROLINE (*working*). *"A few blocks after you pass the two big oil tanks on your left . . ."*

EVERYBODY (*pointing backward*). There they are!

CAROLINE. *". . . you come to a corner where there's an A and P store on the left and a firehouse kitty-corner to it . . .* (*They all jubilantly identify these landmarks.*) *. . . turn right, go two blocks, and our house is Weyerhauser St. Number 471."*)

MA. It's an even nicer street than they used to live in. And right handy to an A and P.

CAROLINE (*whispering*). Ma, it's better than our street. It's richer than our street. – Ma, isn't Beulah richer than we are?

MA (*looking at her with a firm and glassy eye*). Mind yourself, missy. I don't want to hear anybody talking about rich or not rich when I'm around. If people aren't nice I don't care how rich they are. I live in the best street in the world because my husband and children live there. (*She glares impressively at* CAROLINE *a moment to let this lesson sink in, then looks up, sees* BEULAH *and waves.*) There's Beulah standing on the steps lookin' for us.

[BEULAH *has appeared and is waving. They all call out:* "Hello, Beulah – Hello." *Presently they are all getting out of the car.* BEULAH *kisses her father long and affectionately.*]

BEULAH. Hello, Papa. Good old Papa. You look tired, Pa. – Hello, Mamma. – Lookit how Arthur and Caroline are growing!

MA. They're bursting all their clothes! – Yes, your pa needs a rest.

Thank heaven his vacation has come just now. We'll feed him up and let him sleep late. Pa has a present for you, Loolie. He would go and buy it.

BEULAH. Why, Pa, you're terrible to go and buy anything for me. Isn't he terrible?

MA. Well, it's a secret. You can open it at dinner.

ELMER. Where's Horace, Loolie?

BEULAH. He was kep' over a little at the office. He'll be here any minute. He's crazy to see you all.

MA. All right. You men go over to the Y and come back in about an hour.

BEULAH (*as her father returns to the wheel, stands out in the street beside him*). Go straight along, Pa, you can't miss it. It just stares at yuh. (*She puts her arm around his neck and rubs her nose against his temple.*) Crazy old Pa, goin' buyin' things! It's me that ought to be buyin' things for you, Pa.

ELMER. Oh no! There's only one Loolie in the world.

BEULAH (*whispering, as her eyes fill with tears*). Are you glad I'm still alive, Pa? (*She kisses him abruptly and goes back to the house steps.* THE STAGE MANAGER *removes the automobile with the help of* ELMER *and* ARTHUR, *who go off waving their good-bys.*) Well, come on upstairs, Ma, and take off your things. Caroline, there's a surprise for you in the back yard.

CAROLINE. Rabbits?

BEULAH. No.

CAROLINE. Chickins?

BEULAH. No. Go and see. (CAROLINE *runs off stage.* BEULAH *and* MA *gradually go upstairs.*) There are two new puppies. You be thinking over whether you can keep one in Newark.

MA. I guess we can. It's a nice house, Beulah. You just got a *lovely* home.

BEULAH. When I got back from the hospital, Horace had moved everything into it, and there wasn't anything for me to do.

MA. It's lovely.

[THE STAGE MANAGER *pushes out a bed from the left. Its foot is toward the right.* BEULAH *sits on it, testing the springs.*]

BEULAH. I think you'll find the bed comfortable, Ma.

MA *(taking off her hat)*. Oh, I could sleep on a heapa shoes, Loolie! I don't have no trouble sleepin'. *(She sits down beside her.)* Now let me look at my girl. Well, well, when I last saw you, you didn't know me. You kep' saying: "When's Mamma comin'? When's Mamma comin'?" But the doctor sent me away.

BEULAH *(puts her head on her mother's shoulder and weeps)*. It was awful, Mamma. It was awful. She didn't even live a few minutes, Mamma. It was awful.

MA *(looking far away)*. God thought best, dear. God thought best. We don't understand why. We just go on, honey, doin' our business. *(Then almost abruptly — passing the back of her hand across her cheek.)* Well, now, what are we giving the men to eat tonight?

BEULAH. There's a chicken in the oven.

MA. What time didya put it in?

BEULAH *(restraining her)*. Aw, Ma, don't go yet. I like to sit here with you this way. You always get the fidgets when we try and pet yuh, Mamma.

MA *(ruefully, laughing)*. Yes, it's kinda foolish. I'm just an old Newark bag o' bones. *(She glances at the backs of her hands.)*

BEULAH *(indignantly)*. Why, Ma, you're good-lookin'! We always said you were good-lookin'. — And besides, you're the best ma we could ever have.

MA *(uncomfortable)*. Well, I hope you like me. There's nothin' like being liked by your family. — Now I'm going downstairs to look at the chicken. You stretch out here for a minute and shut your eyes. — Have you got everything laid in for breakfast before the shops close?

BEULAH. Oh, you know! Ham and eggs.

[*They both laugh.*]

MA. I declare I never could understand what men see in ham and eggs. I think they're horrible. — What time did you put the chicken in?

BEULAH. Five o'clock.

MA. Well, now, you shut your eyes for ten minutes. (BEULAH *stretches out and shuts her eyes.* MA *descends the stairs absent-mindedly singing:*)

"There were ninety and nine that safely lay
In the shelter of the fold,
But one was out on the hills away,
Far off from the gates of gold. . . ."

AFTER READING

1. For what reasons did the Kirbys decide to go on a trip to Camden?

2. Mention incidents in the play which show:
   a. concern of the various members of the family for one another
   b. pride of each member of the family in the abilities of the others
   c. friendship between the Kirbys and their neighbors.

3. Describe incidents which show that Mrs. Kirby is trying to bring her children up properly.

4. Mrs. Kirby says, "If people aren't nice I don't care how rich they are." Do you agree? Why do you prefer friendliness and integrity to wealth?

5. Caroline says, "I'm spitting out the leather, Ma." To what is she referring?

6. Why was this a happy journey?

7. Does the lack of scenery help or hinder the play? Give reasons to support your opinion.

8. The Stage Manager plays several parts, each in the same lifeless tone. Discuss whether you would have enjoyed the play more if each of these parts was played by a different actor.

CHALLENGES

1. The Parents Association of your school is planning a meeting on "Common Mistakes That Parents Make in Raising Children." The president of the association, who believes that young people should be allowed to express their views on this topic, invites your class to submit a list of such common mistakes for discussion at the meeting. Enumerate some instances of poor parental judgment and explain briefly how parents should behave in each instance.

2. Before setting out on the trip to Camden, Mr. Kirby wrote for reservations to the Y.M.C.A. Compose the letter he wrote.

3. List some common actions and attitudes on the part of young people which make their parents unhappy. As a parent, how would you have these boys and girls change their behavior?

DRAMA WORKSHOP

A hint for playgoers: Learn all you can about the theater.

The more you know about art, dancing, or music, the more you enjoy a painting, ballet, or symphony. Similarly, technical information helps you enjoy a play. In fact, a drama may combine all the arts — including poetry, music, dancing, painting, and even sculpture (the groupings, poses, and movements of the actors) — so that acquaintance with a wide range of the arts is helpful in appreciating drama.

If you want to get the most pleasure from a play or movie, learn all you can about the theater. A good book to start with is Sheldon Cheney's *The Theatre.* Don't try to read it through; just dip into those chapters that interest you. Be sure to read Cheney's discussion of the Chinese theater, beginning at page 119, and notice the Chinese influences in *The Happy Journey* and *The Stolen Prince.* Be sure, too, to look at the remarkable illustrations — there are more than two hundred.

A hint for actors: Observe closely.

A famous movie comedian once was required to play the role of a trolley-car conductor. He spent days preparing for this part by riding trolley cars in order to observe the characteristic gestures and attitudes of conductors. The result was a realistic portrayal which won him wide commendation.

If you want to be an actor, you must first develop your powers of observation. First, notice your own behavior in everyday situations. For instance, go through the motions of removing and folding an imaginary overcoat. Next, actually remove your coat, paying attention to all the movements involved in the act. You'll be surprised at how much you failed to include in your pantomime, mainly because you normally do not observe ordinary occurrences closely.

Second, observe others — an orchestra leader, a teacher, a policeman — and try to reproduce their characteristic movements. In preparation for a presentation of *The Happy Journey,* watch the actions of people riding in an automobile. The behavior of a youngster, for example, in a car differs from that of an adult — regrettably so, if you are an adult!

OTHER COMEDIES YOU WILL LIKE TO READ

The Boor by Anton Chekhov (12). A Russian landowner tries to collect money owed by the late husband of an attractive neighbor, with humorous consequences.

The Constant Lover by St. John Hankin (33). A young man has no difficulty in expressing sentiments of love in rapid succession.

The Dear Departed by Stanley Houghton (6). Just as the two daughters of the supposedly dead father are dividing up the estate he appears with a startling announcement.

A Dollar by David Pinsky (20). A quarrel ensues when a poor troupe of players finds a dollar.

Enter the Hero by Theresa Helburn (16). An imaginative girl writes letters and telegrams to herself from a young man who has been in South America.

The Flattering Word by George Kelly (42). An actor with a good understanding of human psychology persuades a minister and one of his assistants that a play can be worth seeing.

The Ghost Story by Booth Tarkington (28). The difficulties a college student encounters in securing privacy to make a proposal are resolved by his telling a ghost story.

Hyacinth Halvey by Lady Gregory (20). The reputation for goodness turns out to be embarrassing for Hyacinth, who simply cannot get people to think evil of him.

GOD AND TEXAS

BY ROBERT ARDREY

ABOUT THE PLAY

"Remember the Alamo" is almost proverbial, but many who use the expression do not know its full meaning. Likewise, youngsters eventually meet the term "Bowie knife," but some know little about the gallant soldier for whom the knife is named. In this play both the Alamo and Captain Bowie are to be seen in their finest hour.

Historical one-act plays that are well constructed and well written are hard to find, probably because writers cannot exercise much originality in dealing with well-known characters and long-familiar events. It is of course hard to be original with history. During World War II there were many plays written which were designed to help the war effort. Many of them would make dull reading today. *God and Texas* is one of the exceptions. We all can admire the courage of a band of men hopelessly outnumbered, yet unwilling to take the chance to retreat. Our American history is filled with numerous similar incidents, from Bunker Hill to the Battle of the

---

Bulge in World War II. After reading the play, you'll understand better the cry "Remember the Alamo" and perhaps grant a Texan the pride he feels in his native state.

ABOUT THE AUTHOR

Robert Ardrey has been represented on the Broadway stage by four plays: *Star-Spangled, Casey Jones, How to Get Tough about It,* and *Thunder Rock.* He was born and educated in Chicago and was graduated from the University of Chicago. For his excellence in dramatic writing, he was awarded a Guggenheim Fellowship in 1937. For his play *Thunder Rock* the Playwrights' Company awarded him a special prize for the "most promising play by a young American playwright." Mr. Ardrey has worked on a number of motion pictures, including *They Knew What They Wanted* and *The Lady Takes a Chance.* He wrote *God and Texas* as a contribution to the war effort, to be played by and for servicemen. This would account for the all-male cast, even though the play's content could be arranged to include women.

GOD AND TEXAS

Characters

CALLAHAN

COLONEL JAMES BOWIE

CAPTAIN AMOS FOX

COLONEL WILLIAM TRAVIS

COLONEL DAVEY CROCKETT

CAPTAIN BONHAM

GEORGE SMITH

PEDRO GOMEZ

MEXICAN SOLDIERS

PLACE: Texas. TIME: 1836.

SCENE: *A shallow room. A narrow window is indicated. A crucifix hangs on the wall. There's a cot, a chair, a table with a jug of water and a basin. At the table sits a young man named* CALLAHAN. *He holds a pencil poised over a sheet of paper. On the bed lies an officer named* BOWIE. *He's a rugged man about forty, but he's very sick.* BOWIE *lies with his head propped on a makeshift pillow, his folded coat. He wears only his underpants. He's covered by a thin blanket.* CALLAHAN *and the men we see later wear United States Army uniforms, unless otherwise noted. It's night.* BOWIE *is dictating a letter. Occasionally he coughs. As the curtain rises,* BOWIE *lies still, thinking.* CALLAHAN *plays with his pencil. It's very still.*

BOWIE. My dear wife –

[CALLAHAN *writes. There's a dull boom of cannon in the distance. They both look up, and* BOWIE *rises a little, propped on his elbow. There's the slipping, sliding crash of a hit.* BOWIE *rubs his hot forehead slowly.* CALLAHAN *finishes writing his phrase.*]

CALLAHAN. The doctor said you shouldn't sit up, Colonel.

[BOWIE *gives him a look and lies back. He starts to cough.* CALLAHAN *just sits looking at his sheet of paper, playing with his pencil, waiting for* BOWIE'S *coughing fit to pass. He knows how sick* BOWIE *is. Another dull boom in the distance.* BOWIE *stops coughing,* CALLAHAN'S *pencil is still. But this time neither looks up. They wait. No crash.*]

CALLAHAN (*contemptuously*). Miss — some gunnery, eh sir?

[BOWIE *gives him a glance and doesn't smile.* CALLAHAN *lowers his eyes to his paper again.* BOWIE *sighs.*]

BOWIE. My dear wife — (CALLAHAN *waits, pencil poised.*) We've been here seven days. The main army's to the north. We're still hoping for reinforcements —

[CALLAHAN *is writing rapidly.* BOWIE *holds his hot forehead. His words don't come easily.*]

BOWIE (*continuing*). Don't worry about us. You've been married to me long enough to know I like a good fight. (CALLAHAN *smiles as he writes.* BOWIE *struggles for words.*) Oh criminy, Callahan, I wasn't cut out for writing letters to my wife.

CALLAHAN. Go on, Colonel. You're doing fine.

BOWIE. Start over.

[CALLAHAN *shakes his head, throws aside his sheet of paper, and takes another. The doctor enters.* CAPTAIN FOX *is quiet, gentle, inwardly bitter at the predicament of the men he attends. He nods to* BOWIE *as he enters.* BOWIE *just looks at him fixedly.* FOX *feels his forehead and goes on to the table, where he puts down his battered, dusty satchel.*]

BOWIE. How am I?

FOX. Fine, fine.

BOWIE (*sharply*). Don't treat me like a schoolgirl. (FOX *smiles and shrugs.*) How am I?

FOX. You've got pneumonia. Your lungs are jammed. You're burning up with fever. You've got the shakes. And you want to know how you are. (*He goes to* BOWIE'S *side and takes his wrist.*) Your chances, Colonel, are just about the same as the rest of the garrison's.

[BOWIE *looks up at him sharply.* FOX *counts his pulse.*]

BOWIE. What do you mean by that? (*The doctor just counts.*) We're surrounded, all right. We're outnumbered, all right. Things aren't hopeless. You've got no right to say it, Captain.

FOX (*drops* BOWIE's *wrist and returns to the table*). It's about time somebody said something.

[*The cannon booms in the distance. They all freeze. They wait. The slipping, sliding crash of a hit. The doctor starts hunting through his bag.* BOWIE *coughs chokingly. He lies back flat,* FOX *gets out a rag, wets it.* CALLAHAN *has been listening. He's disturbed.* BOWIE *stops his coughing, sighs.*]

BOWIE. My dear wife — (CALLAHAN *starts writing again.*) Oh Lord, Captain, I can't write letters. . . . (*Again dictating.*) My dear wife, Travis thinks we can get a messenger out of here tonight. He can take this letter along. (FOX *puts the wet cloth on* BOWIE's *forehead.*) I'm all right. I have a slight cold. I've asked Colonel Travis to take over command — just for a while. I'm all right though. It's just a slight cold. (FOX *returns to his bag, shakes some pills out of a bottle, pours out some water into a tin cup.* BOWIE *is struggling for words, and* CALLAHAN *is catching up, writing rapidly.*) There isn't much to say. We're fighting a delaying action.

FOX. What a love letter.

BOWIE (*struggling*). Headquarters wants us to hold on as long as we can. (FOX *shakes his head deploringly and hands* BOWIE *the pills and the cup of water.* BOWIE *props himself up, still struggling.*) Our communications seem to be cut —

FOX. What a love letter. (BOWIE *gives him a bitter look and downs his pills.*) No grace, no passion, no sweet, sad sentiments.

BOWIE. Write it yourself! (*He makes a face over the bitter pills and* FOX *laughs.*) Go on! I've got one man writing down the words, I might as well have another one thinking them up! (*He flops out flat.*)

FOX. You mean that? You want me to write it? (BOWIE *doesn't answer. He just lies looking at the ceiling. The doctor rubs his hands and turns to* CALLAHAN.) Well, Callahan, if you can stand it, I can. (CALLAHAN *is looking from one to the other, not quite knowing whether to write or not. He takes another sheet of paper.*) My own sweet wife, my dear one.

BOWIE. Oh Lord. She'll report me. She'll say I'm drinking again.

FOX. Go on, Callahan. Write. (*Quietly.*) My own sweet wife, my dear one — (*There's the thunder of the distant cannon.* CALLAHAN *pauses. They wait, and the doctor's face is sober, meditative. There's the crash of a hit.* CALLAHAN'S *face gets grim. He goes on writing.* FOX *continues:*) Helplessly I turn to you tonight. Why am I here? Why am I alone in the wilderness? (BOWIE *turns his head very slowly, staring at the doctor, and* CALLAHAN *glances up quickly and then goes on writing. The bitterness deepens in* FOX'S *tone.*) My little garrison waits. The walls of my fragile fortress shudder. The enemy, four thousand strong, creeps through the brush. Headquarters, safe in the north, talks about reinforcements. I see no reinforcements. (BOWIE *props himself up suddenly on his elbow. He makes a gesture to stop the doctor.* FOX *goes right on.*) Why are we here? We wonder. In our hearts. We don't say it out loud. (BOWIE *lies back a little, still staring.*) Perhaps, someday, I'll see you. Once again I'll hold you in my arms. And then again perhaps I won't, and these few words are all we'll have.

BOWIE (*low*). Captain Fox?

FOX (*never stops*). In case that's it, then, my darling, good-by. My little garrison — my hundred-odd heroes — we neither fight nor retreat to fight again. We merely wait. (BOWIE *lies out flat, stares at the ceiling.*) I lie here, stricken. I'm ill. Another commands. He tells me we're surrounded. Perhaps we are, perhaps we're not, perhaps he lies. (BOWIE *sits up abruptly.*) Good-by, my love, my wife. God and Texas! — Your obedient husband, James Bowie. (*In a matter-of-fact tone.*) What's the date, Callahan?

CALLAHAN (*automatically, dazed by what he's been writing*). March first.

FOX. Dated this day, March the first, eighteen hundred and thirty-six. San Antonio, Republic of Texas. *He looks up as the cannon booms. He waits for the crash. It comes.*) The Alamo. (*He turns to his bag, replaces the bottle of pills.* BOWIE *swings around on his cot, his naked feet on the floor.*)

BOWIE. Destroy that letter! (CALLAHAN *crumples it.*)

FOX. Lie down, Colonel Bowie. (BOWIE *flings away the wet rag from his forehead, tries to rise, falls back.*) Save your strength for the Mexicans.

BOWIE. Dr. Fox, are we surrounded or aren't we? (FOX *closes his bag, doesn't answer.*) Callahan! Tell Colonel Travis I'll see him immediately. (CALLAHAN *leaves.*) You say Travis lied to me.

FOX (*wearily*). I didn't. I said perhaps.

BOWIE. Travis and I are in joint command. (FOX *looks away.*) He's told me we've got no means of retreat. He's told me the Alamo's encircled.

FOX. You haven't been out of bed since the siege started.

BOWIE. Sant' Anna's got four thousand men. If he hasn't got the Alamo surrounded, why hasn't he?

FOX. I don't know.

BOWIE. Why would Travis lie to me? (FOX *shakes his head.*) What do you know?

FOX. Travis sent out a scout. The scout was wounded. I attended him.

BOWIE. What about it?

FOX. The riverbed's unoccupied. The Mexicans don't even have it covered. (BOWIE *sits back.*) The way to the northeast is clear.

BOWIE. You're positive?

FOX. The scout told Travis. Travis told him not to tell. (BOWIE *rubs his hot forehead.*) I'm a doctor. I have a natural dislike for suicide.

BOWIE (*shaking his head*). Does Crockett know?

FOX. Crockett's a human being. Also, he's a politician. If he knew the Alamo wasn't surrounded, I don't think he'd be here now. (BOWIE *makes a sharp, angry gesture.*) You'd better lie down, Colonel.

BOWIE. Travis wouldn't lie to me.

FOX. I only know what I've said.

BOWIE. That God-forsaken young fool! Why would he tell us we can't retreat—

FOX. To make sure, perhaps, that we won't. (*A pause. Then the doctor wearily picks up his bag, turns toward the door.*) Save your strength, Colonel. Anything else? (BOWIE *shakes his head, lies back on the cot on his side, his head propped up.*) Good night.

[CALLAHAN *enters hurriedly as* FOX *turns toward the door.*]

CALLAHAN. Colonel Travis.

[TRAVIS *enters. He's young, handsome, determined, arrogant. His buttons are polished. His bearing is sharply military. At his side he carries a sword.*]

FOX (*nods grimly*). Colonel Bowie.

TRAVIS (*clicking attention*). Colonel Bowie.

[BOWIE *looks at him grimly for an instant, then speaks to* FOX.]

BOWIE. Find Crockett. Send him in here. Bonham. George Smith. (FOX *nods and leaves.* BOWIE *speaks to* CALLAHAN.) I'll write that letter some other time. (CALLAHAN *leaves.* TRAVIS *looks about curiously.*) Sit down.

TRAVIS. You seem to be recovering.

BOWIE (*grunts, picks up his cup of water from the floor, takes a sip*). Why hasn't Sant' Anna occupied the riverbed? (*For just an instant* TRAVIS *hardly seems to understand the implication of the question. Then abruptly he jumps to his feet. His action reveals the answer* BOWIE *wanted.* BOWIE *nods grimly.*) So he hasn't.

TRAVIS (*in anger*). Who have you been talking to?

BOWIE. Sit down. (TRAVIS *stands rigid.* BOWIE *coughs. He lies back wearily.*) Sit down, Travis, you wear me out.

TRAVIS. Look, Bowie. There are certain tactical problems I haven't wanted to bother you with, you've been sick —

BOWIE (*sitting up in anger*). You arrogant pup! You call the question of stay or retreat a tactical problem?

TRAVIS (*in anger*). We're fighting for the independence of Texas —

BOWIE. Don't for the love of criminy start getting heroic!

TRAVIS. I've got my responsibility to defend the Alamo —

BOWIE. We've got the job of delaying Sant' Anna, that's all!

TRAVIS. I use my judgment —

BOWIE. Your judgment! — What's the purpose of this war, the killing of Texans or the killing of Mexicans? (TRAVIS *stands rigid, his hand clenching his sword.*) You seem to be fascinated by the slaughter of the wrong side.

TRAVIS. Are you calling me a traitor?

BOWIE (*exasperated*). Oh for the love of – Sit down. No.

TRAVIS. What are you trying to insinuate, then?

BOWIE. Merely that you're a romantic kid. You like to make speeches. Death or victory! You like gestures. The idea of holding the Alamo to the last man, to the last bloody corpse – it fascinates you. (*A slight pause.* TRAVIS *looks past* BOWIE *without expression. Gently.*) Bill. We're all of us here in the Alamo for various personal reasons. You like to make gestures, I like a good fight. Crockett, (*A slight smile.*) Davey Crockett's an ex-Congressman. He's a discredited politician. He saw an opportunity for brightening up his somewhat tarnished reputation, and getting back into Congress. (*A slight pause.*) Some of us, I suppose – we're only here because we had no place else to go. (*He coughs a little.* TRAVIS *lowers his head, looks fixedly at the floor.* BOWIE *chokes down his coughing.*) I'm only saying, Bill – you had no right to take your personal desire for making gestures – enforce it on the rest of us –

TRAVIS (*stubbornly*). I have my orders from General Houston. To hold the Alamo –

BOWIE (*sharply*). We have our orders. We're in joint command, Travis. (TRAVIS *looks past him again.*) Why did you lie to me? Why did you tell me we can't retreat?

TRAVIS. Because I don't trust you. (*A slight pause.*)

BOWIE. You God-forsaken pup! Me, Jim Bowie. I've knifed my way out of a thousand saloons! I've killed men for picking their noses! Are you saying I'm afraid to fight?

TRAVIS. I repeat, sir. I don't trust you.

[BOWIE, *with a sudden, agile movement commanding all his strength, whips from under his makeshift pillow the knife he's made famous.*]

BOWIE. You God-forsaken –

[*He's rising.* TRAVIS's *hand goes to his sword but he doesn't draw it.* BOWIE *stands tottering, his knife gleaming in his hand. Three men enter.* DAVEY CROCKETT, *the lean humorous ex-Congressman from Tennessee;* BONHAM, *the young drawling aristocrat from Carolina;* GEORGE SMITH, *a rough Texas rancher. They stand staring at* BOWIE *and* TRAVIS, *astonished.*]

CROCKETT (*after just an instant*). What the heck goes on here? Target practice? (BOWIE *sways dizzily, and falls back on his cot. He drops his knife on the floor.* CROCKETT *whistles softly.*) Good work, men. (*He picks up the knife.*) We've disarmed him.

TRAVIS. Shut up, Crockett. (*Almost tenderly.*) Lie down, Jim. You're sick.

BOWIE (*brokenly*). I've spent my whole life looking for trouble — now here I am in the middle of it — and I'm sick. (*Appealingly.*) Travis! Get us out of here! I hate Sant' Anna, I hate him, I hate his creeping, crawling Mexicans out there — But get us out of here! Give me a chance, a chance to get well! Give me a chance to die fighting! Do I have to die in this God-forsaken bed?

TRAVIS. Lie down. (*Gently, pushing* BOWIE *back on his cot.*) I knew how it was, Jim. I knew it wasn't because you're a coward you'd want to retreat.

CROCKETT. Retreat?

[*A pause.* BOWIE *lies out flat.* TRAVIS *stands erect, speaks quietly.*]

TRAVIS. For the last three days Sant' Anna's left the riverbed uncovered. (*The men stare at each other. The boom of the distant cannon. They all look up. The crash, and the sliding sound of adobe.*) The Alamo's no longer surrounded. We can retreat whenever we choose.

CROCKETT. Holy good — (*He bounds toward the door. Nobody moves. He stares at them.*) Gentlemen! This is the month of March! What are we waiting for, Christmas?

[BONHAM *plunks down in the chair.*]

BONHAM. I'm flabbergasted. (*He wipes his forehead. He looks up at* TRAVIS.) Retreat? We can retreat?

TRAVIS. If we want to, Captain Bonham.

BONHAM (*incredulously*). If we want to! (*He rises, staring at* TRAVIS.) Is there some slight possibility, sir, that we might not want to?

[TRAVIS *looks away. He doesn't answer.*]

GEORGE SMITH (*the rough rancher*). Hey. You, Colonel. Did you say three days?

TRAVIS. Yes.

SMITH. Whyn't you tell us sooner?

[TRAVIS *doesn't answer.*]

CROCKETT. Did you tell Jim Bowie?

TRAVIS. No. (*A pause.*)

CROCKETT (*grimly*). I begin to understand why Bowie was waving his knife around. (*He replaces the knife under* BOWIE's *pillow.* BOWIE *just lies looking at the wall.*)

BONHAM (*quietly*). I'd like to get a few things straight, Colonel. You're sure about the riverbed?

TRAVIS. Yes.

BONHAM. Do you think it's a trap?

TRAVIS. No.

BONHAM. Why not? (TRAVIS *shakes his head.*) Sant' Anna's got four thousand men. The Alamo can't cover more than a couple of acres. If we're not surrounded, why aren't we?

TRAVIS. Sant' Anna wants us to retreat. (*They look at each other.*) Gentlemen. Sam Houston's organizing his army in the north. Sant' Anna doesn't care about us. He wants to get Houston. We've got the good fortune — or the bad fortune, if that's how you want to look at it — to be sitting here right in Sant' Anna's path. He doesn't dare leave us behind him. Can't you see, gentlemen? The longer we hold out, the better's the chance for Houston. And Texas!

SMITH. Houston promised us reinforcements.

TRAVIS. I know.

SMITH. Where are they?

TRAVIS. He can't afford them, he's — (*He just shakes his head.*) Maybe they'll come.

CROCKETT. When they said we'd retreat to the Alamo, I thought the thing was a fort. It's a creeping church.

TRAVIS. I know.

CROCKETT. This isn't any place to make a stand.

TRAVIS. There's no place else for three hundred miles.

CROCKETT. Why didn't I stay in Tennessee? Texas! (*He mutters and turns away.*)

BONHAM (*in his quiet drawl*). Seems to me, gentlemen, all this is off the point. The point is — if we stay here — (*A slight pause. Gently to* TRAVIS.) We may — linger — for quite a while! (TRAVIS *says nothing. His hand clenches his sword, he looks at the floor.*) So we hold up Sant' Anna a few days. What the devil for?

TRAVIS. I've told you! General Houston —

BONHAM. Houston! All right, so he beats Sant' Anna, so he gets to be president of Texas! What about us? (*A slight pause.*) Travis. There's a hundred of us here. Hundred and twenty. We didn't come to the Alamo because it's a church, because it's got a graveyard out behind. (*A slight pause.*) I don't like it.

CROCKETT. You and me, brother.

BONHAM. We came here to fight! If we can't fight here, all right, I say retreat! Fight where we can! In the north, on the Brazos, with Houston — wherever we've got a chance to fight and win! But don't, Travis, for God's sake, don't offer us up like a sacrifice, like cattle in a pen for the Mexicans to slaughter.

CROCKETT. Why did I ever leave Tennessee? (*He shakes his head.*)

SMITH. Jim. (BOWIE, *flat on his back, shakes his head.*) Jim Bowie.

BOWIE (*choked*). I don't know.

SMITH. You're a fighting man. You've fought with the pirate Lafitte. You've fought Indians. The Comanches, they know about you. (BOWIE *just shakes his head.*) Whatever you say, Jim.

BOWIE. I don't know.

SMITH. Whatever you say.

BOWIE. I'm a God-forsaken coward. (*He turns on his side, clutching the edge of his bed.*) I can't help it, Travis. I wasn't built for making speeches — writing letters to my wife — fighting for freedom, for Texas, for independence, for somebody else's amusement. I fight for my own. (*The distant boom of the cannon, and he looks up at the ceiling.*) I don't know. (*The crash of a hit.*) Oh Lord, I want to go, I want to get out of this dump, I want to slit me a Mexican by the throat, I don't want to die, not here in this God-forsaken bed!

SMITH. Whatever you say.

BOWIE *(shaking his head)*. I don't know, Bonham.

BONHAM. Whatever you say.

BOWIE. Davey. Davey Crockett.

CROCKETT. I'm sorry, Jim. I haven't got much interest in dead politicians. I say — what are we waiting for?

BOWIE. Travis.

TRAVIS *(his hand clenches the hilt of his sword, but he speaks quietly)*. It seems to be up to you.

[*A rattle of rifle fire in the distance. They all turn.*]

BOWIE. What was that?

[*They all listen. Several rifle shots.*]

TRAVIS. Bonham! (BONHAM *runs out of the room.*)

BOWIE. Criminy, if those Mexicans have started an attack -- *(He pulls his knife out from under his pillow.)*

CROCKETT. It's night! They can't! They go to bed at night.

[TRAVIS *holds up his hand. They listen. Another rattle of rifle fire.*]

TRAVIS. We'd better get out there —

[CALLAHAN *runs in panting.*]

CALLAHAN. Colonel Travis!

TRAVIS. Out with it!

CALLAHAN. Men approaching — along the riverbed —

TRAVIS. The riverbed!

SMITH. It's a trick! I know it's a trick! Them sneaking Mexicans!

TRAVIS. Report to the guard! Sound the alarm!

CROCKETT *(turning on* TRAVIS*)*. You glory-hunting fool! They gave us three days! Now it's too late!

SMITH. We could of been out of here!

CROCKETT. You swelled-head kid. *(He snatches up his rifle.)*

BOWIE. Let me come! Let me fight! Carry me, for the love of --

TRAVIS. Stay here!

BOWIE. No!

[*The shooting suddenly stops. There's a silence. The men look at each other as they stand about to run out. Distant shouts.* BONHAM *bursts in panting.*]

TRAVIS. Bonham!

BONHAM. Reinforcements!

CROCKETT. Reinforcements!

BOWIE. Lord in Heaven!

BONHAM. Reinforcements! (*He laughs.*) While we debate, should we march out, men march in!

SMITH. Houston's men!

BONHAM. I don't know. (*He's still laughing.*)

BOWIE. How many?

BONHAM. I don't know. But they carry the flag of Texas!

TRAVIS. God, God, I thank you, I thank you.

BOWIE. Creeping Jehosaphat! Give me a few hundred men, we'll stop Sant' Anna where he stands!

TRAVIS. Lie down, Jim!

BOWIE. I can't! It's enough to make a man well!

[*Two soldiers march in.*]

FIRST SOLDIER. Colonel Travis!

TRAVIS. Here!

FIRST SOLDIER. Leader of the reinforcements reporting!

TRAVIS. Send him in! (*The* FIRST SOLDIER *leaves, the second remains at attention.*) Gentlemen!

[TRAVIS *brings himself to stiff attention, standing beside* BOWIE'S *cot.* BONHAM *and* SMITH *click to attention.* CROCKETT *does his best.* BOWIE *sits up straight in his cot, pulls his blanket around him, wipes at his hair. The* FIRST SOLDIER *returns. He looks about at them oddly. But he draws himself to attention. A little grinning Mexican enters. He carries a shotgun taller than he is. He wears fatigue clothes. He's dusty, ragged. His name is* GOMEZ. *He stands blinking, grinning.*]

GOMEZ. H'lo.

[*The men are exchanging bewildered glances.*]

TRAVIS. Who are you?

FIRST SOLDIER. Leader of the reinforcements.

GOMEZ. Yeah. Sure.

TRAVIS. You?

GOMEZ (*grins*). Pedro Gomez. Tha's me.

[*The men stare at each other. A pause.*]

BOWIE. He's a creeping Mexican!

GOMEZ (*agreeably*). Tha's me.

TRAVIS (*to* BOWIE *in sudden anger*). For the love of — ! What kind of men is Houston sending us?

GOMEZ. Who's 'at?

TRAVIS. Houston! General Houston! (GOMEZ *shakes his head. Never heard of him.*) Didn't Houston send you?

GOMEZ. I do' know that fella.

TRAVIS. Who sent you?

GOMEZ. Nobody. (*They stare at each other.*) We jus' come.

TRAVIS. Nobody sent you! Where do you come from?

GOMEZ. Gonzales. Little town down the road. (*They're staring.* GOMEZ *continues reassuringly.*) Nice little town. Sure.

TRAVIS. You're not even soldiers?

GOMEZ. Nah. (*Quickly, brandishing his huge gun.*) Shoot plenty good, you betcha!

BONHAM. Señor Gomez. (GOMEZ *turns to* BONHAM. BONHAM'S *just looking at him, afraid to ask. Then he speaks very slowly.*) Pedro Gomez. How many men have you got?

GOMEZ (*as if he were speaking of regiments*). Twenty. (CROCKETT *sits down slowly in the chair.* BONHAM *looks around at* CROCKETT. *The attitude of stiff attention goes limp.* GOMEZ *is bewildered.*) What I say?

CROCKETT. You're bringing twenty men — twenty men — *into* the Alamo?

GOMEZ. Sure. (*A pause.*)

CROCKETT. Nobody told you to come. You just came.

GOMEZ. Sure. (*A pause.*)

TRAVIS (*takes a deep breath, speaks gently*). Look, Gomez. Maybe you don't know what you're getting into.

GOMEZ. Sure.

TRAVIS. Sant' Anna's got four thousand men out there in the mesquite.

GOMEZ (*shrugs*). So. (*A pause.*)

TRAVIS. We've got a hundred and twenty. (GOMEZ *nods.*) You make it a hundred and forty.

GOMEZ (*shrugs*). So. (*A pause.*)

TRAVIS. Somebody else talk to him.

GOMEZ (*bewildered again*). What' say? I don't talk so good.

CROCKETT. I think we're the ones don't talk so good. You. Gomez. (GOMEZ *turns to* CROCKETT.) Why did you come here?

GOMEZ. Don't understand.

CROCKETT. I say — you're a Mexican.

GOMEZ. Sure.

CROCKETT. You're not even a Texan.

GOMEZ (*shrugs*). I live here.

[CROCKETT *looks about as if for assistance. Nobody can help. He turns to* GOMEZ *again.*]

CROCKETT. I just want to know. What made you come to the Alamo?

GOMEZ (*comprehending*). Oh. Oh sure! Why — somebody they say — that Jim Bowie, he got plenty trouble down to San Anton'. He need plenty help. (*Satisfied, he grins.*) Sure. So we jus' come.

[CROCKETT *looks at* BOWIE. BOWIE *is sitting back on his cot, just staring.*]

CROCKETT. And you wanted a Mexican throat to slit.

[BOWIE *shakes his head vaguely.*]

GOMEZ. 'At fella he don't like Mexicans? (*He frowns at* BOWIE *reprovingly.*) 'At's a fine thing, you don't like Mexicans.

BOWIE (*to* CROCKETT). You got me into this! Get me out!

GOMEZ (*to* BOWIE, *belligerently*). Who you, you don't like Mexicans?

BOWIE. I'm Jim Bowie.

[GOMEZ *falls back bewildered. He scratches his ear.*]

GOMEZ. Don' onderstand.

BOWIE. Neither do I. I'm the guy you came here to help. (GOMEZ *looks about helpless.*) Gomez! Holy criminy — Gomez, you came to help me, all right, help me! If I'm not fighting against your people who am I fighting?

GOMEZ. Sant' Anna!

BOWIE. But he's a Mexican!

GOMEZ. You think Mexican people they like that Sant' Anna? Bah! (*He spits.*) That bad fella? What's a dif'rence Sant' Anna Mexican, Texas, Yankee, what's a dif'rence? Bad fella alla same! (*He sighs, looks around almost sadly.*) Yah. Too bad, huh? So many bad fellas, this world, us good fellas always got to be cut the throat. (*He shakes his head, then brightens.*) Don't you worry, Jim Bowie. We cut the throat.

BOWIE (*low*). Pedro — (*He hesitates.*) — never mind.

GOMEZ (*shrewdly*). You want to know, maybe Pedro scare'? (*A slight pause. He laughs lightly.*) Sure, I'm scare' — Maybe you think that Sant' Anna ain't scare'? All he got, four t'ousan' soldiers. All us hund'erd Texas fellas waiting for him. Maybe you think Sant' Anna ain't scare'?

[CROCKETT *and* BOWIE *exchange a glance.* CROCKETT *shakes his head.*]

BOWIE. Will you do me a favor, Pedro? (*He puts out his hand.* GOMEZ *takes it, shakes it, grins.*)

GOMEZ. Jim Bowie — that's very brave fella — I do anything for Jim Bowie. What you want?

BOWIE. Never mind. You've done it.

[*He looks at his hand, the hand that shook the hand of* PEDRO GOMEZ. *The thunder of the distant cannon. They all look up. The Alamo shakes with the impact.* TRAVIS *draws his sword.*]

TRAVIS. Any of you want to retreat — the way along the riverbed's still open. (*No one moves.*) I intend to stay — here in the Alamo — with Pedro Gomez and his men. (*He looks around.*) All of you that are staying with Pedro and me — (*He draws a line on the floor with his sword.*) Will you cross this line? (*The cannon boom. They stare at the line. None lifts his head. The crash of the sliding adobe.*) For God and Texas — for death, or victory! — will you cross this line? (*A moment and* CROCKETT *rises from his chair.* TRAVIS *in triumph.*) Davey Crockett!

CROCKETT (*as he crosses the line*). Why did I ever leave Tennessee?

TRAVIS (*as* BONHAM *crosses the line*). Bonham! (*As the doctor emerges from the crowd at the door and crosses the line.*) Amos Fox! (*The men by the door are moving in a body across the line.*) Texans!

BOWIE (*propped up on his cot, his knife in his hand*). Gomez! Somebody!

[*A man emerges from the crowd.*]

TRAVIS (*in triumph*). James Bowie!

BOWIE. Carry me across!

[GOMEZ *and the other men are lifting his cot, carrying him across the line.*]

AFTER READING

1. If you were in Colonel Bowie's place and it was up to you to make the decision, what do you think you would do?

2. How would you have acted if you had been Colonel Travis? How can you justify his action?

3. Davey Crockett is a legendary character in American history, famous as local magistrate, state legislator, and Congressman although he had very little formal education. What do you learn of his character from this play?

4. Comment on Gomez's lines: "So many bad fellas, this world, us good fellas always got to be cut the throat." Have times changed since 1836? How?

5. There are many ways of giving the background of the plot of a one-act play. How is it done in *God and Texas?* What would be a better way?

6. Suppose Gomez had not come, what do you think the officers would have decided?

7. Can you think of other instances in history of sieges like the Alamo?

8. It is said that "self-preservation is the first law of nature." What made the people in this play disobey that "law"?

CHALLENGES

1. Write the letter that is finally sent to Mrs. Bowie.

2. During the battle that eventually ensues, Davey Crockett reminisces of his early battles. Consult your history books and write the thoughts that come to his mind.

3. Bonham asks Gomez to explain further why he chose to fight against the Mexicans. Write the dialogue.

4. Colonel Travis leaves a note to General Houston, explaining how the decision to hold the Alamo was made. Write the note.

5. Read the *Autobiography of Davey Crockett* and report on it to the class.

DRAMA WORKSHOP

A hint for playgoers: Look for the climax.

From reading the "Open Letter" at the beginning of this book you will remember that "climax" is derived from a Greek word meaning "ladder." Nowadays the word "climax" means the top rung of the dramatic ladder – the moment of greatest excitement in a story or drama. It is the tense instant which reveals the turning point in the plot.

A play is built around its climax, for the playwright has it in mind from the beginning. All incidents lead up to or away from the climax. For example, the climax of *God and Texas* occurs when Travis draws a line on the floor with his sword and challenges the others to cross it and remain in the Alamo "For God and Texas – for death, or victory!" One by one they cross the line until Bowie remains alone. Will he leave the Alamo and be saved – or will he stay and accept certain death? The author recognized this incident as a tremendously exciting event and made it the climax of his play.

Recognizing the climax adds zest to playgoing, for the success of a play often depends more on it than on any other single ingredient.

A hint for actors: Project your voice.

An actor must be heard and understood. That's rather obvious, isn't it? Yet inaudible or unintelligible speeches by actors are common stage faults. Your problem as an actor is difficult. You must give the impression of carrying on a conversation in ordinary tones, yet you must speak loud enough for a large audience to overhear. A good director starts insisting at the very first rehearsal that the actors display adequate vocal volume and clear diction.

If you think only of *talking louder,* your voice may sound strained and unpleasant. Concentrate instead on *projecting* your voice, on sending it to the back rows of the theater, auditorium, or classroom. Direct as many of your lines as possible to the audience. Glance at the character on the stage to whom you are speaking, but speak most of the lines *front* – that is, direct them beyond the footlights.

OTHER HISTORICAL PLAYS YOU WILL LIKE TO READ

The Boy Bowditch by Riley Hughes (31). Several episodes in the life of Nathaniel Bowditch, America's celebrated mathematician.

The Boy Will by Robert Emmons Rogers (7). A dramatic reconstruction of Shakespeare's leaving Stratford in the company of Peale, a London actor.

Brother Sun by Laurence Housman (5). St. Francis visits the Sultan during a war and tries to persuade the Mohammedan leader to stop fighting.

The Decision at Dawn by R. B. Lawrence (43). Washington is kept from handing in his resignation by the pleas of Mrs. Washington and the good news of Franklin's treaty with France.

Fires at Valley Forge by Barrett H. Clark (31). General Washington is heartened by the offer of two boys to join his ragged forces.

Fortune and Men's Eyes by Josephine Preston Peabody (7). Shakespeare manages to free himself from his infatuation for Mary Fitton.

The Lad of Stratford by Milnor Dorey (35). When Shakespeare is nineteen, Queen Elizabeth happens to see a book of his verses and invites him to London.

Little Father in the Wilderness by Austin Strong and Lloyd Osborne (6). The popular French missionary, Père Marlotte, is made an archbishop by Louis XV after the great General Frontenac kneels in homage.

Franklin & the King

BY PAUL GREEN

ABOUT THE PLAY

Franklin and the King holds our interest in spite of the fact that most of us "already know the story." Here you will find no surprise endings or other dramatic tricks that make some plays successful. Paul Green's play deals with familiar events of the past, but he makes them seem immediate and suspenseful. The reader becomes a spectator of a momentous scene in our country's history. Benjamin Franklin is of course the leading figure in the play, but William Pitt and George the Third also emerge as recognizable personalities. You may have forgotten, in your study of the American Revolution, that a few great Englishmen like William Pitt pleaded the cause of American rights almost as eloquently as the Americans themselves. You may also have forgotten that the differences between England and her young colony were readily capable of being settled peaceably – but these are reminders you will best receive from the play itself.

ABOUT THE AUTHOR

Paul Green is one of the leading dramatists of America today, and he is unequaled in his portrayals of rural life in the South. Although he is most famous as a playwright, he teaches philosophy in the University of North Carolina. He was born on a farm near Lillington, North Carolina, in 1894. During World War I he served with the A.E.F., and upon his return from France he completed his education at the university where he now teaches. His advice to beginning dramatists is worth noting:

"Stay at home, read books, ignore artificial standards and keep a steady job. Those are my precepts for youngsters who want to write. They're the only rules for success I've known and I've followed them religiously. Even if I made a fortune – which does not seem likely – I'd keep my little old job in the University in Chapel Hill and go on living the simple life in the sticks."

The successful plays of Paul Green are numerous, including *In Abraham's Bosom,* which received the Pulitzer Prize in 1926. Some of his one-act plays have become classics. Recently he has been writing plays and pageants about the American heritage, the best known of which is *The Lost Colony*.

FRANKLIN AND THE KING

Characters

GEORGE THE THIRD, *King of England*

HIS MOTHER

LORD NORTH, *Prime Minister*

WILLIAM PITT *the elder, Earl of Chatham, former Prime Minister*

SIR TOBIAS, *a wealthy merchant, and head of the East India Company*

BENJAMIN FRANKLIN

A CHAMBERLAIN

A MESSENGER

TWO FOOTMEN

A FEW LORDS AND COUNSELORS

PLACE: London. TIME: A winter evening, 1774.

The music begins in the auditorium — a piano, organ, or other instrument playing "Rule Britannia." The curtain goes up revealing the stage set to represent an audience room in the palace of King George the Third. Two solitary chairs sit waiting in gilded brightness, one at the right front and one at the left front. At the center back is a door, and to the left of this are heavy red draperies which hang down to the carpeted floor concealing the throne. On the wall opposite the throne is a gilt-framed portrait representative of some ancient king or royal prince of England.

As the music plays, two FOOTMEN *enter from the right front. They are dressed in the fashion of the middle eighteenth century — with velvet knee breeches, wine-colored coats, powdered and beribboned hair, and a show of lace at their throats and wrists. One of them carries a foot warmer and the other a blue tasseled pillow. In time to the music the two march across the room to the left, and with the precision of persons performing a ritual open the heavy curtains, disclosing a th, onelike seat set upon a little platform or dais. They fasten the curtain back, place the pillow on the seat and the foot warmer before it. Then, withdrawing, they stand behind the chairs in stiff and waiting readiness.*

Now entering through the great door at the rear come the KING *and his mother, moving as if in time to the music. The* KING *is a young man in his late twenties, with somewhat pallid face, a large restless roving eye, and nervous moving hands. He is brilliantly dressed and wears an order of merit glowing like a great starry flower on his breast. The* QUEEN MOTHER *is a tall woman with graying hair, beautifully jeweled and gowned, and imperious in her manner. There is a sternness about her face quite in contrast to the young monarch's kindly indecisiveness. She is speaking as they enter through the door, and the music as if in deference to her grows softer.*

QUEEN. It must be decided today. The time has come for action.

KING. But these meetings — these meetings, Mother. We only talk, threaten, and more talk.

QUEEN. Now more than talk is needed — you'll see to that. (*To the* FOOTMEN, *abruptly.*) You may go. (*The* FOOTMEN *bow and retire. As they disappear through the door at the right front, the music stops. The* QUEEN *continues:*) If in these troubled days the very walls have ears, what do we expect from our servants?

KING (*murmuring*). Suspicion, distrust, mutual fear — (*Muttering.*) I wish —

QUEEN. Not wishes, my son, but deeds.

KING (*as he slowly approaches the throne*). Yes, Mother.

QUEEN. And I have your promise to be firm.

KING. I know.

QUEEN. The people demand that a decision be made. You have Lord North's word for it.

KING. But he represents the merchants, the wealthy class, the bankers, men like Sir Tobias.

QUEEN. They are the people — those that count.

KING. But Pitt says otherwise.

QUEEN. Pitt is no longer Prime Minister. He has no power.

KING. He and Benjamin Franklin are opposed to my Lord North's intent about America.

QUEEN (*petulantly*). Ah, and that man Franklin —

KING (*defensively*). He is our friend.

QUEEN. To be a king is to be beyond friends. And you are King.

KING (*suddenly mounting the dais and sitting down on the throne*). Yes, day and night I hear you, Mother — (*As if quoting.*) — George, be a king.

QUEEN. And all must yield before the King. And that goes for the famous Dr. Franklin.

KING. But he is a man with his own ideas. We all know that.

QUEEN. And yet a man. And being so, he has his price.

KING (*laconically*). A short and bitter word — you mean a bribe.

QUEEN. Call it what you will. Men love wealth and honor — and flattery above all. Offer them to him.

KING. And if he refuse?

QUEEN. Increase the price. Promise anything, for to win him is to win the colonies. (*The* CHAMBERLAIN *appears in the door at the right.*) We are ready.

KING (*sighing*). Then summon the honorable gentlemen here.

[*The* CHAMBERLAIN *bows and retires.*]

QUEEN. And now I leave you, my son, but I shall be there — (*Gesturing toward the rear.*) — waiting —

KING. Yes, waiting to give me strength if I should weaken.

QUEEN. But you shall not weaken. The American colonies must be brought to their senses.

[*The* KING *bows his head over on his hands. The* QUEEN *lays her jeweled hand on top of his head affectionately, then bends and places the warmer under his feet. Kissing his brow, she turns and goes out at the rear. For a moment the young* KING *sits bowed in an attitude of weariness, then, looking about him, drops on his knees in silent prayer. Presently he rises and resumes his seat. And now the* CHAMBERLAIN *opens the door at the right and several* COUNSELORS *enter, including* LORD NORTH, *the Prime Minister, a man past middle age, somewhat stout and determined in his bearing. Next to him comes* WILLIAM PITT, *an old broken man making his way haltingly along on a cane and wearing a sort of shawl draped about his shoulders. There are some three or four other* GENTLEMEN, *members of the House of Lords and the Commons, also* SIR TOBIAS, *a wealthy, corpulent merchant. They approach the throne and stand bowed before the* KING. *The* CHAMBERLAIN *retires.*]

LORD NORTH. Your Majesty.

KING. Greetings — (*As they kiss his hand.*) — my Lord North, the Earl of Chatham, you, Sir Tobias, and gentlemen.

[*The elderly* PITT *creeps over and sits in the chair at the left front.* SIR TOBIAS *sits in the one at the right. The rest remain standing.*]

LORD NORTH. Your Majesty, the present crisis moves us to come to you for audience.

KING (*looking out at the group*). I do not see Dr. Franklin.

LORD NORTH. We have heard nothing from him.

KING. He should be here.

LORD NORTH (*ironically*). His action is typical of this new liberty beyond the seas. He comes and goes as he pleases.

FIRST LORD. This is not liberty but license.

SECOND LORD. Aye.

PITT (*in a high voice*). He has been delayed.

LORD NORTH. When His Majesty summons, there must be no delay. (*Unrolling some papers which he has in his hand.*) Your Majesty, the everlasting subject of the American colonies is with us once again. And this time it must be settled. Your Majesty is well acquainted with the long roll of grievances which we hold against them. For ten years they have tried our patience without ceasing. Again and again we have yielded to their demands, hoping that soon or late as loyal subjects to yourself they would see the error of their ways and mend them. Since the conclusion of what some choose to call the French and Indian War, they have grown more and more insolent in their manner. In the passage of the Stamp Act they first exhibited open treason. For the safety of the British Empire we yielded and rescinded the act. Again the necessary and just laws known as the Townshend Act were most stubbornly resisted. Once more to keep the peace we yielded. Far be it from us to criticize His Majesty's attitude in these matters. For then the times were uncertain, our enemies near at home pressed about us, and we could risk no quarrel between us and the strongest of our colonies. But now the times demand a stern hand. Our internal debt has increased by leaps and bounds, a debt in great measure due to the expense of protecting these same colonies, and —

KING (*as* NORTH *turns a leaf of his notes*). Has Dr. Franklin given any further advice upon this subject?

LORD NORTH. None beyond his recent boastful words in Parliament. It is well known what his attitude is. He is in league with such men as Patrick Henry of Virginia, Livingstone of New York, Sam Adams and John Hancock of Boston. It is through their efforts that the people are becoming rebellious and are refusing to accept this recent tax on tea. (*Slapping the sheet of paper in his hand.*) I have here a letter from this same Sam Adams in which he maintains that the act is most malign and diabolical. I ask you, gentlemen, what is so diabolical and unjust about this law as the notorious Sam Adams maintains? (*Turning toward the* KING *again.*) Let us recall, your Majesty, that uninterrupted commerce, trading, the purchase and exchange of commodities, between the different sections of the empire is the very life of that empire. When this is stopped it dies, disintegrates and decays. It is the same as if the lifeblood were choked off from some of the members of the empire. What results? That member, those members perish, and the empire itself is crippled and weakened. The question before us is — shall we allow these bands of misguided zealots three thousand miles across the sea to jeopardize the future glory and greatness of the English nation?

VOICES. No — no!

LORD NORTH. We have developed a great and profitable commerce with the American colonies, and now that they are refusing to buy our goods what can we expect to happen? This tax on tea was voted by an overwhelming majority of both houses of Parliament. It should be collected no matter what the cost.

PITT (*calling out*). And how will you collect it, my lord?

LORD NORTH. We have met here to determine that. As Charles Townshend himself has said before — these American colonies, these children of ours, planted by our care, nourished by our indulgence, have been protected by our arms until they have grown to a degree of strength and wealth almost equal to our own. But again and again they have threatened our trade with ruin. Through their selfishness, their greed, they have strained the patience of His Majesty's Parliament beyond endurance. (*Pausing and then concluding dramatically.*) This time force must be employed.

A murmur arises among several of the statesmen. The KING *looks off before him with abstracted, worried gaze.*]

KING (*as if speaking to himself*). Blood might be shed.

LORD NORTH. I urge that without delay funds be voted for the equipping and sending of ten thousand soldiers into the colonies to impose this tea tax.

VOICES. Yea, we agree.

LORD NORTH. And that such men as Patrick Henry, Livingstone and Adams, Hancock, and others, from the Carolinas to the northernmost colonies — these men who have openly avowed their antagonism to His Majesty's government — be arrested and brought to England for trial.

VOICES. Hear! Hear!

KING (*restlessly*). Where is Dr. Franklin?

A COUNSELOR. He is a philosopher, Sire. Perhaps he has fallen into a well.

A SECOND COUNSELOR. Or is experimenting with his new electricity.

[*Several of the gentlemen laugh.*]

KING (*with a touch of sharpness*). And well he might. He recently sent me lightning rods as a comfort in the summer storms. (*He gestures to* LORD NORTH.)

LORD NORTH. The colonists are able to pay this trifling tax. We have accurate reports on the holdings of the leading colonial citizens. A hundred can be found there whose combined wealth is equal to that of any hundred men in England. For instance, the great landowner Colonel George Washington down in Virginia, John Hancock himself, a man of tremendous wealth. (*Slapping the papers again.)* We have them listed here. Shall we continue to sweat under the burden of taxation and they go exempt?

VOICES. No! No!

[*And now the broken form of* PITT *stirs in his chair.*]

KING (*nodding to him*). The Earl of Chatham.

PITT (*his head propped up on his cane*). It is not that the colonies cannot pay but that they are unwilling to pay.

LORD NORTH (*dryly*). That is one thing we are certain of. (*Curtly.*) Then they must be made to pay. (*Bowing.*) We await your Majesty's decision.

PITT (*attempting to rise and then sinking back into his chair with a groan*). Pardon my illness. (*Looking over at* LORD NORTH.) During my service as Minister I took occasion to study every phase of the colonies' quarrel. The arguments of my Lord North are not only impractical but dangerous. I have come from a bed of sickness to tell him so.

LORD NORTH (*with a touch of sarcasm*). Franklin has been talking with my Lord Pitt again.

PITT. He has, many times. And I have been talking with the common people of England.

LORD NORTH. The burden of this government, sir, is not on the common people but upon those who have the responsibility of taxes and property. (*Indicating the merchant.*) Like Sir Tobias here.

PITT. Your pardon, Sire, but the gentleman is in error. The colonies in America were not planted by our care, were not nurtured by our interest. Tyranny drove them there. (*A murmur of dissent arises among the* COUNSELORS.) They have not been protected by our arms. In the French and Indian War they protected us. They taxed themselves to raise arms, provide munitions and supplies. And that tax which they themselves voted they have continued to pay without murmur or demur.

KING. Are you against England or for the colonies, sir?

PITT. I am for both, your Majesty. (*Now climbing shakily to his feet.*) For an ever and greater British Empire — (*Stretching out his trembling arm.*) — a true Venice of the world, in which the ocean canals flow between the arms and islands of her greatness.

A VOICE. Hear! Hear!

PITT (*with stern conviction*). And if we insist upon these measures with America we shall lose one of our arms, and that the strongest. (*He sinks back into his chair.*)

[*The* KING *sits staring at the floor.*]

LORD NORTH (*coldly*). Then what does the honorable gentleman propose?

PITT. That we yield once more to their demands.

VOICES. No! No!

LORD NORTH. If we do so our prestige is gone in the capitals of Europe, and you know what that means to our commerce.

[*The voice of the* CHAMBERLAIN *calls out from the shadow at the right.*]

CHAMBERLAIN. Benjamin Franklin of Pennsylvania.

[*Everyone looks expectantly around.* FRANKLIN *comes forward into the light. He is now in his late sixties and well preserved, his face genial and ruddy. He wears no wig, and is simply dressed. As he comes foward the* KING *extends his hand, which* FRANKLIN *takes and bows over but does not kiss. With the exception of* PITT *the group show a faint displeasure.*]

KING (*withdrawing his hand*). I feared, Dr. Franklin, we were not to have the pleasure of your company.

FRANKLIN. Your pardon, Sire, I have been at the palace gates this half hour, but was denied admittance. (*With a chuckle.*) The guards said I lacked the proper dress.

[*There is a look among the group which shows that they perhaps think so too.*]

KING. Our major-domo will send you an apology.

FRANKLIN. Oh no, I am used to such things. (*Extending a little rolled paper tied with a ribbon.*) A little gift of friendship to your Majesty – drawings for a new stove which will do much to keep you warm in winter.

KING (*taking the paper and examining it*). My thanks are yours. (*He studies the paper, and then as* LORD NORTH *lets out a little cough he rolls it up.*) At my leisure I will – (*Now with some show of energy.*) Dr. Franklin, we have summoned you here on a serious matter. Because of your standing as a philosopher and your thorough knowledge of the colonies we feel we have a right to your advice.

FRANKLIN (*bowing*). I shall be glad to tell you what I know.

[*The* KING *nods toward* LORD NORTH *again.*]

LORD NORTH. Dr. Franklin, you are acquainted with the present situation as regards the American colonies.

FRANKLIN. I am.

LORD NORTH. And you no doubt recognize the necessity under which our government stands at this present time.

FRANKLIN. I know that like most governments you are hard put to it to raise money for taxes.

LORD NORTH. And do you not agree that all citizens should pay taxes to the government that protects them? To the government to which they owe obedience?

FRANKLIN. It is usually the case that the citizens do pay taxes.

LORD NORTH. And you no doubt are well acquainted with the troubles His Majesty's Government has had in levying and collecting taxes from the American colonies.

FRANKLIN. Naturally.

LORD NORTH. Do you feel that they have been in their right in refusing to accept the Stamp Act, the Townshend Act, the Navigation Act, the Levying and Quartering Act?

PITT (*calling out*). I object to that question.

FRANKLIN. I don't mind answering it. These acts have all been repealed. His Majesty's Parliament realized their injustice.

LORD NORTH. They were repealed only to keep peace, not because they were unjust. Do you not agree?

FRANKLIN. No, I believe they were unjust.

[*Again a murmur arises among the group.*]

LORD NORTH (*abruptly*). Why?

FRANKLIN (*kindly and with perfect politeness*). Because, as I said recently in the parliamentary interview, and as has been said thousands of times, there is a principle involved, the principle of taxation without representation. Is it right or wrong? I say it is wrong to tax a people who have no voice in that taxing.

LORD NORTH. But I thought you just said that citizens should pay taxes to the government under which they reside.

FRANKLIN. Yes, in a representative government — the government which to my mind is the true form of government. I do not believe that any body of lawmakers has the right to tax those who have no representation in that body.

LORD NORTH (*ironically again*). We are all acquainted with that — ah — new rallying cry among the Americans, "No taxation without representation."

KING. I take it, Dr. Franklin, that you wish to have parliamentary representatives chosen from the colonies to hold seats in the house here in London.

FRANKLIN. I did not say so, your Majesty.

A VOICE. He did not say so — what did he say?

LORD NORTH. Philosophers are well known for their ability to confuse the issue.

FRANKLIN (*still kindly and polite*). It is not my intent to confuse. I say that I along with most of my countrymen deny the right of Parliament to tax us unless we are represented in Parliament, unless we have someone to speak for us, to defend us. On the other hand, I do not say that we should be represented in Parliament.

LORD NORTH. Then just what do you mean?

FRANKLIN. Briefly, I mean that our own assemblies in America, the General Assembly, the House of Burgesses, or whatever form each colony's government takes — these bodies should have the right to tax us, and none other.

LORD NORTH (*throwing up his hands*). That's treason.

FRANKLIN. It's not treason, but sense.

LORD NORTH. Treason, I tell you. It means self-government, gentlemen, and that means, sharp and to the point, that the honorable gentleman here recommends that the American colonies be a free and independent country.

FRANKLIN. I have not said that we owe no allegiance to the King, but I do say that we owe no allegiance to Parliament in such matters as affect us so vitally.

PITT (*suddenly applauding*). Hear, hear!

[*For a moment there is a murmur among the* GENTLEMEN, *and* NORTH *paces back and forth with his head bent down.*]

SIR TOBIAS (*presently turning sharply on* FRANKLIN). Do you know, sir, that the East India Company of merchants is facing ruin if America continues in her present attitude?

FRANKLIN. I have heard so.

SIR TOBIAS. The East India Company has built up a vast trade with the American colonies. And now, due to their misunderstanding as to the mother country's intent, they are refusing to buy my company's goods. Do you know what that means, sir?

FRANKLIN. I presume that it means the East India Company is in hot water.

SIR TOBIAS. And do you know that this great trading company is vitally important to the life and welfare of this nation?

FRANKLIN. I do.

LORD NORTH (*jerking his head up*). And do you know that if it fails, goes bankrupt, a panic may strike the nation, the government may fall and perhaps those ancient enemies of England, Spain and France, will seize the opportunity to attack not only us but America too?

FRANKLIN (*smiling*). We needn't count our chickens till they are hatched.

LORD NORTH. Beg pardon –

FRANKLIN. I mean – not cross a bridge till we come to it.

SIR TOBIAS. And do you know that seventeen millions of pounds of tea are rotting in our warehouses at this moment, that cargoes of many ships are spoiling in the American harbors because your people won't let them unload?

FRANKLIN. I have heard that to be the case.

SIR TOBIAS. Then what would you recommend to save the situation?

FRANKLIN. I don't think you can make one wrong right by committing another wrong.

LORD NORTH. Bah – (*He paces the floor again.*)

KING. Dr. Franklin, in the light of these facts, what do you advise?

FRANKLIN. I would still say – the tax on tea should be repealed.

LORD NORTH. Never! Never!

[*The* COUNSELORS *and* SIR TOBIAS *echo "Never," and the* KING *sits with bowed head.*]

PITT (*quaveringly*). It seems, ah – Franklin, that you and I are in the minority. (*To the* KING.) On the one hand we run the risk of creating a rebellion among the Americans. On the other hand we run the risk of destroying the greatest trading institution in the world and thereby creating a panic here in England and destroying our credit. Which shall we do? (*Loudly.*) Your Majesty, I say we must do the right thing irrespective of the consequences.

LORD NORTH. And the right thing is not to jeopardize the greatness of this English nation.

PITT. If you antagonize the American colonies too far you certainly jeopardize it.

LORD NORTH. And if we allow the English banks to close, unemployment and hunger will sweep the country and civil war may result. And — (*He throws out his hands again helplessly.*) — this law must be imposed.

VOICES. Hear! Hear!

FRANKLIN (*quietly but intensely*). Your Majesty — gentlemen. Year after year I have hoped and trusted and with the only means at my command, my voice, have urged that England and America might settle their differences in a friendly way, might remain as one nation united in the ways of peace, as I would nations everywhere might do. But the course of events seems to conspire against us. The people in America are still loyal to His Majesty. There is no question of that. But every act of your Ministry, Sire, brings us nearer a dreadful separation. With all respect to the Prime Minister here, it would seem that in future generations the historians may say that a blind and misguided Parliament apparently did all that it could to create friction between the mother country and her most powerful colonies. The advice of using force seems to me but another illustration of that fact, for it will only aggravate the trouble. The matter is not any longer an economic one. For prior to all things among my people now is the question of this representative government. To them it has become an ideal, an ideal that once actuated the earlier pioneers and which has grown and been developed in the conquering of that wilderness. The nation is now gradually growing up. Every day new voices rise to speak this truth of freedom abroad. It is fast becoming a religion. Every act of antagonism by your Parliament but increases it. And in defense of their religion men will — in a simple word — fight. I beg of you, repeal this law, meet with the representatives of the colonies, and seek a reconciliation before it is too late.

LORD NORTH (*crying out*). It is England's place to command and not to beg. (*Turning more vehemently toward the* COUNSELORS.) Gentlemen, Dr. Franklin but confirms our view of the American mind. Every day faith in our Government is being weakened by this delay. Every succeeding hour is fraught with danger. What is your voice?

VOICES. Let us act now. Force. Let us use force if it is necessary.

FRANKLIN. Gentlemen, I beg of you. Your Majesty — I —

KING (*raising his head and staring before him as they all wait*). Ah, why can't we be at peace? Why do they deny my sovereign command? (*Muttering.*) That's what hurts. It hurts me here — in my heart.

FRANKLIN. They do not deny your sovereign command, your Majesty. But they deny the action of the Parliament.

KING (*looking out at the* COUNSELORS *with a lonely boy's grieving face*). I want to be a good king. I want my subjects to love me. (*Shaking his head.*) But I fail. No one can tell me differently. Every day England plunges deeper into debt. Vast schemes are moving around me in the East, the Orient, and in the West. Something seems to sweep us all on, circumstances, happenings. We cannot stop to be reasonable. Gentlemen, what is your advice?

LORD NORTH (*ironically, as no one speaks*). His Majesty's will must be supreme.

KING (*after a moment*). Dr. Franklin is right. I feel in my heart he is right. If we use force the Americans will fight. And that means — (*With a groan.*) — civil war too. For we are all Englishmen under God. We have the same blood. We have the same ideals, the same history behind us. The ties that bind us together span these few thousand miles of sea. (*Shuddering.*)

These ties must not be broken. We must find some peaceful way to settle these differences.

LORD NORTH (*with hidden anger*). I have laid my advice before your Majesty. If it is wrong, then my resignation is in your hands.

KING (*staring at him astonished*). That would — would — (*Shaking his head.*) I cannot accept it. We must — we must — (*He looks helplessly at* FRANKLIN.) Dr. Franklin, I appeal to you — out of your wisdom — help us —

FRANKLIN. I have only one thing to say. The law is wrong and must be repealed.

LORD NORTH (*loudly*). The law will stand and America must yield.

FRANKLIN. Then it means war. There is no other way out.

[*For a moment the group is silent.*]

KING (*finally looking up at* FRANKLIN). Yes, there is a way out, Dr. Franklin, and war could be averted.

FRANKLIN. Thank God if there is.

KING. And that way is through you, through your great influence.

FRANKLIN (*staring at him*). Then you do not know the temper of my people, Sire.

KING. I know your greatness and in what respect you are held in America. You could persuade them.

FRANKLIN (*coldly*). And become a traitor?

KING. No, Dr. Franklin. (*Pleadingly.*) Rather become one who saved the British Empire from breaking in pieces.

VOICES. Hear! Hear!

KING (*hurrying on*). You have been sent to London to represent the affairs of Pennsylvania and Massachusetts — two of the most powerful colonies. That is true?

FRANKLIN. Yes, that it is.

KING. And what you advise they will be inclined to listen to?

FRANKLIN. Perhaps.

KING (*with fierce earnestness*). And Pennsylvania at least would act as you advise.

FRANKLIN (*quietly*). I think she might.

KING. And then New Jersey would follow. And already New York is kindly disposed to us, as my Lord North informs me. She would agree, and one by one the other colonies would yield, and the horrible disaster of rebellion, of civil war, would be averted. (*Vehemently.*) We appeal to you, Dr. Franklin, in this critical hour we beg you to persuade them to yield.

FRANKLIN (*as the* KING *stares beseechingly at him*). You have asked an impossible thing, your Majesty.

KING. You could, you could do it. At this moment you have the power to decide whether the English people shall remain as one or perhaps be divided forever.

LORD NORTH (*sharply*). And power to save your people from the invasion of arms and waste of blood.

KING. You are a scientist and philosopher, Dr. Franklin. You have great dreams of invention and human progress. Here in England you might bring them to pass. Our universities, our scholars, our accumulated learning are yours to use as you see fit. Honor and wealth await you here. There in the wild frontier of America your great gifts will be neglected, die in that arid soil. You owe it to the world, to England and America, to act as I request. Do it, I beg you. (*He stares at* FRANKLIN *with wide pleading eyes.*)

FRANKLIN (*gazing kindly at the young* KING). Your Majesty, I respect whatever motives may impel you. And yet I must refuse. All the wealth and all the honor of the world could not hire me to betray the people for whom I speak. (*The* KING *bows his head over in his hands.*) America is wild and uncouth, arid if you will, and lacking in the arts and sciences and culture of your Europe. But even so on our vast continent it may yet be possible to build a nation the like of which the world has never seen. Already the idea of a democratic government is abroad among the people. It will take years to work it out, generations maybe, centuries even. True, there may be bloodshed and tragedy ahead for us. But if they must come, then let them. The cause for which we suffer them will the more endure. And so, to speak brief and to the point, I'd rather help bring this new government of man to pass and die forgot than have all the fame and riches Europe could command. Pardon me, your Majesty, but so I must refuse your request. And rather than try in this hour to save England or her colonies I prefer to cast my lot with something bigger than either — an idea, a dream, if you will, of liberty and free men. (*He stands silent.*)

PITT (*applauding*). Bravo, Franklin.

LORD NORTH (*as the* KING *sits with bowed head*). And so to the practical matter at hand. It seems there is no alternative but force against the colonies. And I agree.

KING (*in a choked voice*). But that would mean war, I tell you. Once more, Dr. Franklin —

[*He twists his hands helplessly together. And now entering from the rear sweeps the dowager-like* QUEEN. *She comes over and stands by the young* KING. *He reaches out and convulsively grasps her hand. The* GENTLEMEN, *including* FRANKLIN, *bow in honor to her.*]

QUEEN (*in a clear ringing voice as she enters*). Then let it be war!

FRANKLIN (*presently*). And if England loses —

QUEEN. The man is mad. (*Venomously.*) Braggart!

FRANKLIN. No, your Majesty, I am simply suggesting that you may not be able to conquer America.

VOICES (*angrily*). Treason! Treason!

FRANKLIN (*retaining his kind but serious calm*). You might put down rebellion in one center, but it would break out in another. America is a vast country.

LORD NORTH. But it is idiocy to say ten million people cannot conquer three million.

FRANKLIN. But you will not have ten million. You will only be able to spare a few — say a hundred thousand soldiers at most. If you weaken your home forces, immediately Spain and France would be entering at your back door.

LORD NORTH. We do not fancy your threats, Dr. Franklin.

FRANKLIN. It is not a threat. It is a simple fact. And England should repeal this unjust tax law now — before it is too late.

LORD NORTH (*appealing to those around him*). If the American colonies are allowed longer to defy England, then India and others may follow. We shall be shorn of our strength, and the glory common to us all will be lost. (*To the* KING.) Your Majesty, we beg you to act.

QUEEN (*as the* KING *remains silent*). The question is simple. Are we to continue our greatness by struggling for it, or are we to sink to insignificance in world affairs? It must be decided now — yes or no.

VOICES. Yes, yes!

[*A* FOOTMAN *brings in a document and hands it to* LORD NORTH. *He looks at it, an exclamation breaks from him and everyone stares at him questioningly.*]

KING (*uneasily*). What is it?

LORD NORTH (*with a touch of patronizing triumph*). Our husbandry bears luscious fruit. The people of Boston have destroyed the cargoes of tea and torn down the statue of the King. The governor appeals for troops. (*Whirling on* FRANKLIN.) And I accuse this man of being a party to it.

[*He hands the document up to the* KING, *but it is taken by the* QUEEN. *She bends down and whispers in her son's ear.*]

KING (*after a moment, his face averted*). Dr. Franklin, you are free to go now.

[FRANKLIN *looks about him in anger and grief.*]

FRANKLIN. Your Majesty, it is not too late. You must —

QUEEN (*loudly, as she steps in front of the* KING). No.

PITT. We must not take this fatal step until every resource for peace is exhausted.

QUEEN (*suddenly straightening up and calling out in a loud voice*). Where has the manhood of our country gone? Have you heard that this my son, the King of England, has been openly defied — that the jeweled scepter of our empire has been flaunted, desecrated, trampled in the mire? In God's name I would take up arms myself before this insult shall pass.

VOICES. It must be avenged. We must act!

[FRANKLIN *looks from one to the other and at the* KING'S *bent head.*]

FRANKLIN (*bowing*). In your faces I read the verdict. (*Solemnly.*) Then war it must be. Gentlemen, this may mean the loss of your liberty, but it shall mean the birth of ours.

[*The* QUEEN *once more bends vehemently down by the* KING.]

KING (*in a low choking voice*). You are dismissed, Dr. Franklin, from our presence.

FRANKLIN (*quietly*). Your Majesty commands. (*He turns and goes swiftly away at the right.*)

LORD NORTH. His words are empty boasting, Sire. The colonists have no means with which to fight. This rebellion will be easily put down. I beseech your authority to act.

KING (*after an instant's silence*). We yield to Lord North's judgment.

[*There is loud applause.* PITT *bows his head. The* QUEEN *whispers to the* KING *again, and he straightens up.*]

LORD NORTH. And in this great trust I shall not fail. First I do request that all dispatches sent by Franklin to America shall be held up.

KING. I agree.

[*The* COUNSELORS *murmur their approval.* PITT *snaps his fingers toward the right, and a servant comes out to help him away.*]

LORD NORTH. And that the necessary steps to raise arms and men be taken.

[*The* KING *nods his head.*]

PITT (*bowing a bit lower as he goes*). Your Majesty, I beg to be excused. (*His voice almost breaking.*) Centuries will not wipe out the error of this day. Gentlemen — (*He hobbles out at the right.*)

QUEEN (*suddenly and dramatically*). Long live the King!

VOICES (*in triumphant cheers*). Long live the King!

KING (*murmuring, after an instant of silence as he stands up suddenly*). Long live England!

QUEEN (*fervently*). Amen.

KING (*looking at her*). Ah, Mother.

VOICES (*repeating*). Amen.

[*At a gesture from the* QUEEN *the* COUNSELORS *turn and move from the room. The* KING *stands staring before him. The* QUEEN *reaches out and takes his hand.*]

KING (*as the door closes behind the* COUNSELORS). Things happen, events come to pass, and only God knows what lies ahead. (*He clings to his mother.*)

QUEEN. Come, my son, you are the King. (*She leads the way out at the rear as the music begins again.*)

[*The two* FOOTMEN *enter from the right as before. They close the curtains over the throne, pick up the pillow and the foot warmer, and march out in military precision the way they came. The music continues.*]

AFTER READING

1. Find incidents in the play which show the Queen's influence upon her son.

2. Name the characters who uttered the following lines, identifying them, if possible, without referring to the play:

   a. I urge that without delay funds be voted for the equipping and sending of ten thousand soldiers into the colonies to impose this tea tax.

   b. Do you know, sir, that the East India Company of merchants is facing ruin if America continues in her present attitude?

   c. All the wealth and all the honor of the world could not hire me to betray the people for whom I speak.

   d. Where has the manhood of our country gone? . . . In God's name I would take up arms myself before this insult shall pass.

   e. Your Majesty, I beg to be excused. Centuries will not wipe out the error of this day.

3. Contrast the arguments of Lord North and William Pitt, Earl of Chatham.

4. Why did Lord North request that all dispatches sent by Franklin to America be held up?

5. How did Franklin in this play resemble the Franklin you had pictured in your mind from your study of history? How did he differ from that picture?

6. How could you defend the viewpoints of Lord North and Sir Tobias?

7. Suppose the Stamp Act had been repealed, as Franklin requested. Would we still be members of the British Empire today?

8. In what ways were the origins of the American Revolution made clearer to you as a result of this play?

CHALLENGES

1. Read Franklin's *Autobiography* and report on it to the class. Be sure to discuss those personal characteristics of Franklin which earned him international respect and admiration.

2. List ten proverbs of Franklin. Suggested sources: *Poor Richard Comes to Life* by Bessie W. Johns; *Benjamin Franklin* by Carl Van Doren; and *Benjamin Franklin, First Civilized American,* by Phillips Russell.

3. Write a letter from Franklin to a member of the Pennsylvania Legislature in which the substance of this play is narrated.

4. William Pitt and Franklin discuss the King's decision later that night. Write the dialogue.

5. Sir Tobias tells a meeting of the stockholders of the East India Company of his part in swaying the King to make his decision. Write what he says.

DRAMA WORKSHOP

A hint for playgoers: Consider the characterization.

There are six main characters in *Franklin and the King,* each one distinct from the others. Each is a living creature, not just a type or a marionette. Creating such lifelike characters is difficult, as any playwright will tell you. A playwright brings his characters to life for us by various means. We come to know them by what they do, by what they say and how they say it, and by what other characters say about them.

Franklin and the King contains instances of each of these methods. Before Franklin's appearance, the King describes him as a man with his own ideas, one Counselor remarks that he is a philosopher, and another points out that he is a scientist. Franklin's actions and opinions when he finally appears before the King show that these descriptions are correct. We recognize the King's indecisive nature and his mother's domineering influence on him by several incidents. Her urgings at the opening of the play, her interference in the deliberations of the council, and her whispered advice to the King at critical moments reveal her powerful influence. As the King leaves the chamber he clings to her while she reassures him. Her actions and statements as well as her imperious manner and commanding tone reveal her character and show that her son is like a puppet in her hands.

Notice that the lines of *Franklin and the King* cannot be transferred from one character to another without hurting the play. The dialogue is good because it is tailored to fit the characters who speak it.

A hint for actors: A master gesture helps establish character.

Everybody has distinctive mannerisms. For example, each of your teachers and classmates has certain habits of movement or speech which differentiate him or her from everybody else. These habitual gestures, postures, and inflections make each of us stand out as an individual.

If you want the role you are enacting to be distinctive and vivid, use a master gesture — one that the character uses unconsciously and habitually and one which is part and parcel of his personality. A miser, for example, may rub his hands; a flighty typist, chew gum; a teen-age girl, giggle. Perhaps the King in *Franklin and the King* nervously taps his fingers on the arms of the chair when he cannot make up his mind, or perhaps Lord North has an arrogant way of handling snuff and Sir Tobias a pompous way of clearing his throat before speaking.

OTHER HISTORICAL PLAYS YOU WILL LIKE TO READ

The Feast of Ortolans by Maxwell Anderson (24). On the eve of the fall of the Bastille a group of aristocrats and intellectuals hear prophecies of their future.

Little Known Louisa by Marion Wefer (31). A documentary drama about Louisa May Alcott as actress and nurse.

Man of Destiny by Bernard Shaw. Napoleon matches his wits with a woman spy in one of his campaigns.

Marie Curie, Dreamer and Scientist by Evva Brinker (31). An episodic treatment of the life of Madame Curie from her schooldays to the time she discovers radium.

Mozart and the Grey Steward by Thornton Wilder (39). Mozart is asked to write a requiem for the late Countess but dies before he can complete it.

The Night of "Mr. H." by Harold Brighouse (6). Charles Lamb's farce *Mr. H.* has been a miserable failure. His friends have accompanied him to his home to cheer him up.

A Passenger to America by Clinton Hancock Miller (31). The French diplomat Talleyrand en route to America meets Benedict Arnold in an English inn and asks for a letter of introduction.

This Is Villa by Josephine Niggli (24). Pancho Villa, Mexican revolutionary leader, is pictured as a man of many moods, with brute courage predominating.

THE STOLEN PRINCE

BY DAN TOTHEROH

ABOUT THE PLAY

Many things about Chinese drama seem strange to our Western eyes. Realistic scenery is unknown, and the actors' costumes, even those of the minor characters, are elaborate and stylized. The musicians sit on the stage in full view of the audience, playing their shrill and — to our ears — monotonous songs. The spectators don't

---

pay the same close attention to the happenings on the stage that we are trained to give; in fact during the performance, which may last six or seven hours, they are likely to converse, greet friends, drink, and walk about.

But perhaps the most striking difference is to be found in the property man. He strolls about the stage during the play, handing actors the properties they need or removing articles no longer required by them. He is always on stage, moving about freely among the actors in plain view of the audience. He is a very important personage, but the spectators pay no attention to him because — since he is dressed in black — he is invisible. The Property Man in *The Stolen Prince* is not very bright, as you will see, and not very energetic either, but some of his faults arise from overwork. He has to act as a peach tree, make duck noises, set boat sails, roll and unroll a river, give the Executioner his ax and the duck his fish, and perform many more such arduous duties. No wonder he's so tired!

Chinese acting uses suggestion, rather than realistic portrayal, more than Western acting. An actor walks several times around the stage to suggest a long journey or steps high several times to indicate that he is climbing a flight of stairs. Several instances of this nonrealistic acting are indicated in *The Stolen Prince*.

ABOUT THE AUTHOR

Dan Totheroh began writing plays while he was still a high-school student in San Rafael, California. After graduation he played in vaudeville for a while, but when the United States entered World War I he joined the army and served overseas. In 1921 he won an award for the best play written by a Californian. This prize play, *Wild Birds,* a tragedy in three acts, was successfully produced in New York four years later. He is also the author of *Distant Drums* and *Moor Born,* both Broadway productions, and a number of screen plays, including *The Dawn Patrol* and *The Count of Monte Cristo.*

THE STOLEN PRINCE

Characters

LONG FO, *the little son of the royal cook*

WING LEE, *his little sister, daughter of the royal cook*

THE ROYAL NURSE

HI TEE, *a poor but honest fisherman*

LI MO, *his wife*

JOY, *the stolen Prince*

LEE MEE, *the duck*

TWO SOLDIERS *of the royal Court*

THE EXECUTIONER

THE CHORUS

THE PROPERTY MAN

THE ORCHESTRA

There is no stage setting except for a backdrop of curtains, and two black chairs, center. A lacquered box for the PROPERTY MAN *stands in the left-hand corner. On the extreme right, separated from the players by a railing, is the* ORCHESTRA, *composed of three or more children dressed as Chinamen. They have no leader and they play without notes. Any instruments may be used, but there must be a gong. The music must be shrill and squeaky and, to our ears, discordant. Combs, covered with tissue paper, give a very good effect.*

A gong is struck by the gong-bearer and the CHORUS *enters. He is dressed in a long mandarin coat and wears a headdress of feathers and beads. He walks very proudly to the center of the stage and bows. The gong is struck again and the* CHORUS *raises his hand.*

CHORUS. I am the Chorus and I am here to tell you all about the play that my honorable actors are about to act upon this stage. They are all waiting behind the curtain with their make-up on and they are very anxious to begin, so I shall be brief.

[*The* ORCHESTRA *plays a few notes, stopped by the* CHORUS *raising his hand.*]

The name of our play is *The Stolen Prince*. It is a sad story at first, but do not weep too hard, because it has a happy ending.

[*He claps his hands together. The* PROPERTY MAN, *a funny fellow in a black coat and trousers and a long queue, enters and walks downstage, standing beside the* CHORUS.]

This is the Property Man. Bow!

[*He strikes the* PROPERTY MAN *on top of the head with his fan and the* PROPERTY MAN *bows.*]

He will change the scenery and will hand the properties to the honorable actors when they have need of them. And he will take especial charge of Lee Mee, the duck.

[*The* PROPERTY MAN *goes "Quack! Quack!" and the* CHORUS *strikes him again on the head with his fan.*]

Silence! It is not time for that! Are all your properties ready?

[*The* PROPERTY MAN *nods his head.*]

The first scene of our play takes place in the garden of the Emperor Lang Moo, in the Middle Flower Kingdom, a thousand and one years ago.

[*The gong-bearer strikes the gong.*]

It is springtime and the blossoms are on the peach trees. It is a very important time in the household of the Emperor Lang Moo, because a child is about to be born to him and he prays it will be a son. (*To the* PROPERTY MAN.) Where is the blossoming peach tree?

[*The* PROPERTY MAN, *who has been dreaming, starts and blinks, then shuffles up to the property box. He takes up a branch of imitation peach blossoms and, crossing to the two chairs, he stands behind them, holding the branch over them. Now and then he becomes tired of holding the branch in one hand and he carelessly shifts it to the other.*]

CHORUS. Long Fo and Wing Lee, a little sister and a little brother, children of the chief cook in the royal household, come under the peach tree to play together.

[*The* CHORUS *bows and steps to the left, where he stands throughout the play. There is music as* LONG FO *and* WING LEE *enter.*]

LONG FO. Will you help me fly my kite, Wing Lee?

[*At the word "kite," the* PROPERTY MAN *drops the peach branch and goes to the box, where he finds a paper kite on a short string. He gives it to* LONG FO, *then takes up the peach branch again.*]

WING LEE (*sitting down on one of the chairs*). There is not enough wind, Long Fo. Let us sit here beneath the branches of the peach tree and wait for news about the baby who is coming today.

LONG FO. I do hope it will be a boy.

WING LEE. Yes. If it is a girl the Emperor will have her killed at once. Poor little thing.

LONG FO. Why are you so sorry for her? It is the law to kill girl babies because they are worth so little.

WING LEE. You say that because you are a boy, but I am very sorry for her.

LONG FO (*with contempt*). You are a weak, weeping girl. I am a big strong man and I am going to fly my kite.

WING LEE. You cannot fly your kite, because there isn't any wind.

LONG FO (*sitting down*). Then I shall wait patiently until the wind shakes the branches of the peach tree.

[*The gong-bearer strikes the gong three times, rapidly.*]

WING LEE (*jumping up*). What is that?

LONG FO. The new baby has come to the Emperor's palace.

WING LEE. Oh, I tremble with excitement!

LONG FO. I feel sure it is a boy.

WING LEE. And I feel sure it is a girl.

[*There is music. Enter the* ROYAL NURSE.]

LONG FO. Nurse! Nurse! Tell me! Is it a boy?

WING LEE. It is a girl, is it not, Nurse?

NURSE. It is both, my children!

WING LEE. Both?

LONG FO. How could that be?

NURSE. It is twins, my children. A boy and a girl.

[*The gong is struck. The* NURSE *and the two children bow. They go out. The* PROPERTY MAN *takes the branch back to the corner and sits down on the box to rest.*]

CHORUS (*bowing*). The next scene of our illustrious play takes place in the same garden. Three days have passed. The nurse is walking in the royal garden with the royal twins. The day is warm and full of the perfume of peach blossoms.

[*The* PROPERTY MAN *returns with the peach branch and stands behind the chairs. The* NURSE *enters, carrying two dolls, one on each arm. One doll has a string of jade around its neck. That is the boy. The other doll is dressed in white and is the girl.*]

NURSE (*sitting on one of the chairs and singing a little song to the twins*). Go to sleep — Go to sleep — The wind is in the crooked tree.

[*The* PROPERTY MAN *waves the peach branch back and forth.*]

And it sings a song to you.
In the pool the goldfish three
Are sleeping too.
Go to sleep — Go to sleep — Go to sleep.
Go to sleep — Go to sleep — The moon is in the purple sky,
And it smiles a smile at you.
By the pool the dragonfly
Is sleeping too.
Go to sleep — Go to sleep — Go to sleep.

NURSE (*speaking*). Ah, my pretty babies, I love you both, but one of you must leave me. (*To the girl doll.*) Tomorrow you must die because you are a little girl.

[*The* PROPERTY MAN *hands her an embroidered silk handkerchief and she wipes her eyes, first one and then the other.*]

NURSE (*holding up the doll with the string of jade around its neck*). Ah, little one, you are the chosen of the gods because you were born a little boy. You will spend your happy childhood playing by the fishpond in the royal gardens. You will hear the Emperor's golden parrot sing and you will hear the sacred scarlet fish telling secrets to the sacred dragonfly. When you become a man you will become the Emperor of this great and mighty Middle Flower Kingdom. Bright is your shining star. (*Holding up the girl doll.*) Ah, dark is your star, little one. It is almost set. Tomorrow, at the hour of seven gongs, you die.

[*She wipes her eyes again. The gong is heard and there is music.*]

NURSE (*looking off to the left*). By the great green catfish, what do I see? A robber in the garden stealing cabbages as plain as can be! I'll run and scare him away!

[*She places the two dolls on the chairs and runs off, waving her hands in the air. There is music.* LONG FO *and* WING LEE *enter.*]

WING LEE. Here they are. The nurse has left them alone. Now is our chance.

LONG FO. I do not approve of this, Wing Lee. If we are found out we will both have our heads cut off.

WING LEE. You promised to help me if I gave you my gold ball.

LONG FO. Oh, I'll help you all right. I never go back on my word, but I don't see what you want to save a girl for. They're so useless.

WING LEE. Quick! Don't talk any more. The nurse is coming back. Which is the girl?

LONG FO (*lifting up the doll with the jade beads*). This one, of course. She has jade beads around her neck.

WING LEE. Give her to me. Now let's run to the river.

[*They run off to the right. The* NURSE *returns and goes to the chairs. She starts back in surprise. She cannot believe her eyes — looks again — looks all about her — beats her breast.*]

NURSE. Oh! Oh! Oh! The Prince has been stolen! Oh! Oh! Oh! I will have my head cut off for this! Oh! Oh! Oh! I must run away and hide myself in the mountains where they will never find me! Oh! Oh! Oh!

[*She runs off right, crying, taking the girl doll with her. The* ORCHESTRA *makes a terrible din.*]

CHORUS (*bowing and raising his hand for silence*). Our scene changes now. The action of our play moves from the garden of the Emperor Lang Moo to the green banks of the river Chang Hi. The Property Man will show you the river.

[*The* PROPERTY MAN *puts the peach branch back into the box and takes out a piece of blue cloth. He unrolls it on the floor. He walks up and down on it, pulling up the legs of his trousers to show you the river is wet. Then he goes back to his box and sits down on it. He goes to sleep. There is music.* LONG FO *and*

WING LEE *enter running very fast and looking over their shoulders.* WING LEE *carries the doll with the jade necklace. She almost runs onto the blue cloth.*]

LONG FO. Be careful! Do not go too near the river, Wing Lee. You will fall in and be drowned!

WING LEE. Where is the tub?

LONG FO (*glancing at the* PROPERTY MAN, *who is still asleep*). Yes, where is the tub?

[*The* PROPERTY MAN *snores.* LONG FO *looks helplessly at the* CHORUS.]

CHORUS (*calling to the* PROPERTY MAN). The tub! The tub!

[*The* PROPERTY MAN *answers with another snore.*]

CHORUS (*to the audience*). Excuse him, my good friends, for he is very stupid. We only keep him because we get him cheap.

[*He claps his hands loudly. The* PROPERTY MAN *jumps up as if he had been stuck with a pin. He looks about, bewildered.*]

CHORUS (*severely*). The tub!

[*The* PROPERTY MAN *takes a small wooden tub from the box and places it on the edge of the blue cloth. Then he goes back to his seat on the box.*]

WING LEE. Ah, there is the tub. We will put the little girl in the tub. The tub will float down the great river and some kind person will see it and give the poor little girl a home. (*She kisses the doll and puts it in the tub.*) Good-by, little girl. When I get back to the palace I shall burn a stick of incense to the gods for your safe voyage down the great river. Ah, now it is in the current. There it goes!

[*The* PROPERTY MAN *shuffles over and pulls the tub slowly down to the other end of the blue cloth.* WING LEE *and* LONG FO *wave their handkerchiefs.*]

LONG FO. Now it has turned a bend in the river. It is out of sight. Let us go back to the palace, Wing Lee. I want to fly my kite.

WING LEE. There is not enough wind to fly your kite, Long Fo.

LONG FO. Oh, you always say that. Come on!

WING LEE (*looking sadly down the river*). There are many things can happen to her. A storm may rise and sink the tub. The terrible dragonfish may see her and swallow her alive. Poor little girl, I fear for her. (*She wipes her eyes with her handkerchief.*)

LONG FO. Do not cry any more. You will get your eyes all red and then they will begin asking questions at the palace. Come along! Come along!

[*He takes her hand and they go out. There is music.*]

CHORUS. And now we follow the wooden tub on its long journey down the great river of Chang Hi. It sails all that night and all the next day and stops, at last, before the houseboat of Hi Tee, a poor but honest fisherman.

[*He signals to the* PROPERTY MAN, *who fetches a stick with a white piece of cloth tacked to it to represent a sail. He sets it above the two chairs. Then he returns to the box and takes out the duck,* LEE MEE, *a stuffed duck with a big yellow bill, and places it in the center of the blue cloth. He stands back with arms folded as music and the gong are heard and* HI TEE *enters, followed by his wife* LI MO. *They bow and sit side by side on the chairs.* HI TEE *rows the boat with imaginary oars.*]

HI TEE. I am that poor but honest fisherman named Hi Tee. This lady beside me is my wife, Li Mo. That (*Pointing to the duck*) is our little duck, Lee Mee. He is a trained duck and the fish that he catches with his big bill he gives to us. We are very happy, but we long for a child. Do we not, Li Mo?

LI MO. That is all that we need to make us completely happy.

HI TEE. All day long we sail and sail down the great river Chang Hi, and little Lee Mee swims merrily behind us, catching us fishes as we go. See, the wind is shaking our sails. (*The* PROPERTY MAN *shakes the stick with the white cloth.*) Faster and faster now we go! The wind is so kind I shall not have to row any more today. I'll just sit still and watch the scenery go by. (*He stops rowing with the imaginary oars. There is music.*) But, merciful catfish, what do I see? A tub floating by just as plain as can be!

LI MO. So it is! A tub — with a baby in it!

HI TEE. I'll jump into the water and save the child. A short way down the stream the dreadful rapids start. The tub will be upset and the baby will be drowned.

LI MO. Oh, save the child, Hi Tee!

[HI TEE *jumps from the chairs onto the blue cloth and, making swim-*

ming motions with his arms, he picks up the tub and brings it back to the chairs.]

LI MO. Give the poor little baby to me. I shall take care of it and bring it up as my own child.

[*She takes the doll and holds it in her arms.*]

HI TEE (*looking at it*). It is a baby of high degree. It wears a beautiful chain of jade about its neck.

LI MO. The gods have answered our prayers.

HI TEE. Lee Mee, our faithful little duck, we have another mouth for you to feed. Now, three times a day, you must catch three extra fish to feed our baby here.

[*The* PROPERTY MAN *gives an answering "Quack! Quack!" and shakes the sail.*]

LI MO. Here we go! Here we go! Floating down the water. We thank the gods for this little child — be it son or daughter!

[*The* PROPERTY MAN *quack-quacks again.* HI TEE *and* LI MO *rise, bow, and go out, right. The* PROPERTY MAN *puts the wooden tub back in the box. The gong crashes. The* PROPERTY MAN *sits on his box and yawns. The* CHORUS *comes down and raises his hand.*]

CHORUS. The first act of our illustrious play is now over. You will excuse my actors while they are served a drink of tea to refresh themselves for the remainder of the performance? It is not easy work being actors, and they are tired.

[*He bows and goes out to the left. The curtain is not pulled. The* ORCHESTRA *spends its time tuning up, and then the actress who has played the* NURSE *enters with a tray of tea in little Chinese bowls and serves tea to actors and* ORCHESTRA. *They drink and return the bowls to the tray. The* NURSE *goes to serve tea to the* PROPERTY MAN, *but finds him asleep, so, shrugging her shoulders, she leaves, drinking his bowl of tea herself. The gong is sounded. The* CHORUS *re-enters and takes the center of the stage. He bows.*]

CHORUS. Now that my actors have refreshed themselves, we will proceed with our play. Nine years have passed away. We are once more on the river Chang Hi, looking at the fishing boat of Hi Tee and his loving wife Li Mo.

[HI TEE *and* LI MO *enter and bow.* HI TEE *is wearing a gray cotton beard, the strings of which are tied around his ears.*]

CHORUS. As you can see by Hi Tee's beard, he is not as young as he used to be. His wife, Li Mo, is not as young as she used to be either, but she keeps her hair black by putting fish grease on it.

[HI TEE *and* LI MO *take their places on the chairs.*]

CHORUS. And now you will see the hero of our play, the little Prince who was stolen. He does not know he is a prince, and you who are sharing the secret must not tell him or you will spoil him and he will become unhappy, longing for something he cannot have. His foster parents have named him Joy, which is a very good name for such a bright and laughing boy.

[*There is music.* JOY *runs in and bows. He wears the same chain of jade around his neck. It looks very strange with the rest of his coarse brown fishing costume. He turns to the chairs and waves to* HI TEE *and* LI MO. *They beckon him to come to them. He runs over to the chairs and sits between them.*]

HI TEE. Where have you been all day, my little Joy?

JOY. I have been digging mud turtles with my friend Kee Hee, but we did not find any. Then we looked for fish with our nets, but we could not find any fish either. I am hungry now, dear Mother.

LI MO (*shaking her head sadly*). Alas, my poor boy, I am hungry too, and so is your poor father, but there are no fish in the great river.

JOY. Why are there no fish in the great river?

HI TEE. Because, my son, the gods are angry. They have tied strings to all the fishes' tails and are holding them prisoners in the tall mountains where the river begins.

LI MO. If they do not untie the strings and let the fish float down to us, very soon we will all die.

JOY. I will climb up the tall mountains to the place where the river begins and untie the fishes' tails. I am not afraid, Mother.

LI MO. The gods would kill you, my little son, and then what would I do without you?

JOY. Cannot Lee Mee, our faithful little duck, find any fish either?

LI MO. Can you find us any fish, Lee Mee?

[*They wait for a "Quack, Quack" from the* PROPERTY MAN, *but he is still asleep. The* CHORUS *turns and sees him sleeping. He crosses to him with great dignity and taps him on the head with his fan. The* PROPERTY MAN *leaps up, blinking.*]

CHORUS. You will be discharged after the play is over. You have not given us a "Quack"!

PROPERTY MAN (*staring stupidly*). Quack! Quack!

JOY. What does our little duck say?

PROPERTY MAN. Quack! Quack! Quack! Quack!

LI MO. He says he will search every river and every pond and every lake the whole world over until he finds a fish for us to eat.

JOY. I will go with him.

HI TEE. No! You must stay with us. Go, my good Lee Mee, and bring a fishie back to poor Hi Tee.

[*The* PROPERTY MAN *shuffles forward and picks up the duck and tucks it under his arm. He shuffles off with it, giving a solemn "Quack! Quack!"*]

LI MO. If there is a fish left in the river, the lake, or the pond, Lee Mee will find it for us. He is the most faithful duck in the whole Middle Flower Kingdom.

JOY. I love Lee Mee!

[*There is music.*]

CHORUS. An hour passes by and Lee Mee returns.

[*The* PROPERTY MAN *enters with the duck. He has put into the beak of* LEE MEE *a fish carved out of wood and painted a bright scarlet. He sets* LEE MEE *down close to the chairs, then returns to his box.*]

HI TEE. Look! Look! Lee Mee has found a fish for us!

LI MO. Oh, good Lee Mee!

JOY. I have never seen such a beautiful fish before. It is as red as blood.

HI TEE. It is very beautiful. Where did you get it, Lee Mee?

PROPERTY MAN. Quack! Quack!

LI MO. He says he will not tell.

JOY. Let us eat it at once. I am very hungry.

[HI TEE *reaches down and takes up the fish.*]

HI TEE. You may have the tail, Li Mo. I will have the head, and our son, the little Joy, may have the middle because it is the sweetest and the fattest. Give me my knife.

[*The* PROPERTY MAN *takes a long wooden knife with a curved blade from the box and gives it to* HI TEE. HI TEE *puts the fish on the edge of the chair and raises the knife over his head. The gong and loud music are heard.* TWO SOLDIERS *enter carrying tall bamboo poles. They point at the scarlet fish and rush at* HI TEE.]

FIRST SOLDIER. You are my prisoner!

HI TEE. What have I done?

PROPERTY MAN (*mournfully*). Quack!

FIRST SOLDIER. Come along! (*He picks up the fish. To the* SECOND SOLDIER.) Bring the rest of them.

[*He starts off with* HI TEE. *The* SECOND SOLDIER *follows with* LI MO *and* JOY. *As they are about to go out* JOY *brushes aside the bamboo pole of the* SECOND SOLDIER *and rushes back to* LEE MEE, *the duck. He tucks it under his arm.*]

JOY. I would never leave you, Lee Mee! Never in the world.

PROPERTY MAN. Quack! Quack!

[JOY *rushes back to the* SECOND SOLDIER *and they all depart. The gong and music are heard.*]

CHORUS. And now we are back once more to the garden of the Emperor Lang Moo. It is the next morning.

[*The* PROPERTY MAN *rolls up the blue cloth, and takes the sail down from the chairs.*]

It is autumn time when the leaves are falling.

[*The* PROPERTY MAN *takes a handful of imitation autumn leaves from the box and walks solemnly across the stage, scattering them to left and right as he goes.*]

It is the sad time of the year and all the Emperor's Court is sad because the Emperor is very ill. Everybody knows that the great Lang Moo will soon die and will pass above to the Celestial Kingdom. This is indeed sad in itself, but when an emperor dies without a son to take his throne, then it is tragedy.

[*The gong is struck and the* ROYAL NURSE *enters. She is walking with a cane, for she is now very old and bent.*]

NURSE (*looking about her*). Ah, me—ah, my—many years have

passed since I was banished from this royal garden. I am a very wretched old woman. It is all my fault because the mighty Emperor is dying without a son. Ah, me — ah, my — (*She sits on one of the chairs and the* PROPERTY MAN *gives her a large silk handkerchief to weep into. She weeps, wiping first one eye and then the other.*) I do not know what brought me back today, but something whispered in my ear and said that I should come. I left my mountain hiding place and walked for three long nights and three long days. I am now so very old that no one will ever recognize me, so I am safe.

[LONG FO *and* WING LEE *enter. They are now grown up and wear older headdresses.*]

WING LEE. It is here the execution will take place.

LONG FO. Yes, and the Executioner should be here now. He is always on time.

NURSE. Pardon me, my children, but may I ask who is going to be executed?

WING LEE. Oh, don't you know?

NURSE. No. I am a stranger here.

WING LEE. Four heads are coming off this morning. The head of a fisherman, the head of his wife, the head of his son, and the head of a duck, Lee Mee.

NURSE. What have the poor souls done?

WING LEE. They have —

LONG FO. Let me tell her, Wing Lee. You are only a woman and you will get the story mixed up. (*To the* NURSE.) The little duck, Lee Mee, stole the Emperor's sacred scarlet fish from the royal fishpond and brought it to the fisherman and his family for them to eat.

NURSE. But if the duck stole the fish, why should they execute the fisherman and his family, too?

LONG FO. Because the duck belonged to the fisherman and the fisherman should have taught him better manners.

WING LEE. Oh, here comes the Executioner!

[*The* EXECUTIONER *enters, walking very proudly. The* PROPERTY MAN *hands him a wooden ax. The* EXECUTIONER *stands to one side as the gong sounds.* HI TEE *walks in very slowly with his head bent.*

LI MO *enters next, then* JOY, *carrying the duck* LEE MEE. *They are followed by the* TWO SOLDIERS. HI TEE, LI MO, *and* JOY *form a straight line. The* TWO SOLDIERS *stand in front of them. The* PROPERTY MAN *gives the* FIRST SOLDIER *a scroll.*]

FIRST SOLDIER (*reading from the scroll before him*). Today, Hi Tee, fisherman on the river Chang Hi, his wife, Li Mo, their son, Joy, and the most evil, bad-mannered duck, Lee Mee – (*The* PROPERTY MAN *quacks sadly.*) – will die under the ax of the Executioner. (*The* EXECUTIONER *swings his ax.*) The first to die will be the little boy named Joy, so that his parents may have the extreme pleasure of seeing the ax fall on his neck.

[*He motions to the* EXECUTIONER, who steps forward. JOY *kisses his father and his mother good-by and then kisses* LEE MEE, *the duck, handing it to* HI TEE. *Then he steps bravely forward. He sinks to his knees and bows his head. The chain of jade is plainly seen around his neck. The* EXECUTIONER *raises his ax to strike.*]

WING LEE (*to* LONG FO). I'm sure I've seen that chain of jade somewhere before.

FIRST SOLDIER. Wait, Executioner! I will remove this chain of jade. It is too beautiful to be cut by the Executioner's sword. I will keep it for my wife. (*He takes the chain from* JOY'S *neck.*)

NURSE (*jumping up*). Oh, stay a moment! Where did he get that chain of jade?

FIRST SOLDIER. Who are you, old woman?

NURSE. You do not recognize me, for I am so very old, but I am Sing Lo, the royal nurse who long ago was banished from the Court because the little Prince was stolen while in my care. Do you remember?

WING LEE (*suddenly beginning to weep*). Oh! Oh! Oh!

FIRST SOLDIER. What is the matter with you?

LONG FO. She is not feeling well, sir.

NURSE (*to* JOY). Where did you get that chain of jade?

JOY. It has always been around my neck as long as I can remember.

NURSE (*to* HI TEE). Is this your son?

HI TEE. Y – yes.

NURSE. Your true son?

LI MO (*breaking down*). He is not our true son, I must confess. We do not know who he is. We found him in a wooden tub, floating down the river, when he was only a tiny baby.

WING LEE. Oh! Oh! Oh!

NURSE. He is the stolen Prince!

FIRST SOLDIER. What?

WING LEE. It's true.

FIRST SOLDIER. What do you know about it, Wing Lee?

WING LEE. I was the one who stole him.

NURSE. You?

WING LEE. Yes, when I was a little child. The nurse had left the twins beneath the peach tree. They were going to kill the little girl, so I thought I would steal her away. By mistake, I stole the little Prince. I sent him down the river in a wooden tub, with that chain of jade around his neck.

JOY (*jumping up*). What are you all talking about? Aren't you ever going to cut off my head? I'm tired of waiting.

NURSE (*taking him in her arms*). We are not going to cut off your head. Instead, we are going to put a crown on it. You are the royal son of the mighty Emperor Lang Moo, who now is dying in his royal bed. The throne of the Middle Flower Kingdom will soon be yours.

FIRST SOLDIER. I will run and tell the Emperor.

SECOND SOLDIER. And so will I!

[*They run out.*]

LONG FO (*to* WING LEE). What did you say anything for? Now we will be beheaded.

NURSE. Oh no you won't. The Emperor will be so glad to get his son back that he will smile to the end of his days.

JOY. Is it really true I am the Prince? Mother, is it really true?

LI MO. Yes, my little Joy. (*She weeps.*)

JOY. Why do you weep, Mother?

LI MO. Because you will become the Emperor and I shall never see you again.

JOY. Oh yes you will, Mother. You will always be next to my heart. You and Father and Lee Mee will always be my dearest dears.

PROPERTY MAN. Quack! Quack!

[*The* FIRST *and* SECOND SOLDIERS *return.*]

FIRST SOLDIER. Little Prince, the Emperor awaits you in the royal bedchamber. Will His Royal Highness come?

JOY. May I bring my family along, too?

FIRST SOLDIER. Of course, your Highness.

JOY (*taking* LI MO's *hand*). Come along, Mother. You and I will go in together. Hi Tee, you and Lee Mee follow close behind.

[*Music and gong are heard as in procession,* JOY *and* LI MO, *followed by* HI TEE, *carrying* LEE MEE, *go out. The* TWO SOLDIERS *close in at the last.*]

LONG FO (*to the* EXECUTIONER). Why do you pull such a long face, Executioner? Are you angry because you couldn't use your ax?

EXECUTIONER (*growling*). Burrrr! (*He shoulders his ax and stalks off.*)

NURSE. Let us tiptoe down to the royal hall and peek through the royal keyhole into the royal bedchamber. I would like to see the Emperor greet his little son.

[*There is music. With fingers on lips and stepping very high on tip-toes, they start off in line, led by the* NURSE. *The* PROPERTY MAN *starts to follow.*]

CHORUS. Stop! (*The* PROPERTY MAN *stops. The others go out.*) You cannot peek through the royal keyhole, because you are only the Property Man.

PROPERTY MAN (*hanging his head*). Quack! Quack!

CHORUS (*stepping forward and bowing*). My good and patient friends, our play is over. For your kind attention, I bow, and bow, and bow. (*He bows three times. The* PROPERTY MAN *bows three times. The* CHORUS *turns and sees him. Snapping his fan open with great dignity.*) You are discharged!

[*He sweeps off to the left. The* PROPERTY MAN *shrugs his shoulders and goes out to the right.*]

The curtain is pulled back, showing tableau of all the characters grouped around JOY, *who is seated on one of the black chairs with a crown on his head. In his arms he holds* LEE MEE, *the duck.* LI MO *stands next to him and, on the other side,* HI TEE.

AFTER READING

1. Why is *The Stolen Prince* classified as a fantasy?

2. Find instances of humor resulting from:
   a. unexpected actions
   b. inappropriate or inadequate scenery
   c. droll remarks
   d. sound effects
   e. fanciful occurrences
   f. puns (note, for example, the name of the Royal Nurse)

3. If you were directing *The Stolen Prince,* what music would you instruct the Orchestra to play as important incidents occur?

4. Nothing is told about the baby Princess whom the Royal Nurse carried off to the mountains. Tell the story of her return to the Emperor as the author might relate it.

5. Often in fantasies the characters are types rather than individuals. Is this true in *The Stolen Prince?* In a sentence or two for each, point out the characteristics of the Chorus, the Property Man, Hi Tee, Long Fo, and Wing Lee.

6. Find examples of nonrealistic acting required in the stage directions.

CHALLENGES

1. Write the scene in which the Emperor greets his son.

2. In *The Happy Prince and Other Stories* by Oscar Wilde you will find a number of tales that can be successfully dramatized. Select one and use it as the basis for a one-act play of your own writing.

3. Compare *The Stolen Prince* with any one of the following fantasies, giving reasons why you prefer one to the other:
   a. *Cabbages and Kings* by Rose Fyleman (in *Types of Modern Dramatic Composition* by LeRoy Phillips and Theodore Johnson)
   b. *The Emperor's Doll* by E. Vanderveer and F. Bigelow (29)
   c. *The Sleeping Beauty* by Margaret Ellen Clifford (43)
   d. *The Gooseberry Mandarin* by Grace Dorcas Ruthenburg (13)

4. If *The Stolen Prince* is presented in class or assembly, write a review for possible publication in your school paper. In preparation for this assignment read several dramatic criticisms by motion-picture and theatrical reviewers in your daily newspapers, noting their methods and styles.

DRAMA WORKSHOP

A hint for playgoers: Classify the play.

Recalling what was said in our introductory "Open Letter" about classifying plays as comedies, tragedies, farces, melodramas, or fantasies, what kind of play is *The Stolen Prince?*

Is it a comedy? The Property Man makes the audience laugh, and some of the lines and incidents are quite droll.

Is it a tragedy? The little Prince was lost for many years, and the Royal Nurse was banished for losing him while he was in her care.

Is it a farce? Some of the humor is far-fetched and depends on situation more than character.

Is it a melodrama? There is excitement when the Executioner is about to behead the fisherman, his wife, their son Joy, and the duck.

Is it a fantasy? The characters have a make-believe quality and the plot is certainly not realistic.

Or is it a combination of two of these? if so, which two?

Classifying a play is more than a pleasant pastime. It is an exercise in understanding. Try it and see.

A hint for actors: Relax and remember.

Ever wind an alarm clock so tight that it wouldn't go? The clock stopped because the spring was too tense. A beginning actor sometimes "runs up" on his lines (that is, forgets his part) because of stage fright. The explanation is simple. He expends so much nervous energy in tensing his body muscles that he hasn't enough left for thinking and remembering clearly.

At ease! Be relaxed in body and composed in mind. If your body is free from strain and you keep performing the actions your role requires, your lines will come to you at the moment you need them.

Act all the time. There is no danger of forgetting if you relax and keep acting.

OTHER FANTASIES YOU WILL LIKE TO READ

Poor Maddalena by Louise Saunders (15). A brief visit to the earth convinces Pierrot and Pierrette that they are better off in the land of make-believe.

The Princess Marries the Page by Edna St. Vincent Millay (41). A page with whom the Princess falls in love turns out to be a king.

Sam Average by Percy MacKaye (23). American soldiers of the War of 1812 are dissuaded from deserting by a stranger.

The Shoes That Danced by Anna Hempstead Branch (37). An artist who has painted the Madonna on the soles of a pair of dancing slippers must decide whether to give them to the Queen or to Columbine, who has rejected his suit.

The Slave with Two Faces by Mary Carolyn Davies (41). Two ways of looking at life: it will do your bidding if you command, but it is a tyrant to those who cringe.

Three Pills in a Bottle by Rachel Field (42). Three magic pills are used by a boy to cure the sickness of three who pass by.

Will-o'-the-Wisp by Doris F. Halman (26). The wife of a poet who has befriended a mysterious waif is eventually led to her destruction in the sea.

THE GOLDEN DOOM

BY LORD DUNSANY

ABOUT THE PLAY

The Golden Doom is typical of Lord Dunsany's plays in its language, its oriental setting, and its simplicity of plot and characterization. Our imagination is stirred to transport us to a time when kings believed in the stars; when few people could read and writing was considered sacred and mysterious; when strange interpretations were placed on the simplest happenings. Lord Dunsany does not picture the world of the early twentieth century in his plays or his short stories. Instead, he creates new worlds, names them, peoples them, and gives them histories. Appropriately he uses a language almost Biblical in its simplicity and poetic quality.

The ease with which Lord Dunsany's artistry is turned to fantasy is revealed in a recent letter he wrote the editors: "I wrote *The Golden Doom* on August 19, 20, and 21, 1910 in this house [Dunsany Castle, County Meath], probably working on each occasion for an hour or two after tea. I do not think I intended any special meaning. It is just a simple story, though of a far country. Any ironies in it are clear enough to be seen."

ABOUT THE AUTHOR

Lord Dunsany is a name that has been familiar to lovers of fantasy and romance for the past three decades. Born in London in 1878 as Edward John Moreton Drax Plunkett, he succeeded his father to the title of Lord Dunsany, which dates back to the fifteenth century. He was educated at Eton and Sandhurst, the English military academy. He served in the South African War and World War I, and at the time of the German invasion of Greece in World War II, he was Professor of English Literature at the University of Athens.

He made his debut in literature with a collection of tales, *The Gods of Pegana* (1905) in which he wrote of a strange world fashioned more after his imagination than after the world of reality. His first play to be produced was *The Glittering Gate,* at the famous Abbey Theatre in Dublin. Since then Lord Dunsany has written over fifteen collections of short stories and over a score of plays. The richness of his imagination is summed up in another Irish writer's account of a visit to Lord Dunsany: "I have watched him sketch a scenario for a play, write a little story, and invent a dozen incidents for tales, in the course of a morning, all the time talking imaginatively."

THE GOLDEN DOOM

Characters

THE KING
CHAMBERLAIN
CHIEF PROPHET
GIRL
BOY
SPIES
FIRST PROPHET
SECOND PROPHET
SECOND BOY
FIRST SENTRY
SECOND SENTRY
STRANGER
ATTENDANTS

SCENE: *Outside the King's great door in Zericon.*

TIME: *Some while before the fall of Babylon.*

Two SENTRIES *pace to and fro, then halt, one on each side of the great door.*

FIRST SENTRY. The day is deadly sultry.

SECOND SENTRY. I would that I were swimming down the Gyshon, on the cool side, under the fruit trees.

FIRST SENTRY. It is like to thunder or the fall of a dynasty.

SECOND SENTRY. It will grow cool by nightfall. Where is the King?

FIRST SENTRY. He rows in his golden barge with ambassadors or whispers with captains concerning future wars. The stars spare him!

SECOND SENTRY. Why do you say "The stars spare him"?

FIRST SENTRY. Because if a doom from the stars fall suddenly on a king it swallows up his people and all things round about him, and his palace falls and the walls of his city and citadel, and the apes come in from the woods and the large beasts from the desert, so that you would not say that a king had been there at all.

SECOND SENTRY. But why should a doom from the stars fall on the King?

FIRST SENTRY. Because he seldom placates them.

SECOND SENTRY. Ah! I have heard that said of him.

FIRST SENTRY. Who are the stars that a man should scorn them? Should they that rule the thunder, the plague, and the earthquake withhold these things save for much prayer? Always ambassadors are with the King, and his commanders, come in from distant lands, prefects of cities and makers of the laws, but never the priests of the stars.

SECOND SENTRY. Hark! Was that thunder?

FIRST SENTRY. Believe me, the stars are angry.

[*Enter a* STRANGER. *He wanders toward the* KING'S *door, gazing about him.*]

SENTRIES (*lifting their spears at him*). Go back! Go back!

STRANGER. Why?

FIRST SENTRY. It is death to touch the King's door.

STRANGER. I am a stranger from Thessaly.

FIRST SENTRY. It is death even for a stranger.

STRANGER. Your door is strangely sacred.

FIRST SENTRY. It is death to touch it.

[*The* STRANGER *wanders off. Enter two children hand in hand.*]

BOY (*to the* SENTRY). I want to see the King to pray for a hoop.

[*The* SENTRY *smiles.*]

BOY (*pushes the door: to the* GIRL). I cannot open it. (*To the* SENTRY.) Will it do as well if I pray to the King's door?

SENTRY. Yes, quite as well. (*Turns to talk to the other* SENTRY.) Is there anyone in sight?

SECOND SENTRY. Nothing but a dog and he far out on the plain.

FIRST SENTRY. Then we can talk awhile and eat bash.

BOY. King's door, I want a little hoop.

[*The* SENTRIES *take a little bash between finger and thumb from pouches and put that wholly forgotten drug to their lips.*]

GIRL (*pointing*). My father is a taller soldier than that.

BOY. My father can write. He taught me.

GIRL. Ho! Writing frightens nobody. My father is a soldier.

BOY. I have a lump of gold. I found it in the stream that runs down to Gyshon.

GIRL. I have a poem. I found it in my own head.

BOY. Is it a long poem?

GIRL. No. But it would have been only there were no more rhymes for sky.

BOY. What is your poem?

GIRL.

I saw a purple bird
    Go up against the sky
And it went up and up
    And round about did fly.

BOY. I saw it die.

GIRL. That doesn't scan.

BOY. Oh, that doesn't matter.

GIRL. Do you like my poem?

BOY. Birds aren't purple.

GIRL. My bird was.

BOY. Oh!

GIRL. Oh, you don't like my poem!

BOY. Yes I do.

GIRL. No you don't; you think it horrid.

BOY. No. I don't.

GIRL. Yes you do. Why didn't you say you liked it? It is the only poem I ever made.

BOY. I do like it. I do like it.

GIRL. You don't, you don't!

BOY. Don't be angry. I'll write it on the door for you.

GIRL. You'll write it?

BOY. Yes, I can write it. My father taught me. I'll write it with my lump of gold. It makes a yellow mark on the iron door.

GIRL. Oh, do write it! I would like to see it written like real poetry.

[*The* BOY *begins to write. The* GIRL *watches.*]

FIRST SENTRY. You see, we'll be fighting again soon.

SECOND SENTRY. Only a little war. We never have more than a little war with the hillfolk.

FIRST SENTRY. When a man goes to fight, the curtains of the gods wax thicker than ever before between his eyes and the future; he may go to a great or to a little war.

SECOND SENTRY. There can only be a little war with the hillfolk.

FIRST SENTRY. Yet sometimes the gods laugh.

SECOND SENTRY. At whom?

FIRST SENTRY. At kings.

SECOND SENTRY. Why have you grown uneasy about this war in the hills?

FIRST SENTRY. Because the King is powerful beyond any of his fathers, and has more fighting men, more horses, and wealth that could have ransomed his father and his grandfather and dowered their queens and daughters; and every year his miners bring him more from the opal mines and from the turquoise quarries. He has grown very mighty.

SECOND SENTRY. Then he will the more easily crush the hillfolk in a little war.

FIRST SENTRY. When kings grow very mighty the stars grow very jealous.

BOY. I've written your poem.

GIRL. Oh, have you really?

BOY. Yes, I'll read it to you. (*He reads.*)

I saw a purple bird
Go up against the sky
And it went up and up
And round about did fly.
I saw it die.

GIRL. It doesn't scan.

BOY. That doesn't matter.

[*Enter furtively a* SPY, *who crosses stage and goes out. The* SENTRIES *cease to talk.*]

GIRL. That man frightens me.

BOY. He is only one of the King's spies.

GIRL. But I don't like the King's spies. They frighten me.

BOY. Come on, then, we'll run away.

SENTRY (*noticing the children again*). Go away, go away! The King is coming, he will eat you.

[*The* BOY *throws a stone at the* SENTRY *and runs out. Enter another* SPY, *who crosses the stage. Enter a third* SPY, *who notices the door. He examines it and utters an owllike whistle.* NO. 2 *comes back. They do not speak. Both whistle.* NO. 3 *comes. All examine the door. Enter the* KING *and his* CHAMBERLAIN. *The* KING *wears a purple robe. The* SENTRIES *smartly transfer their spears to their left hands and return their right arms to their right sides. They then lower their spears until their points are within an inch of the ground, at the same time raising their right hands above their heads. They stand for some moments thus. Then they lower their right arms to their right sides, at the same time raising their spears. In the next motion they take their spears into their right hands and lower the butts to the floor, where they were before, the spears slanting forward a little. Both* SENTRIES *must move together precisely.*]

FIRST SPY (*runs forward to the King and kneels, abasing his forehead to the floor*). Something has been written on the iron door.

CHAMBERLAIN. On the iron door!

KING. Some fool has done it. Who has been here since yesterday?

FIRST SENTRY (*shifts his hand a little higher on his spear, brings the spear to his side, and closes his heels all in one motion; he then takes one pace backward with his right foot; then he kneels on his right knee; when he has done this he speaks, but not before*). Nobody, Majesty, but a stranger from Thessaly.

KING. Did he touch the iron door?

FIRST SENTRY. No, Majesty; he tried to, but we drove him away.

KING. How near did he come?

FIRST SENTRY. Nearly to our spears, Majesty.

KING. What was his motive in seeking to touch the iron door?

FIRST SENTRY. I do not know, Majesty.

KING. Which way did he go?

FIRST SENTRY (*pointing left*). That way, Majesty, an hour ago.

[*The* KING *whispers with one of his* SPIES, *who stoops and examines the ground and steals away. The* SENTRY *rises.*]

KING (*to his two remaining* SPIES). What does this writing say?

FIRST SPY. We cannot read, Majesty.

KING. A good spy should know everything.

SECOND SPY. We watch, Majesty, and we search out, Majesty. We read shadows, and we read footprints, and whispers in secret places. But we do not read writing.

KING (*to the* CHAMBERLAIN). See what it is.

CHAMBERLAIN (*goes up and reads*). It is treason, Majesty.

KING. Read it.

CHAMBERLAIN.

I saw a purple bird
  Go up against the sky,
And it went up and up
  And round about did fly.
I saw it die.

FIRST SENTRY (*aside*). The stars have spoken.

KING (*to the* SENTRY). Has anyone been here but the stranger from Thessaly?

SENTRY (*kneeling as before*). Nobody, Majesty.

KING. You saw nothing?

FIRST SENTRY. Nothing but a dog far out upon the plain and the children of the guard at play.

KING (*to the* SECOND SENTRY). And you?

SECOND SENTRY (*kneeling*). Nothing, Majesty.

CHAMBERLAIN. That is strange.

KING. It is some secret warning.

CHAMBERLAIN. It is treason.

KING. It is from the stars.

CHAMBERLAIN. No, no, Majesty. Not from the stars, not from the stars. Some man has done it. Yet the thing should be interpreted. Shall I send for the prophets of the stars?

[*The* KING *beckons to his* SPIES. *They run up to him.*]

KING. Find me some prophet of the stars. (*Exeunt* SPIES.) I fear that we may go no more, my chamberlain, along the winding ways of unequaled Zericon, nor play dahoori with the golden balls. I have thought more of my people than of the stars and more of Zericon than of windy Heaven.

CHAMBERLAIN. Believe me, Majesty, some idle man has written it and passed by. Your spies shall find him, and then his name will be soon forgotten.

KING. Yes, yes. Perhaps you are right, though the sentries saw no one. No doubt some beggar did it.

CHAMBERLAIN. Yes, Majesty, some beggar has surely done it. But look, here come two prophets of the stars. They shall tell us that this is idle.

[*Enter two* PROPHETS *and a* BOY *attending them. All bow deeply to the* KING. *The two* SPIES *steal in again and stand at back.*]

KING. Some beggar has written a rhyme on the iron gate, and as the ways of rhyme are known to you, I desired you, rather as poets than as prophets, to say whether there was any meaning in it.

CHAMBERLAIN. 'Tis but an idle rhyme.

FIRST PROPHET (*bows again and goes up to the door. He glances at the writing*). Come hither, servant of those that serve the stars.

[*The attendant approaches.*]

FIRST PROPHET. Bring hither our golden cloaks, for this may be a matter for rejoicing; and bring our green cloaks also, for this may tell of young new beautiful things with which the stars will one day gladden the King; and bring our black cloaks also, for it may be a doom. (*Exit the* BOY; *the* PROPHET *goes up to the door and reads solemnly.*) The stars have spoken.

[*Re-enter the attendant with cloaks.*]

KING. I tell you that some beggar has written this.

FIRST PROPHET. It is written in pure gold. (*He dons the black cloak over his body and head.*)

KING. What do the stars mean? What warning is it?

FIRST PROPHET. I cannot say.

KING (*to* SECOND PROPHET). Come you then and tell us what the warning is.

SECOND PROPHET (*goes up to the door and reads*). The stars have spoken. (*He cloaks himself in black.*)

KING. What is it? What does it mean?

SECOND PROPHET. We do not know, but it is from the stars.

CHAMBERLAIN. It is a harmless thing; there is no harm in it, Majesty. Why should not birds die?

KING. Why have the prophets covered themselves in black?

CHAMBERLAIN. They are a secret people and look for inner meanings. There is no harm in it.

KING. They have covered themselves in black.

CHAMBERLAIN. They have not spoken of any evil thing. They have not spoken of it.

KING. If the people see the prophets covered in black they will say that the stars are against me and believe that my luck has turned.

CHAMBERLAIN. The people must not know.

KING. Some prophet must interpret to us the doom. Let the Chief Prophet of the stars be sent for.

CHAMBERLAIN (*going toward the left exit*). Summon the Chief Prophet of the Stars that look on Zericon.

VOICES OFF. The Chief Prophet of the Stars. The Chief Prophet of the Stars.

CHAMBERLAIN. I have summoned the Chief Prophet, Majesty.

KING. If he interpret this aright I will put a necklace of turquoises round his neck with opals from the mines.

CHAMBERLAIN. He will not fail. He is a very cunning interpreter.

KING. What if he covers himself with a huge black cloak and does not speak and goes stuttering away, slowly with bended head, till our fear spreads to the sentries and they cry aloud?

CHAMBERLAIN. This is no doom from the stars, but some idle scribe hath written it in his insolence upon the iron door, wasting his hoard of gold.

KING. Not for myself I have a fear of doom, not for myself; but I inherited a rocky land, windy and ill-nurtured, and nursed it to prosperity by years of peace and spread its boundaries by years of war. I have brought up harvests out of barren acres and given good laws unto naughty towns, and my people are happy, and lo, the stars are angry!

CHAMBERLAIN. It is not the stars, it is not the stars, Majesty, for the prophets of the stars have not interpreted it. Indeed, it was only some reveler wasting his gold.

[*Meanwhile, enter* CHIEF PROPHET *of the stars that look on Zericon.*]

KING. Chief Prophet of the Stars that look on Zericon, I would have you interpret the rhyme upon yonder door.

CHIEF PROPHET (*goes up to the door and reads*). It is from the stars.

KING. Interpret it and you shall have great turquoises round your neck, with opals from the mines in the frozen mountains.

CHIEF PROPHET (*cloaks himself like the others in a great black cloak*). Who should wear purple in the land but a King, or who go up against the sky but he who has troubled the stars by neglecting their ancient worship? Such a one has gone up and up increasing power and wealth, such a one has soared above the crowns of those that went before him, such a one the stars have doomed, the undying ones, the illustrious. (*A pause.*)

KING. Who wrote it?

CHIEF PROPHET. It is pure gold. Some god has written it.

CHAMBERLAIN. Some god?

CHIEF PROPHET. Some god whose home is among the undying stars.

FIRST SENTRY (*aside to the* SECOND SENTRY). Last night I saw a star go flaming earthward.

KING. Is this a warning or is it a doom?

CHIEF PROPHET. The stars have spoken.

KING. It is, then, a doom?

CHIEF PROPHET. They speak not in jest.

KING. I have been a great king — let it be said of me "The stars overthrew him, and they sent a god for his doom." For I have not met my equal among kings that man should overthrow me; and I have not oppressed my people that man should rise up against me.

CHIEF PROPHET. It is better to give worship to the stars than to do good to man. It is better to be humble before the gods than proud in the face of your enemy, though he do evil.

KING. Let the stars hearken yet and I will sacrifice a child to them — I will sacrifice a girl-child to the twinkling stars and a male child to the stars that blink not, the stars of the steadfast eyes. (*To his* SPIES.) Let a boy and a girl be brought for sacrifice.

(*Exit a* SPY *to the right, looking at footprints.*) Will you accept this sacrifice to the god that the stars have sent? They say that the gods love children.

CHIEF PROPHET. I may refuse no sacrifice to the stars nor to the gods whom they send. (*To the other* PROPHETS.) Make ready the sacrificial knives.

[*The* PROPHETS *draw knives and sharpen them.*]

KING. Is it fitting that the sacrifice take place by the iron door where the god from the stars has trod, or must it be in the temple?

CHIEF PROPHET. Let it be offered by the iron door. (*To the other* PROPHETS.) Fetch hither the altar stone.

[*The owllike whistle is heard off right. The* THIRD SPY *runs crouching toward it. Exit.*]

KING. Will this sacrifice avail to avert the doom?

CHIEF PROPHET. Who knows?

KING. I fear that even yet the doom will fall.

CHIEF PROPHET. It were wise to sacrifice some greater thing.

KING. What more can a man offer?

CHIEF PROPHET. His pride.

KING. What pride?

CHIEF PROPHET. Your pride that went up against the sky and troubled the stars.

KING. How shall I sacrifice my pride to the stars?

CHIEF PROPHET. It is upon your pride that the doom will fall, and will take away your crown and will take away your kingdom.

KING. I will sacrifice my crown and reign uncrowned among you, so only I save my kingdom.

CHIEF PROPHET. If you sacrifice your crown which is your pride, and if the stars accept it, perhaps the god that they sent may avert the doom and you may still reign in your kingdom, though humbled and uncrowned.

KING. Shall I burn my crown with spices and with incense, or cast it into the sea?

CHIEF PROPHET. Let it be laid here by the iron door where the god came who wrote the golden doom. When he comes again by night to shrivel up the city or to pour an enemy in through the iron door, he will see your cast-off pride and perhaps accept it and take it away to the neglected stars.

KING (*to the* CHAMBERLAIN). Go after my spies and say that I make no sacrifice. (*Exit the* CHAMBERLAIN *to the right; the* KING *takes off his crown.*) Good-by, my brittle glory; kings have sought you; the stars have envied you.

[*The stage grows darker.*]

CHIEF PROPHET. Even now the sun has set who denies the stars, and the day is departed wherein no gods walk abroad. It is near the hour when spirits roam the earth, and all things that go unseen, and the faces of the abiding stars will be soon revealed to the fields. Lay your crown there and let us come away.

KING (*lays his crown and scepter before the iron door; then to the* SENTRIES). Go! And let no man come near the door all night.

SENTRIES (*kneeling*). Yes, Majesty.

[*They remain kneeling until after the* KING *has gone. The* KING *and the* CHIEF PROPHET *walk away.*]

CHIEF PROPHET. It was your pride. Let it be forgotten. May the stars accept it. (*Exeunt left.*)

[*The* SENTRIES *rise.*]

FIRST SENTRY. The stars have envied him!

SECOND SENTRY. It is an ancient crown. He wore it well.

FIRST SENTRY. May the stars accept it.

SECOND SENTRY. If they do not accept it, what doom will overtake him?

FIRST SENTRY. It will suddenly be as though there were never any city of Zericon, nor two sentries like you and me standing before the door.

SECOND SENTRY. Why! How do you know?

FIRST SENTRY. That is ever the way of the gods.

SECOND SENTRY. But it is unjust.

FIRST SENTRY. How should the gods know that?

SECOND SENTRY. Will it happen tonight?

FIRST SENTRY. Come! We must march away. (*Exeunt right.*)

[*The stage grows increasingly darker. Re-enter the* CHAMBERLAIN *from the right. He walks across the stage and goes out to the left.*

Re-enter SPIES *from the right. They cross the stage, which is now nearly dark.*]

BOY (*enters from the right, dressed in white, his hands out a little, crying*). King's door, King's door, I want my little hoop. (*He goes up to the* KING'S *door. When he sees the* KING'S *crown there, he utters a satisfied:*) O-oh!

[*He takes it up, puts it on the ground, and, beating it before him with the scepter, goes out by the way that he entered. The great door opens; there is light within; a furtive* SPY *slips out and sees that the crown is gone. Another* SPY *slips out. Their crouching heads come close together.*]

FIRST SPY (*hoarse whisper*). The gods have come!

[*They run back through the door and the door is closed. It opens again and the* KING *and the* CHAMBERLAIN *come through.*]

KING. The stars are satisfied.

AFTER READING

1. Lord Dunsany in a letter wrote: "I will say first that in my plays I tell very simple stories — so simple that sometimes people of this complex age, being brought up in intricacies, even fail to understand them." Discuss *The Golden Doom* in the light of the quotation.

2. Millions of dollars are spent annually for horoscopes, so-called prophecies obtained by studying the stars. How would you explain this interest?

3. It has been said that Dunsany's language at times is rhythmic and exalted, influenced by his reading of the Bible. Find evidences of this influence. Try reading them aloud.

4. What do you consider the central idea of the play to be?

5. What, in your opinion, will be the effect of this experience upon the King's behavior in the future?

CHALLENGES

1. One of the sentries discusses the strange occurrences of the day with his wife. Write the conversation.

2. The Boy explains to his father how he came by the golden hoop. Write the dialogue.

3. At the next court reception the King explains why he abandoned his crown. Try writing his speech in the style of Dunsany.

4. Can you think of another ending to this play?

DRAMA WORKSHOP

A hint for playgoers: Judge acting by its effect on you.

The next time you hear someone remark that "so-and-so's a fine actor," ask him to tell you why. You'll probably discover that his reasons are vague, or else that he makes the common error of confusing an actor's personality with his roles.

It's very difficult to judge acting intelligently. Good acting is largely a matter of detail and variety, according to the famous playwright John Drinkwater. By this standard, a good actor is one whose inventiveness, staying power, and versatility can hold you spellbound throughout a play. Actors who lack these qualities or whose resources are limited will always play "bit" parts. Occasionally an actor is urged to "live your part" and "become the character you portray," but this advice of itself is not enough. The important thing is not what the actor feels, but what the audience feels as a result of his acting. As a playgoer you should judge by what he does to you; if he makes you feel as you think the dramatist intended you to feel, he is acting competently.

A hint for actors: Pick up your cues quickly.

Sometimes high-school play productions drag, and as a result audience interest is weakened. The tempo is slowed usually because pauses occur between the last words of one speaker and the first words of another.

"Pick up a cue as if it were a cricket ball to be smartly fielded," advises Bernard Shaw. Picking up cues swiftly gives lightness and life to a production. You should almost – but not quite – interrupt the speech of the preceding actor, except when the script calls for intervening action.

OTHER FANTASIES YOU WILL LIKE TO READ

Aria da Capo by Edna St. Vincent Millay (33). The senselessness of war is demonstrated by a Pierrot play.

The Exchange by Althea Thurston (20). People who are dissatisfied with their present lot come to the judge to request changes in their lives.

Figureheads by Louise Saunders (12). When the Prince woos the Princess in the guise of a fisherman, she accepts but only after considerable excitement.

The Fisherman by Jonathan Tree (25). Audrey and her sweetheart have died in a plane crash. Audrey has no difficulty in getting into Heaven.

Gods of the Mountain by Lord Dunsany (27). Crime does not pay for seven beggars who, posing as gods, defraud the populace.

King Argimenes and the Unknown Warrior by Lord Dunsany (42). With the help of a sword which he digs up while working as a slave, King Argimenes defeats his former conqueror.

Maid of France by Harold Brighouse (7). Joan of Arc comes to life in the vision of two sleeping soldiers.

Maker of Dreams by Oliphant Downs (7). It takes a third person to inform Pierrot that the lady of his dreams is really Pierrette.

Manikin and Minikin by Alfred Kreymborg (32). Two porcelain figures on the mantelpiece have a quarrel, but like human beings they make up.

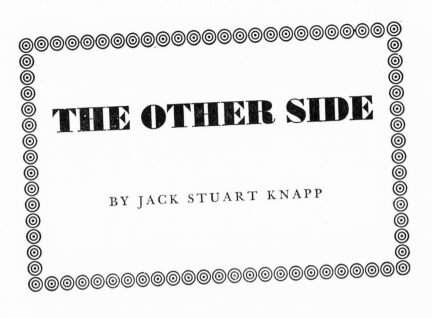

THE OTHER SIDE

BY JACK STUART KNAPP

ABOUT THE PLAY

A callous reporter comes to a state prison on the night of an electrocution with an unusual assignment. He is not to write the story of the actual execution—another reporter will take care of that. Instead, he is to report the gruesome event as it is reflected in the actions, emotions, and comments of the executioner. The reporter happens upon a more sensational story than he had ever dreamed of obtaining.

The four characters—the nervous prison guard, the kindly warden, the uncommunicative executioner, and the tough newspaperman—are vividly defined. Each prepares for the execution in a different way, as his business requires, and each regards it in the light of his own temperament and previous experience. A surprising development momentarily unnerves the warden and the executioner, revealing an unexpected weakness in one. The plot moves swiftly; the style is lean and restrained; the closing scene is sheer theater.

ABOUT THE AUTHOR

Jack Stuart Knapp has been interested in the theory of play production as well as the practice of playwriting. Among his published one-act plays are: *The Son's Wife, Four Hundred Nights, The Duke, The Heritage, The Command Performance,* and *Minnetonka.* His writings about the stage and play production include the books *Lighting the Stage with Homemade Equipment* (1933) and *How to Produce a Play* (1937), based on a series of articles in the magazine *Recreation.* For many years he was associated with the National Recreation Association. As a playwright he has contributed significantly to the recreation of amateur theater groups with a number of easily produced and effective plays like *The Other Side.*

THE OTHER SIDE

Characters

HALEY, *the guard*

QUINN, *the reporter*

ALLISON, *the executioner*

COUGHLIN, *the warden*

The action of the play takes place in a state prison. The time is night.

SCENE. *The stage is shallow but fairly wide. A well-defined spotlight from above reveals a desk and two chairs on the left side of the stage. This is* WARDEN COUGHLIN'S *office. Another well-defined spotlight on the right side of the stage reveals a chair and a section of the upright wall. There is a small barred window in the wall about six feet from the floor. Just to stage right of the window is a big knife switch. This is the executioner's chamber. The two spotlights are never on at the same time. When one is on the rest of the stage is in complete darkness. No other lights are used.*

AT RISE. *When the curtain rises the right spotlight is on, revealing* HALEY *pacing nervously back and forth, puffing on a cigarette. He wears a prison guard's uniform. He is about twenty-eight years old, and is pale and nervous. He looks at the grim switch on the wall and shudders.* QUINN *enters, an ageless young man, cigarette hanging from his lips, hat on the back of his head, wrinkled overcoat hanging unbuttoned.* HALEY *sees him and starts in surprise.*

QUINN. Sorry. I didn't mean to startle you.

HALEY. That's all right. I'm just a bit nervous.

QUINN. I don't blame you. This isn't exactly a picnic.

HALEY. No. I don't believe I know who you are.

QUINN (*slouching into the chair and puffing his cigarette*). Quinn. Reporter.

HALEY. Oh, I see. The Warden let you in, I suppose?

QUINN. Yeah. I came to get the story. I'm on the *Chronicle.*

HALEY (*nervously*). I'm waiting for Allison. I have to help him test the chair. This whole business gives me the shivers.

QUINN (*very little interested*). New here, aren't you?

HALEY. Yes. Have you seen . . . many executions?

QUINN. Too many to sleep well sometimes. I've covered lots of them.

HALEY (*shuddering*). This is my first. I'm only hoping I can get through with it. Every time I think of a man twisting and burning in that chair in there (*Nodding at the window.*) I get sick all over. I have to help strap him in . . .

QUINN (*interrupting*). Better forget it, buddy, or you'll go to pieces. You'll get used to it in time. How's Brown taking it?

HALEY (*with nervous quickness*). Better than the rest of us. He's the coolest one in the place. Talks and jokes with the guards. You wouldn't think that in less than an hour he was going to . . . die.

QUINN. I wonder if Brown's his real name?

HALEY. I guess so. They haven't been able to find any relatives or anything, but he's belonged to this gang for two years and they all knew him by that name. Queer, how a kid like that, only twenty-two years old, has to die in the electric chair. There must be something wrong, some place.

QUINN (*He is pretty hard-boiled about this*). Yeah. Lots of kids go wrong. They don't mean to, maybe, but it's easy. A kid wants some excitement and meets the wrong guys. He gets a twisted idea about the world and himself. Starts in to make some easy dough, via the hold-up route. Then some gink refuses to part with his hard-earned cash and gets bumped off. Then the chair for the kid. It's happened to lots of them. Brown's younger than most — that's all.

HALEY. He's young . . . and brave . . .

QUINN (*callously*). Tough, you mean. The gang makes 'em that way, but I know how you feel. Felt that way the first time I saw somebody in the hot seat. I never did get over it. I'm glad I don't have to watch this one.

HALEY. I thought you said you were covering it?

QUINN. I am, but from the other side, the executioner's side. I'm going to watch Allison's reaction when he throws the switch, try and get him to tell how it feels to kill a man in cold blood. It ought to make a wow of a story. D'you know Allison?

HALEY. I've seen him. He ought to be here any minute. Do you think he'll give you a story? The papers have been rather rough on him—called him some pretty bad names.

QUINN. I don't expect to get much out of him in the way of conversation, but he can't stop me watching him. Even then I probably won't get much reaction from him. This is old stuff to him, and he's as cold as a fish. (*Yawning.*) Oh well, that's what I've got an imagination for.

HALEY (*with morbid curiosity*). I wonder how he happened to get into this . . . business. It is a business for him. Three hundred dollars every time he throws the switch. (*He glances at it.*)

QUINN (*pleased*). The execution business . . . public murder at three hundred dollars a head. Thanks, buddy, that's a good line for my story.

HALEY. Three hundred dollars! Not much to sell your soul for . . .

QUINN. Allison never had a soul, buddy, or a heart. He's as feelingless as a wall. The only thing in that bird's life is money.

HALEY. Careful . . . here he comes!

[ALLISON *enters. He is about sixty years old, with white hair and cold blue eyes. He is dressed neatly in dark clothes and moves without a sign of age. He is calmly smoking a pipe. He stops and looks at the two men.*]

HALEY (*not offering to shake hands*). Hello, Mr. Allison. I'm Haley The Warden detailed me to help you.

ALLISON. Hello. (*He looks at* QUINN *inquiringly.*)

QUINN (*rising*). I'm Quinn from the *Chronicle*. I'd like a story.

ALLISON. No.

QUINN. Wait a minute. All the papers have been roasting you, calling you inhuman, cold-blooded. Here's your chance to tell your side.

ALLISON (*uninterested*). No.

QUINN. I promise to give you a good write-up, turn sentiment in your favor. You owe it to yourself. Tell me, what do you think of when you throw the switch?

ALLISON (*brushing by him*). Haley, I'm going in and test the chair. When I call, throw on the juice. (*He exits.*)

QUINN. Of all the cold-blooded fish! I'll give him a story all right. I'll make him a devil on earth. I'll make a murderer look like a saint beside him!

HALEY. He didn't help you much, did he? (*Taking hold of the switch.*) God! I hate to touch this thing, even when I know there's no one in the chair. How Allison must feel . . .

ALLISON (*off stage*). Now! (HALEY *throws the switch. It sputters and crackles. The light grows dim.*) All right, throw it off.

[HALEY *throws off the switch. The light gets brighter again.* ALLISON *enters.*]

ALLISON. All right, Haley. Go and tell the Warden everything's ready.

HALEY (*wiping his forehead*). Yes, sir. (*He exits.*)

QUINN (*confidentially*). See here, Mr. Allison, give me a break, won't you? I've got to get a story or the skipper will fire me. If you don't want to talk about the execution, tell me something about yourself. How did you happen to get into this work? (ALLISON *seats himself and silently puffs on his pipe.*) If you don't want to talk about that, where do you come from? (*No answer.*) Have you any family? (*No answer.*) Well, if you won't talk, I'll write my own story, that's all, and listen, you cold-blooded turnip, you can't buffalo me. I'm going to see the Warden right now, and get him to let me watch you throw that switch. You'll get a story all right, and will it be a story!

[QUINN *exits whistling.* ALLISON *sits quietly smoking his pipe. The light fades out and the left spotlight fades on, revealing* WARDEN COUGHLIN *seated at his desk chewing nervously on the butt of a dead cigar. He is young for his position, somewhere in the middle thirties. He looks at his watch, then at the telephone on his desk.* HALEY *enters hurriedly.*]

COUGHLIN (*looking up*). Everything ready?

HALEY. Yes, sir.

COUGHLIN (*half turning in his chair*). How's Brown taking it?

HALEY. Calm, sir. He's sure hard-boiled; wouldn't have anything to do with the chaplain. He sits there smoking and kidding the guards.

COUGHLIN. I hope he doesn't break. It's bad when they do that. That Greek last month had every man in the place screaming.

HALEY. I don't think Brown will break, sir. He's like iron, cold, calm . . . almost like Allison. After all, they're both killers, only Allison's killings are lawful. They've both got nerve, too. The only difference is that Brown's so young.

COUGHLIN. He may be young, but these baby-faced killers are usually the worst. How they get that way is beyond me. Think of this kid, twenty-two years old, smart, good-looking, and dying tonight in the electric chair. That's what comes of wrong company. A tough gang, a hold-up, a dead clerk, and the chair.

HALEY (*after a pause*). Any chance of the Governor . . . ?

COUGHLIN. I don't think so, but I've got the line clear just in case . . . but there's not a chance. Brown deserves what he's getting. Even he admits it. What's the matter, Haley? You're shaking like a leaf!

HALEY (*his voice a trifle uncertain*). I'm sorry, sir, but this thing's getting my nerves. I'm on the detail tonight to strap him in the chair. I've never seen a man . . .

COUGHLIN. I forgot. This is your first detail of this kind, isn't it? Sorry I can't ask one of the other boys to take your place, but you'll have to get used to it. It's part of your job.

HALEY. I suppose in time I'll get more like Allison. He's in there now (*Nodding right.*) as cold as a fish. You'd think he was going to a tea, instead of going to send a man's soul to . . . to wherever it goes. He gives me the shivers. How many men has he . . . ?

COUGHLIN. Executed? I don't know. I don't believe he does. He's been executioner for seven states for over ten years.

HALEY (*shakily*). He must have sent hundreds . . . ! What a way to make a living!

COUGHLIN (*prosaically*). Someone's got to do it. I'm mighty glad to have Allison. (*Looking at his watch.*) In twenty minutes someone's got to push that switch in there. If Allison wouldn't do it, I'd have to, but I don't mind telling you that I'd rather cut off my right arm.

HALEY. I wish I had his nerve for the next half hour.

COUGHLIN. Buck up, Haley. You're not responsible. All you do is help the other boys place him in the chair. Allison is the one who throws the switch. If there is any blame, it's on his head—(QUINN *enters.* COUGHLIN *stares at him.*) Who let you in?

QUINN (*sinking into a chair beside the desk*). Nobody. I walked.

COUGHLIN (*half angry*). Quinn, you've got more brassbound nerve than any lousy reporter in the city.

QUINN. That's why I'm the best reporter. Got a drink?

COUGHLIN. I have not. What do you want? Spit it out and beat it. I'm busy tonight.

QUINN. I came to see your executioner. I want to get a story.

COUGHLIN (*firmly*). You can't see him.

QUINN (*coolly*). That's all right. I've already seen him.

COUGHLIN. You've what? How in —

QUINN (*grinning*). A ten-dollar bill looks big to a guard.

COUGHLIN. What dirty —

QUINN. Just one of the boys around here. I don't know his name. In fact I wouldn't know him if I saw him. I'm that way.

HALEY. But you told me the Warden had let you in.

QUINN (*grinning*). I do have the worst habit of lying sometimes. Can't seem to break myself of it.

COUGHLIN. Haley, better get on the job. Not much time left.

HALEY. All right, sir. Any further instructions?

COUGHLIN. No, you know what to do.

[HALEY *exits.* QUINN *stares after him.*]

QUINN. Your guard's got a bad case of nerves.

COUGHLIN. He's new, but he'll come through. (*Half threateningly.*) If I find that bird who let you bribe him . . . !

QUINN (*impatiently*). Aw, what's the difference? I was trying to get in, not out.

COUGHLIN (*curiously*). What'd Allison tell you?

QUINN (*disgusted*). Nothing. He wouldn't talk.

COUGHLIN (*triumphantly*). I thought not! There's one man that's got more nerve than you have.

QUINN. I admit it. The man's as cold-blooded as a werewolf. He just sat there and grunted "no." The more I talked the stiller he was. (*Yawning.*) Oh well, that's all right, too. If he'd of talked I'd have to have written what he said. Since he didn't, I can write what I please.

COUGHLIN (*looking at his watch*). Fifteen minutes. Queer how slow time goes on execution nights, all except for the poor devil in the death cell. I wonder if he's counting the minutes too, watching them slip through his fingers . . . (*Shrugging his shoulders.*) Well, if you're covering this story you'd better be going. The witnesses have to be in the death chamber ten minutes before the execution.

QUINN. I'm not going to see the execution. Donahue's covering that. I'm going to watch Allison throw the switch.

COUGHLIN. What's the big idea?

QUINN. The skipper had a brain wave. He said to get a story from the other side, the executioner's side. Something new . . .

COUGHLIN. I don't know whether I can let you do that or not. It might bother Allison.

QUINN (*rising leisurely*). Bother that icicle? Don't make me laugh. He's got the feelings of a fish and the heart of a stone idol. He's so cold that . . .

[*The left spot fades out and the right spotlight fades on, revealing* ALLISON *smoking quietly in his chair.* HALEY *enters, white and shaking.* ALLISON *looks at him keenly.*]

ALLISON. Something wrong?

HALEY. I just saw Brown . . . laughing . . . I've got to get away! I can't see it through.

ALLISON (*calmly*). See what through?

HALEY. The murder! That's what it is, legalized murder! And I've got to help, I've got to hold him while they strap him in the chair.

ALLISON (*coldly*). If you don't like your job, why don't you quit?

HALEY. I can't. I need the money. I've got a family. I've got to stick if it drives me crazy.

ALLISON (*indifferently*). You'll get over it.

HALEY. I suppose so. You seem to have. It doesn't seem to bother you to know that you're going to kill a man in a few minutes. (*Hysterically.*) Don't you know that when you push that switch a man, a boy, is going to die twisting and writhing in the chair on the other side of that window?

[*He begins to sob.* ALLISON *rises.*]

ALLISON (*with a touch of pity in his voice*). Sit here a minute, son. (*He pushes* HALEY *into his chair.*) Pull yourself together and look at this thing sensibly. Heaven knows our job isn't easy, but someone's got to do it. (HALEY *looks up.*) Oh, I know, that's a weak excuse. (*Pause.*) You say you've got a family?

HALEY (*head in his hands*). Yes.

ALLISON. Kids?

HALEY. Two.

ALLISON. You've got to stick it out then, haven't you?

HALEY (*dully*). I've got to stick it out.

ALLISON. Maybe I can help you. I've been on this job a long time.

HALEY. I wish you could. Tell me, how do you keep your nerve? If only this boy weren't so young . . . only twenty-two . . .

ALLISON (*sharply*). Stop it. I don't want to know anything about him. That's the first thing, know nothing about them, don't talk about them or listen to anything about them. Never read the papers. I haven't read a paper for ten years, for fear I'd see something about one of them. When I push that switch I don't kill a man. I merely erase a number. This one is Number 4386. That's all I know, all that I want to know.

HALEY. You mean you don't know who's in the chair in there?

ALLISON. No.

HALEY. That's a good idea. I won't know, after this. Tell me some more, talk to me so I won't think. What time is it?

ALLISON (*taking out a beautiful gold watch and fob*). Ten minutes.

HALEY (*laughing shakily*). What a beautiful watch to tell when a man is going to die.

ALLISON (*correcting him sharply*). When a number is going to be erased. (*He looks at his watch.*) I bought two of these just alike, four years ago.

HALEY. Why two?

ALLISON. One for a graduation present for my son. I had a jeweler engrave them just alike.

HALEY (*interested*). I didn't know you had a family. How queer . . . your son, what does he think of your . . . ?

ALLISON. My job? He doesn't know about it. Allison isn't my real name.

HALEY. Tell me about him . . . anything. Keep on talking. It helps. What's his job?

ALLISON. Billy's got a job in a brokerage house. He's a fine kid, steady, reliable, always careful with money. He's had his job four years, ever since he left high school. (*He sighs*). I haven't seen him for two years. He's been making business trips for the firm. I think a lot of Billy. You see he's the only thing I have.

HALEY. I wonder . . . if you took your job for the same reason I took mine.

ALLISON. Just about. You see ten years ago Billy took sick, had to have an operation to live. I'd been out of work . . . no money. Billy was all that I had. His mother died when he was born. Billy was twelve then . . . too young to die. I was about crazy — then this chance came. Three hundred dollars for pushing a switch. I took it.

HALEY. I see.

ALLISON. He got better, and we were pals, camping together, fishing, hiking, all that. This job gave me money to raise him well. I sent him to high school. He was tickled with his watch. Said he'd never part with it . . . that having the only two like it in the world made us closer together . . . as though anything could make us closer together! Then I wanted him to go to college, but he didn't want to go. He wanted to go into business. He always had a head for making money, and he's been doing fine. He's made this job of mine worth while. (*He looks at his watch.*) It's time for you to go. Think you can see it through now?

HALEY. I think I can . . . now. You've helped a lot. Thanks.

ALLISON (*rising*). Remember it's for your family. He's just a number, not a man — just a number. I push the switch and I take the blame. That's what I'm paid for. I wouldn't have it otherwise.

HALEY. I'll remember.

[*He exits.* ALLISON *watches him go, glances at his watch and seats himself.* QUINN *enters.* ALLISON *glances at him and lights his pipe.*]

QUINN (*nonchalantly*). The Warden says I can watch you push the switch. Hope it won't bother you.

ALLISON (*shrugging*). No.

QUINN. Thanks, I didn't think it would. (*Dryly.*) I see where I'm going to have to make up all the sob stuff in this story. (*He goes to the barred window and gazes into the death chamber.*) Here they come . . . they're bringing him in. He's walking by himself. His head's up. He's taking it well. They're putting him in the chair . . . they're all whiter than he is. God, he's young . . .

ALLISON (*harshly*). Shut up!

QUINN (*glancing at him*). Sorry. Here comes the Warden.

[COUGHLIN *enters.* ALLISON *stands beside the switch.* COUGHLIN *wipes his forehead with his handkerchief.*]

COUGHLIN. He didn't break. Hard as they come. Game all the way through. Ready, Allison?

ALLISON (*quietly*). Yes.

[*He places his hand on the switch.* COUGHLIN *gazes into the death chamber through the window.* QUINN *watches* ALLISON. COUGHLIN *puts his hand into the side pocket of his coat and pulls out a gold watch and fob. Without looking he hands it to* ALLISON.]

COUGHLIN. Here, Allison. He asked me to give this to the bird who pushed the switch. Queer, how they make grandstand plays . . .

[ALLISON *slowly puts out his left hand and takes the watch. He gazes at it in horror. He reaches into his pocket and pulls out his own. They are alike. He sags back against the wall.*]

COUGHLIN (*raising his hand*). Ready? Now! (ALLISON *does not move but stands with his eyes closed.* COUGHLIN *turns and looks at him.*) Quick! Throw the switch! Allison, what's the matter with you? Throw that switch!

ALLISON (*groaning*). I can't . . . I can't!

COUGHLIN (*grasping him by the shoulder*). You've got to! He's in the chair – you're prolonging his agony – My God, throw that switch!

ALLISON (*shaking his head weakly and whispering*). I can't.

COUGHLIN. He's in the chair, I tell you! Throw that switch! Come out of it. (ALLISON *does not move.*) If you don't I'll have to. (*Whispering.*) I'll be a murderer, too. (*Desperately.*) Please, Allison, don't make a murderer out of me. He's in the chair . . . suffering. Throw the switch . . . For God's sake, Allison, are you going to make a murderer out of me?

[ALLISON *opens his eyes and gazes at him. He shakes his head slowly. His right hand slowly grasps the switch.*]

ALLISON (*hoarsely*). I'll . . . not . . . make . . . a murderer . . . out of you . . .

[*He pushes the switch. The spotlight grows dim as the switch sputters.* ALLISON *sags back against the wall, his white face upturned, his arms outstretched as though crucified.*]

AFTER READING

1. Why is the play called *The Other Side?*

2. Quinn says: "Allison never had a soul, buddy, or a heart. He's as feelingless as a wall." Point out lines or incidents in the play to support or refute this point of view.

3. All the roles in this play are clearly drawn and sharply differentiated. In a few sentences for each, point out the chief characteristics of Haley, Quinn, Allison, and Coughlin.

4. In what ways did Brown resemble his father?

5. The warden lays the blame for Brown's delinquency on bad company. What other causes for juvenile delinquency can you suggest? To what extent do you think Allison was responsible for his son's lawbreaking?

6. Give some reasons why you think the playwright omitted a scene between the father and the son.

7. Should Allison have pulled the switch? Give reasons for your answer.

8. Is the ending of the play logical and satisfactory? Suggest another possible ending. Is the author's the more dramatic?

CHALLENGES

1. Imagine you are Quinn. Write the story of the execution for the *Chronicle* as he might have written it.

2. Read one of the most famous one-act plays ever written, *The Valiant* by Holworthy Hall and Robert Middlemass. Like *The Other Side,* it deals with a young prisoner who refuses to disclose his identity even though he is about to be executed. In what ways are the two plays alike? In what ways dissimilar? Which do you prefer? Why?

DRAMA WORKSHOP

A hint for playgoers: Read dramatic reviews.

A very good way of learning how to judge a play or movie is to read the dramatic reviews that appear in reputable newspapers and in national news magazines. Most reviewers include enough about the plot and the characters in their accounts of a play to enable a reader to decide for himself whether he wants to see the play. In addition, a good reviewer comments, either favorably or unfavorably, on such matters as direction, acting, setting, lighting, theme, musical background, and entertainment value. Make a habit of reading reviews and you will be surprised how quickly you will steep yourself in the lore of the theater, and how your own ability to evaluate plays will increase.

A hint for actors: Understand the inner life of the character you are portraying.

Suppose the script calls for one character to pace back and forth and, then, to be startled at the entry of another, as in *The Other Side.* A mechanical and stilted performance will result if you walk from one side of the room to the other and abruptly express surprise only because the script requires you to do so. Many productions are marred because the actors move about without apparent purpose.

Get deep into the character you are acting. Ask yourself such questions as: Why is the Warden pacing up and down the room? What is disturbing him? Why does he shudder when he sees the switch on the wall? Why is he startled at Quinn's entrance? Whom does he expect? In other words, before you begin to concern yourself with gestures and other physical actions, you must first try to think and feel as the character thinks and feels. If you re-create this inner life, the outward appearances will come more easily and naturally.

OTHER MELODRAMAS YOU WILL LIKE TO READ

The Game of Chess by Kenneth Sawyer Goodman (15). Brain, in the person of a Russian nobleman, is pitted against brawn, in the person of a peasant with fanatical courage.

The Ghost of Jerry Bundler by W. W. Jacobs and Charles Rock (29). To convince a skeptic that the inn at which they are staying is haunted, an actor impersonates a ghost.

In the Net by Percival Wilde (41). A crook uses his ventriloquism to open a burglar-proof safe while posing as an F.B.I. agent.

The Man without a Head by Lloyd Thanhouser (41). What begins as a prank ends with the death of one friend and the suicide of another.

The Monkey's Paw by Louis N. Parker and W. W. Jacobs (22). A monkey's paw given by a friend returned from service in India brings tragedy to a quiet English household.

Moonshine by Arthur Hopkins (36). A revenue officer has a tight squeeze in a battle for his life with a moonshiner.

A Night at an Inn by Lord Dunsany (7). A Hindu idol which has lost a precious ruby calls four English soldiers to their destruction.

On Vengeance Height by Allan Davis (15). In this feud between two Tennessee families the last male of one family faces the surviving male of the other family.

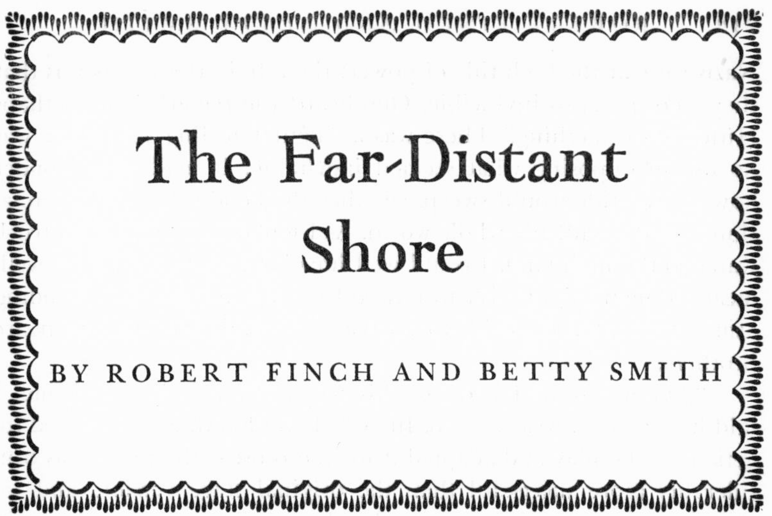

The Far-Distant Shore

BY ROBERT FINCH AND BETTY SMITH

ABOUT THE PLAY

This is Robert Finch's account of the origin of *The Far-Distant Shore:* "One evening in 1937 I walked along the shore at Oyster Bay, Long Island. Far across the water on the mainland the lights glittered and twinkled, magically, as though they were lights from a land that could never be seen except at a distance. In those days the

---

Nazis were at the high tide of power; the talk in the streets was that they were perhaps invincible. One heard the remark that 'perhaps Hitler has something.' There was a singular feeling that there was no use in opposing what seemed inevitable. It made one wonder how far the tide would sweep, whether the flood of race discrimination would engulf the whole world. As I looked over the light-struck water to the mainland, I could well imagine how an innocent, well-meaning man might wish to escape from the tense and foreboding atmosphere of the world, to escape to a land where all men are brothers.

"The first draft I wrote of this play did not quite satisfy me; I laid it away for a year or two. In 1941 Betty Smith and I worked together on the play and adapted it for radio use — the result was considerably more successful than the original stage version, and we were encouraged to incorporate the changes into a new and greatly improved stage version, which is the play as it is printed here."

ABOUT THE AUTHORS

Betty Smith is widely known as the author of the best-selling novel *A Tree Grows in Brooklyn,* and her more recent book, *Tomorrow Will Be Better.* She was born in the Williamsburg section of Brooklyn, the locale of her novels. At eleven she had two poems published, and since then her literary career has included not only her novels but seventy one-act plays written alone or in collaboration. With the prize awarded to her for her play *Francie Nolan,* she bought a typewriter and enlarged the play into her novel *A Tree Grows in Brooklyn.* Writing at the rate of two pages a day before breakfast, she took five years to finish it. The book has sold 3,000,000 copies, has been translated into sixteen languages, and has enjoyed a record film run.

Robert Finch was born in Marion, Iowa, in 1911. He was raised in Montana, but moved East to study the theater at the Yale Drama School and the University of North Carolina. After appearing as an actor in several New York stage productions, he was awarded a playwriting fellowship in 1940–1941 and a National Theatre Conference playwriting fellowship in 1947. He is the author of more than thirty plays, both one-act and full-length.

THE FAR–DISTANT SHORE

Characters

DAVID LEVINE

LEAH, *his daughter*

JOSEPH, *his son*

RUTH, *his wife*

THE STRANGER

PLACE. A dock landing in Brooklyn.

TIME. The present. Nearly midnight of an evening at the end of summer.

A pier's end with sea-whitened piles. A worn lifesaver with faded lettering "S.S. Paradise" hangs from a nail. A rusted anchor and a tired coil of rope keep it company. There are two lanterns at either end of the pier, one red, one green. It is a dock landing in Brooklyn.

It is one of the last evenings of summer. There is a chill in the air, and a fugitive sea wind moves the lanterns from time to time. Across the water may be seen the twisting blinking lights of a bridge and the slow-wheeling lights of a Ferris wheel in some obscure amusement park.

As the curtain rises, there is the mournful throb of a distant boat whistle, and the strains of an orchestra playing in a ship going out to sea.

DAVID *comes hurrying on. He is a disappointed passenger for the departed boat. He is a gentle, slender man in well-worn clothes, and with his coat collar turned up against the wind. He sets down a battered suitcase and speaks sadly as he looks out to sea, where the boat is disappearing in the darkness.*

DAVID. Gone! (*Gazes back in the direction from which he came, then looks out to sea again.*) Well . . .

[*He leans dejectedly against one of the piles. He is startled when he hears a little girl's voice.*]

LEAH. Papa! Papa! (*She runs in, a twelve-year-old with long braids, a short skirt, and a sailor blouse. She carries a little straw suitcase. Usually she is a serious child. But now she's excited.*) Oh, Papa! It's gone! The boat's gone.

DAVID. You shouldn't have come out, Leah. It's chilly. I didn't even want you to know I was going. Why did you follow me?

LEAH. But look at the boat, Papa.

DAVID (*nods*). Yes. There she goes. All her lights strung out like on a Christmas tree.

LEAH (*her head to one side*). I can hear the music.

DAVID (*sadly*). And the orchestra plays all the way across.

LEAH. Holler! Maybe the boat will turn back.

DAVID. No, Leah. No boat would turn back for me. (*Sighs.*) I felt I was going to be too late.

LEAH (*stricken*). Oh! I forgot! (*Calls.*) Hurry up, Joseph.

DAVID. Did you bring Brother, too?

LEAH. Yes, only he couldn't keep up with me. And now he's afraid that you're going to scold him.

DAVID. You both ought to be home in bed, but . . . (*Calls in a resigned tone.*) Well, come along, son, now that you're here.

JOSEPH (*as he comes on panting*). She wouldn't wait for me. (*He's a little fellow of eight, wearing knickerbockers, sneakers, and a sailor blouse, and a sailor hat on the back of his head. His shirttail hangs out, and he carries a little suitcase which bangs against his knees as he carries it with two hands. He is disillusioned.*) Aw, phooey! I *knew* we were going to miss it.

LEAH (*pointing*). See it, Brother? See it? There goes the boat. Like a merry-go-round. Only more lights.

DAVID (*trying to be stern*). Children, why did you follow me?

LEAH (*avoiding the issue*). Look at the lights shine on the water! They wiggle and they make a road clear to the boat.

DAVID (*still trying to be stern*). What are you doing here, children?

LEAH. We thought you were going somewheres and we didn't want to be left. So we packed our suitcases and then made out like we went to bed. But we just sat in the dark and listened when you went. Then we followed you.

JOSEPH. Leah's got the pajamas. But I got *lunch* in my suitcase.

DAVID (*worried*). You didn't wake up Mama?

LEAH. No-o-o. It seemed like you didn't want her to know. (*She is puzzled, but the father gives no explanation.*)

JOSEPH. I wanted to ride on the boat with you. And now we went and missed it! (*Disgusted, he drops suitcase to the ground, and kicks it.*)

LEAH. Joseph! Don't kick the lunch!

DAVID. At least we saw the boat, anyway. (*Looking out over the water.*) It's beautiful, isn't it?

LEAH. It sure is, Papa. (*Breathing the name.*) The *Paradise*. That's its name.

DAVID (*nodding*). The S.S. *Paradise.*

JOSEPH (*agonized*). Ain't there *another* boat?

LEAH. No, there ain't. Not till this one comes back at three A.M. in the morning.

DAVID (*patiently*). Don't say "ain't."

JOSEPH. Aw, *Papa!* It don't matter what we say when we missed the boat. And after all the trouble we had sneaking out of the house, too.

LEAH (*troubled*). What'll we do now, Papa?

DAVID. I'm going to stay and wait for the boat. You and Brother will have to go right back home and go to bed.

JOSEPH (*wailing*). Aw . . . !

LEAH. Can't we wait and go on the boat with you, please, Papa?

DAVID. No!

JOSEPH. Why?

DAVID. Because I'm going a long ways away. (JOSEPH *wails louder.*) Hush, son.

LEAH. But if we go home now, we might wake up Mama. And if she asks, we'll have to tell her where you are.

DAVID. That's right. Well — look here, children. If I let you stay awhile, will you promise to go right home when the boat comes?

LEAH. You're *sure* we can't go with you?

DAVID. No, Leah. You can't.

LEAH. We'll stay then, just till the boat comes in.

JOSEPH. Oh boy! Stay out all night! Pretty near all night, anyhow. (*But already he yawns loudly.*)

LEAH (*laughing at him*). He's sleepy already, and it ain't midnight yet.

JOSEPH (*valiantly pulling himself together*). I am not sleepy. I'm just *hungry.* (*He opens his suitcase.*) And I'm gonna eat now. (*He takes out a misshapen sandwich and munches on it.*)

LEAH. Mama was saving that meat for tomorrow. There wasn't much of it, either.

JOSEPH (*at first conscience-stricken, then reconciled*). Well, I can't put it back. I already licked on it.

LEAH. Put it back for dinner tomorrow.

JOSEPH (*puts it back into the suitcase; something else catches his eye*). I brought fishing tackle too, Papa. Can I fish? Can I?

DAVID. If you want to. Here! Give me a piece of that meat. I'll bait the hook for you. (*He does so.* JOSEPH *takes the line, which is rolled on a stick, and throws the hook into the water and watches it wide-eyed.*) Do you like it here, children?

LEAH. I like it because I've never been out so late before. (*Peers after the receding boat.*) The boat's almost out of sight now.

DAVID. Away out on the sea where I'd be now, if . . .

LEAH. And now you can't hear the music any more.

[*It is remarkably still all at once.*]

JOSEPH (*pulling in the line*). I guess the fish is all sleeping.

LEAH. I bet Mama's mad.

DAVID. I don't think she knows. (*Looks back at the house on the hill.*) There's no light. House is all dark. She must be asleep.

JOSEPH. Poor Mama!

DAVID. Now, son. (JOSEPH *sniffs.*) What's the trouble?

JOSEPH (*nearly sobbing*). Lonesome.

DAVID. I told you not to follow me.

JOSEPH (*afraid of being sent back*). I don't mean lonesome. (*Finding an excuse.*) I just don't like the water. It sounds funny sloppin' round down there — like it's deep.

LEAH. Sure it's deep. But we're not in it. We're up here.

JOSEPH (*feebly*). But it never was black when I was here before.

LEAH (*shivers suddenly*). I'm cold.

DAVID (*taking off his coat*). Sit close to Brother and I'll put my coat around you both.

[*They sit close together in the shadows. He puts his coat about them.*]

JOSEPH. I'm *scared.* Seems like there was something comin' over the water that I can't see – and I'm scared.

DAVID. You're just tired. Lie down with Sister, close together, and keep each other warm.

LEAH. If we fall asleep, will you wake us when the boat comes?

DAVID. Yes. Go to sleep now.

[JOSEPH *yawns and lies down.*]

LEAH. When I play the music box – just once.

[*She takes a tiny battered music box from her suitcase. She turns the catch and it tinkles out a tiny childish tune, which sounds mysterious in the night.*]

DAVID. Sleep now.

[*The song tinkles on to the end. The children go to sleep.*]

STRANGER. Evening.

[*He appears without a sound, at the top of the pier, seeming to rise out of the sea. He is hatless, and wears a seaman's jacket and boots. His hair is somewhat long and he is unshaven.*]

DAVID (*starts in alarm*). Where did you come from?

STRANGER (*with a kindly smile*). From the water.

DAVID. But you're not wet.

STRANGER. No.

DAVID. Oh! You came in a rowboat. Of course. (*A bit frightened.*) But I didn't hear any oars.

STRANGER. Very few people hear me come.

DAVID (*glancing at him sharply*). What did you say?

STRANGER. Perhaps you were listening to the music. (*He indicates the music box, which has now run down.*)

DAVID. It's a present I gave her when she was very small. She plays it every night before she goes to sleep.

STRANGER. Yes.

DAVID. It's long past their bedtime. We're waiting for the three-o'clock boat.

STRANGER. Children going with you?

DAVID. Where I go, I go alone.

STRANGER. You are making a mistake, Levine.

DAVID (*starts*). You know my name?

STRANGER. I know your name.

DAVID. Oh! You work for the boat company.

STRANGER. In a way.

DAVID. I didn't sign anything when I bought my ticket for the boat this morning. (*Enlightened.*) But I guess the ticket seller knew me.

STRANGER. Perhaps. (*He leans on a post and looks out to sea.*) I wish — I wish you'd change your mind about this trip, Levine.

DAVID. I wouldn't change my mind now. (*Vehemently.*) I should say not. (*Suddenly facing the* STRANGER.) Why shouldn't I go? (*Bitterly.*) That is one of the few rights still left to me.

STRANGER. That's true, in a way.

DAVID. Well?

STRANGER (*calmly*). It's just that everything is so unsettled these days. A man ought to be mighty clear in his mind before he goes on a trip. (*Slowly.*) Especially such a long one.

DAVID. You don't know . . .

STRANGER (*puts out his hand and* DAVID *stops talking*). And it's getting cold too. The wrong time to start out, seems like. (*Silence as both gaze out to sea.*) Yet the lights look sort of pretty on the other side, don't they?

DAVID. Beautiful! (*He speaks more intimately.*) Seems like I been looking at them all my life — the merry-go-round and the Ferris wheel over there. Sometimes you can hear the music from them when the wind is right.

STRANGER. Listen!

[*He holds up his left hand, palm outward toward the sea. Music fades in as from a distance and is clearly heard.*]

DAVID (*pleased*). Yes. I hear it now. (*The* STRANGER *lowers his hand and the music fades away. Now* DAVID *seems more friendly to the* STRANGER.) You know, every night when I lock up the house and start up to bed, I always stop a minute and look out of the upstairs window at the lights on the other side, and listen for the music. Our house is quite high up, and sometimes the music seems to come clearer there.

STRANGER (*nodding back over his shoulder*). That's your house. The white one on the hill.

DAVID (*astonished*). Why, yes! (*Looks closely at the* STRANGER.)

STRANGER. It's a very neat place.

DAVID. Ruth, my wife, loves it and keeps it spotless.

STRANGER. There's a nice yard for the children to play in.

DAVID. Only there's not much room. It's full of flowers, mostly chrysanthemums now. It's getting into fall.

STRANGER. It must be a good life: a wife, children, your home, flowers . . .

DAVID. No, it isn't good. It isn't good because the world isn't good. The landlord says we can stay in the house but two weeks longer. My wife cries in secret. Even the flowers, they are not ours.

STRANGER. You planted them and tended them.

DAVID. To sell on the streets, from house to house, for a few pennies.

STRANGER. Even so.

DAVID. But summer's gone now and the flowers died with the first frost last night. Winter's coming on and there won't be enough for the five of us. There's a baby at home, you know.

STRANGER. There will be other work.

DAVID. Not for me. I'm a machinist — was a machinist. I did good work, earned good money, and then — things changed. I'm not American.

STRANGER. So you are getting out of it.

DAVID (*passionately*). What else can I do?

STRANGER. You can endure and hope — and live, Levine.

DAVID. You do not understand. (*Simply.*) I am a Jew.

STRANGER. You are a Jew.

DAVID. I always tried to live right. I worked hard, was accepted at my worth. And then the world caught on fire.

STRANGER (*sighs heartbrokenly*). I know.

DAVID. I got letters from those who knew my folks in the old country. They suffered persecutions, humiliations, concentration camps — and then death.

STRANGER. Old injustices, since the world began.

DAVID. It was all right here at first. Then things changed. No Jews wanted. One man told me if I'd change my name . . . But I wouldn't.

STRANGER. It's a good name, Levine.

DAVID. It's a thousand years old. But it's against me in these times.

STRANGER. So you were going out on that boat and never coming back.

DAVID (*in a whisper*). Yes. There is no other way out. Our landlord tells me I have to move by the first. He speaks of real estate values.

STRANGER. And Ruth?

DAVID. My wife is not Jewish. After I go, there will be a little insurance. She can give the children her father's name and start life new somewhere else.

STRANGER. When Ruth took you, she took your people. She would not want you to leave her. Your people are her people and your God, her God.

DAVID. But you do not know what it is to be persecuted.

STRANGER. I know. I too am a Jew.

DAVID. You? (*The* STRANGER *nods.*) But not a workman?

STRANGER. I used to be a carpenter.

DAVID. You were persecuted by the Gentiles?

STRANGER. By the Gentiles and Jews both. (*Sadly.*) And I did not *want* to die.

DAVID (*sits down and buries his face in his hands*). I don't want to die. But I don't know how to live in this world.

STRANGER. Levine, remember who you are. You come of an old people, a people who will endure until the ending of all recorded time.

DAVID. In spite of terrors and persecutions?

STRANGER. In spite of tortures and crucifixions.

DAVID. I don't know . . . I don't know.

STRANGER. Lift up your heart, Levine. Remember that the first Christian was a Jew. According to the Gentile faith, God chose a Hebrew child to be His Son on earth.

DAVID. What must I do? What must I do?

STRANGER (*in a tone of authority*). Levine! (DAVID *gets to his feet and fastens his eye on the* STRANGER'S *face.*) You must not die now. You must live . . .

DAVID. Live to endure the things . . .

STRANGER. Live until you die – or as it may be, until you are put to death. It may be that you will be destined to die for your faith. When that time comes, you must die with faith and courage, so that your people will live and be brave enough to endure. So dying, you will come to something. This way, no.

DAVID. But my wife . . . Sometimes I think Ruth looks at me accusingly, as though marrying me had set her apart from others.

STRANGER. Even now she weeps in her sleep, dreaming that you are leaving her. (*Pause.*) Look!

[*They look toward the house. The* STRANGER *raises his left hand.*]

DAVID. Why, the lights are coming on in my house!

STRANGER. Your wife is leaving her bed and is coming to take you home.

DAVID (*stares a long time at his house, then turns slowly and speaks fearfully*). Who – are you?

STRANGER. Levine . . . ?

[*He shows his hands to* DAVID, *holding the palms out.*]

DAVID (*stares at his hands. Then his eyes go to the* STRANGER'S *face. His voice is a tense whisper*). No! (*He backs away, his eyes on the* STRANGER'S *face. His whisper is louder.*) *No!*

STRANGER (*holds up his left hand in gentle command.* DAVID *stands still*). Remember me. (*He backs into the shadows and is gone.*)

DAVID (*stands awed, then speaks quickly*). Leah, wake up!

LEAH. I wasn't asleep, Papa.

DAVID. Then you saw him?

LEAH. Who?

DAVID. The man who was here.

LEAH. I didn't see anybody.

JOSEPH (*wakes up, rubbing his eyes*). Has the boat come yet, Papa?

DAVID. No, son.

JOSEPH. Will it come soon?

DAVID. We're going home.

JOSEPH. You're not going away on the boat?

DAVID. Not now, son.

RUTH (*hurries in. She looks frightened. She wears a long coat over her nightgown. She gives an exclamation of relief when she sees her husband*). David!

DAVID. How did you know I was here, Ruth?

LEAH. Mama!

[*Runs and takes her hand.* JOSEPH *clings to the other hand.*]

RUTH. Oh, David, I had a dream. I dreamed you were leaving us, and I cried in my sleep. Then I awoke and knew just where to come.

JOSEPH. The boat went away.

DAVID. I spoke with a stranger . . .

LEAH (*patiently*). There was no one, Papa.

DAVID. He just left — in a boat.

RUTH (*looking out over the water*). There is no boat on the water, David.

DAVID. I thought . . . (*He passes his hand over his eyes.*)

RUTH. Oh, David, why did you go through it alone? I knew what they were doing to you. Why didn't you tell me?

DAVID. I never knew you suspected. I didn't want you to be hurt, too.

RUTH. I'm your wife. I have a right to share your troubles.

DAVID. Oh, Ruth . . .

RUTH. We can go somewhere else. This is a big free country. There's a place for us — somewhere — in it. We'll find a bit of land where we'll build a home of our own — somehow. It's a good country, David. Things will never happen here that happen in other parts of the world. Take heart, David.

DAVID (*as if to himself*). He knew. Because he was persecuted too.

RUTH. You've had a dream. Come home with us now.

JOSEPH. I'm so sleepy. (*Yawns.*)

DAVID. Yes, we'll go home now.

[*He picks up the boy.* RUTH *and* LEAH *each take a suitcase and start to go.* DAVID *lingers alone, holding his son and looking out over the water.*]

RUTH (*calling from off stage*). Come, David, beloved.

[DAVID *straightens himself up and, carrying his now sleeping son, follows his wife. He holds his head high with new courage.*]

AFTER READING

1. Music is used in this play. Why did the authors introduce it on the boat? From Leah's music box?

2. Did David have a dream, or was his meeting with the Stranger real?

3. What do you think of the Stranger's garb? Was it appropriate? What do you think of his manner of speaking?

4. Why did the authors use the boat journey as a symbol of leaving this life? (You might care to read Sutton Vane's *Outward Bound,* which also represents a boat as the transport from this world to the next.)

5. What do you think will happen to David and Ruth?

6. What part do the children play in this drama? Were they necessary? Could the play have been as effective with just David and the Stranger alone?

7. Is there any special significance in placing the setting on a pier in Brooklyn? In placing David's house so near the pier and on a hill?

8. State in your own words the central idea of this play.

CHALLENGES

1. David and Ruth discuss their experiences of this evening. Write the dialogue.

2. If you were directing this play how would you explain, at the first meeting of the cast, its significance and your attitude toward it?

3. Leah and Joseph talk about their night at the pier. The conversation takes place the following day. Write the dialogue.

4. Leah has a dream about her experience. What might it be?

DRAMA WORKSHOP

A hint for playgoers: Good dramatic writing avoids what is known as "the god from the machine."

In ancient Greek plays the characters often became involved in intricate situations which could be solved only by the intervention of some supernatural power. At the climax of a difficult situation in these plays a large box was lowered from the top of the stage by means of pulleys. Out of it stepped one or more gods who unraveled the plot and brought it to a happy conclusion. This device was called "the god from the machine" or *deus ex machina.*

Nowadays we use the expression *deus ex machina* to describe a solution to a dramatic conflict that is brought about by the unexpected intervention of an outside or extraordinary agency, rather than by a reasonable and natural turn of events. Obviously, the use of such a device weakens a play. Consider the ending (or denouement) of *The Far-Distant Shore,* which you have just read. Decide whether it's plausible — that is, whether the ending could reasonably be expected to happen as an outgrowth of the characterization and the mood the authors have created throughout the play — or whether it is impossible and artificial and shows the weakness of a *deus ex machina* climax.

A hint for actors: The stage is a picture.

The stage arch (proscenium) is like a picture frame and the stage itself is like a canvas on which a picture is painted. The picture constantly changes as the actors enter, move about, and leave, but at all times it must be pleasing to the eye. To maintain a pleasing pictorial effect, a good director arranges the actors' positions so that the stage is always balanced, with the character who is the center of interest placed in the strongest position, generally upstage center. He avoids grouping all his actors on one side of the stage unless the action of the play demands such an unbalanced arrangement. As emphasis shifts from one character to another during the course of a scene, he arranges his actors so as to focus attention on the one who is the current center of interest.

You as an actor can help a director in this important matter of stage grouping by being careful not to stand directly in front of another character, and by avoiding the tendency to huddle close to others on the stage. When you make an entrance, advance toward the center, being sure not to remain beside the door.

OTHER DRAMAS YOU WILL LIKE TO READ

The Earth Is Ours by William Kozlenko (23). A railroad agent uses ruthless tactics against a Polish-American farmer who refuses to sell his land to the company.

Knives from Syria by Lynn Riggs (4). A farm woman consents to the marriage of her daughter to a Syrian peddler whom she fears.

The Lord's Prayer by François Coppée (37). The memory of her brother's kindness to all makes a Frenchwoman shelter a soldier from the same forces that killed her brother.

Nerves by John Farrar (35). Determined to redeem himself from the charge of cowardice, a young aviator goes up again into air battle.

Twenty-Five Cents by W. Eric Harris (23). In the days of the Great Depression a family suffers a series of calamities.

The Violin-Maker of Cremona by François Coppée (35). A hunchback apprentice to a violin-maker wins his master's daughter as the prize for having made the finest violin, but he does not keep her.

A Way Out by Robert Frost (6). A stranger fleeing from the police kills a lonely old bachelor and impersonates him.

Finders Keepers

BY GEORGE KELLY

ABOUT THE PLAY

Have you at one time or another lost something you treasured? It may have been valuable, such as a piece of jewelry, a large sum of money, or a good fountain pen, or it may have had a sentimental association though little intrinsic worth, such as a keepsake or a souvenir. But whatever it was, you longed to get it back and you hoped that the finder would return it.

If the finder was honest and made every effort to return your property, you were pleased. On the other hand, if the finder was not scrupulously honest, you may have become a little bitter as the days went by without sign of your lost article. "Isn't anyone honest?" you may have complained. But how honest are you yourself, really, when put to the test of disregarding that old saying "finders keepers"?

The theme of *Finders Keepers* is the common temptation to keep what is found. How strikingly this theme is handled may be judged from Mr. Kelly's description of a characteristic effect his play had on audiences: "During the time that *Finders Keepers* was being presented through the country on the professional stage . . . managers used to report that for weeks after the engagement of the play the box offices were literally cluttered with every kind of worthless article that anyone had found in the theater. Everything from an old glove to a five-cent piece was faithfully turned in, with elaborate detail of the circumstances of its finding." Mr. Kelly concludes that "poor humanity may be better than we depict it; and needs only to be shown the better way to follow it."

ABOUT THE AUTHOR

George Kelly has been part of the American stage for more than thirty-five years as actor, director, producer, and playwright. He started his career as an actor when he was just out of his teens, and after playing juvenile roles for five years on the regular stage, turned to vaudeville, touring the country in dramatic sketches of his own composition. *The Torch-Bearers,* produced in 1922, brought him national recognition. In subsequent years he wrote *The Show-Off, Craig's Wife,* and *The Fatal Weakness. Craig's Wife* gained him the Pulitzer award for 1925. *The Show-Off* has been called the best comedy yet written by an American. His one-act plays include *Poor Aubrey, The Flattering Word,* and *The Weak Spot.*

Mr. Kelly is generally acknowledged to rank among the first of American dramatists. His plays show him to have a sympathetic and acute understanding of middle-class American life; he is a keen observer of human nature and a painstaking craftsman.

FINDERS KEEPERS

Characters

EUGENE ALDRID

MRS. ALDRID, *his wife*

MRS. HAMPTON, *a neighbor*

SCENE. The action of the play takes place in the living room of Mr. Aldrid's home, located in an outlying suburb of the city of Philadelphia, Pennsylvania.

The time is about five o'clock of a late September afternoon.

After a second's stillness, a door closes out at the right, and immediately MRS. ALDRID *hurries through the archway in the upper right-hand corner of the room and crosses down to the center table. She has evidently been "in town" shopping, and has several little parcels in her hands. These she deposits on the table, then straightens up and draws a deep breath. She is a trim blonde in her late twenties, very modishly dressed, and with a certain deft, well-co-ordinated manner. Before she has had time to draw the second breath, the clock on the mantelpiece at the left strikes five. She glances at it.*

MRS. ALDRID. Heavens, five o'clock! (*She hastily removes her fur neckpiece and hat, tossing them onto the sofa in front of the mantelpiece; then, with a glance at her hair in the mantelpiece mirror, hurries down to the door at the left and goes out. There is a slight pause. Then* MR. ALDRID *comes through the archway, carrying a roll of blueprints in one hand and the evening newspaper in the other. He is a tall, thin, rather serious-looking man, probably thirty-three years of age, wearing a business suit of a dark color. He puts the roll of blueprints on the table, and then* MRS. ALDRID *calls to him from out at the left.*) Is that you, Gene? (*He looks in the direction of the voice.*)

ALDRID (*with the suggestion of a smile, and crossing to a flat-topped desk down at the right*). Yes.

MRS. ALDRID. You must have been right behind me.

ALDRID (*carefully laying the folded newspaper down between the upper side of his desk and the wall*). Did you just get in?

MRS. ALDRID (*coming into the room again, adjusting a bungalow apron*). This minute. I've been in town shopping. I had no idea it was so late.

ALDRID (*picking up a telegram from the desk and opening it*). It's after five.

MRS. ALDRID. I know it is, and there isn't a thing ready; you'll have to wait hours for your dinner. Did you come out on the four fifty-three?

ALDRID (*without looking up from the telegram*). Yes — you weren't on it, were you?

MRS. ALDRID. No — I'd intended coming out on the train, but — something happened that made me change my mind.

[ALDRID *stands looking straight ahead, tapping the telegram against his hand.*]

ALDRID (*thoughtfully*). Spaulding — (*Turning suddenly to his wife.*) What? Why, what happened?

MRS. ALDRID (*lowering her voice, and stepping toward the back of the room*). Wait till I tell you. (*She glances keenly out into the hallway, to assure herself that no one is within hearing, then comes forward mysteriously — her husband watching her curiously.*) You know I went into town this afternoon, to get some georgette crepe for that new blouse of mine —

ALDRID. Yes.

MRS. ALDRID. Well, as I went into the Market Street entrance of Blum's — you know, there's a glove counter right inside the Market Street door — (ALDRID *nods.*) Well, I went over to ask the saleslady where I could get the georgette; and as I leaned over to ask her, I stepped on something — it felt like a bracelet or something — rather soft — and yet it was metallic —

ALDRID. Yes.

MRS. ALDRID. Well, I didn't pay any attention to it at first. I thought it might be a joke or something; you know they're always doing that sort of thing in those department stores.

ALDRID. Yes, I know.

MRS. ALDRID. But as I started away from the counter, I just glanced down at the floor, and what do you suppose it was?

ALDRID. What?

MRS. ALDRID. A purse — one of those little gold-mesh purses.

ALDRID. Anything in it?

MRS. ALDRID. Well now, wait till I tell you. I didn't open it right away — I was afraid someone might be looking; so I waited till I got up to the writing room, and *what* do you suppose was in it?

ALDRID. What?

MRS. ALDRID. *Four hundred dollars.*

ALDRID. Four hundred dollars?

MRS. ALDRID. Um-hum.

[*There is a slight pause.*]

ALDRID. Where is it?

MRS. ALDRID. In my pocketbook.

ALDRID. Are you sure it's real money?

MRS. ALDRID. Of course it is — I'll show it to you in a minute. You know, I could scarcely believe my eyes at first, because, you know, *I've* never found anything in all my life; and then to suddenly pick up *eight* fifty-dollar bills — Positively, Gene, I don't know how I ever got home.

ALDRID. Were they all fifties?

MRS. ALDRID. Um-hum, and brand-new ones at that. They look as though they'd just been taken out of a bank.

[ALDRID *turns suddenly and leans on the chair in front of his desk, then looks at her.*]

ALDRID. Can you imagine *losing* that?

MRS. ALDRID. *Losing* it? Can you imagine *finding* it? I thought I was *seeing* things.

[*She starts away, toward the left door, her husband watching her. When she has almost reached the door he speaks.*]

ALDRID. Did you say anything about it?

[*She stops and turns.*]

MRS. ALDRID. How do you mean?

ALDRID. At the "Lost and Found"?

MRS. ALDRID. No, of course I didn't — what do you think I am?

ALDRID. You might have gotten in touch with the owner.

[MRS. ALDRID *smiles indulgently, and moves back slowly toward him.*]

MRS. ALDRID. Positively, Gene, you talk like a boy from the country.

ALDRID. Why so?

MRS. ALDRID. Because you do. Don't you know that if I were to turn that amount of money into a "Lost and Found" desk I'd stand just about as much chance of ever seeing it again as I would of seeing the North Pole?

ALDRID. Well, you wouldn't expect ever to see it again if it were returned to the owner.

MRS. ALDRID. And how would I know that it *had* been returned to the owner?

ALDRID (*turning away*). Oh, everybody isn't dishonest. (*He glances at the telegram again.*)

MRS. ALDRID. Well, you let people get their hands on four hundred dollars — you'll find out how many of them are honest. (*Moving toward the left again.*) Hand that amount of money to one of those "Lost and Found" clerks — he'd soon find an owner for it, believe *me.*

ALDRID (*crushing the telegram quietly in his hand*). What are *you* going to do with it?

[*She stops and looks back at him. He throws the telegram with a slow overhand movement into the wastebasket below his desk.*]

MRS. ALDRID. I'm going to keep it. (*He makes a sound of amusement.*) What do you think I'm going to do with it, throw it away? It's as good in my pocket as it is in anybody's else. (*He turns smoothly and looks at her, in a way that disconcerts her slightly; but as he withdraws his eyes in turning to his desk, she regains herself and comes a step or two farther into the room.*) I can get awnings for this whole house for that, and one of those new radios I was telling you about, too.

ALDRID (*coming over to the center table for his blueprints*). You'd better not count your chickens before they're hatched.

MRS. ALDRID. What do you mean?

ALDRID. Why — there'll very likely be an ad for it in one of the morning papers.

MRS. ALDRID (*looking away*). Well, what if there is?

ALDRID (*looking at the prints*). Nothing — only you'd simply have to return it, that's all.

[*There is a slight pause, during which* MRS. ALDRID *shifts her eyes and thinks, with an expression of sullen calculation.*]

MRS. ALDRID (*almost to herself*). I don't see why I should.

[*Her husband simply raises his eyes above the top of the prints and looks at her, quizzically.*]

ALDRID. You don't see why you should return lost property to the person who lost it?

MRS. ALDRID. That depends.

ALDRID. Upon what?

MRS. ALDRID. Whether or not I was sure he'd lost it.

ALDRID. Couldn't you make sure?

[*She turns her head and looks at him.*]

MRS. ALDRID. How?

ALDRID. Identification.

[*She turns away again, shaking her head slightly, and with a touch of smugness.*]

MRS. ALDRID. Not in this case.

ALDRID. Why not?

MRS. ALDRID (*turning back to him*). Because there isn't a solitary thing about it by which it could *possibly* be identified — not a card or a paper of any kind.

ALDRID. How about the purse?

MRS. ALDRID (*slightly annoyed at his persistence*). There are a million exactly like it — a plain gold-mesh bag. (*Indicating the desk at the right.*) I've had one in that top drawer there for the past year.

ALDRID. Couldn't the money be described?

MRS. ALDRID. That wouldn't be any identification.

ALDRID. Why not?

MRS. ALDRID. Why, because money is simply money, Gene — unless it's marked; and this isn't — for I've examined it very carefully. (*She turns away.*)

ALDRID (*resting one end of the roll of prints on the table, and leaning his elbow on the other*). So you don't see any possible way by which this money could be returned to its owner?

MRS. ALDRID. Not unless I took his word for it. (*She turns and looks at him.*) And really I don't see why I should do that.

[*He holds her eye for the fraction of a second—then speaks in a very level, even tone.*]

ALDRID. What are you trying to do, make yourself believe it belongs to *you?*

[*She gives a little shrug of her shoulders and turns away.*]

MRS. ALDRID. I *found* it.

ALDRID. And somebody else *lost* it.

MRS. ALDRID. I suppose so.

ALDRID. Possibly some poor man or woman.

MRS. ALDRID (*turning to him*). Now please don't get sentimental, Gene.

ALDRID (*with a touch of impatience, and taking a couple of steps toward her*). That isn't sentiment at all.

MRS. ALDRID (*incisively*). No very poor man or woman has any eight fifty-dollar bills to lose. (*She turns away, and smooths her hair back on the left side. And he stands looking at her, steadily.*) And no matter who lost it, it'll be a very good lesson to him to be a little more careful in the future.

ALDRID (*dryly*). I see. Well, why should he pay *you* four hundred dollars for that lesson?

MRS. ALDRID. Nobody's paying me any four hundred dollars.

ALDRID. You've often lost things yourself, haven't you?

MRS. ALDRID (*turning to him quickly*). Yes, and I never got them back, either.

ALDRID. Whose fault was that?

MRS. ALDRID (*turning away again*). I don't know whose fault it was.

ALDRID. Well, try and think.

MRS. ALDRID. Unless the people who found them weren't honest enough to return them. (ALDRID *turns away, unable to follow her logic, and moves across toward his desk. A door closes out at the right, and he glances in the direction of it.* MRS. ALDRID *steps nervously toward the back of the room to peer out into the hallway.*) Who's that? (*She begins to remove her apron.*)

ALDRID (*casually*). Somebody at the door.

[*The apron is whipped off and tossed onto the sofa, and* MRS. ALDRID *starts across toward the archway.*]

MRS. ALDRID (*in a lowered tone, as she crosses*). Don't say anything about this. (*She reaches the archway.*) Oh, it's you, Mrs. Hampton!

[ALDRID *reaches down between the upper side of his desk and the wall, and picks up the evening newspaper.*]

MRS. HAMPTON (*in the hallway*). Yes, it's me.

MRS. ALDRID (*rather nervously effusive*). Come right in.

[*She extends her arm and leads* MRS. HAMPTON *into the room.* MRS. HAMPTON *is very pale—and dark, with something of a Madonna-like quality in her expression and personality. She appears to be about* MRS. ALDRID'S *age—maybe a year or two younger.*]

MRS. HAMPTON (*entering*). Good evening.

MRS. ALDRID. Good evening, dear, how are you?

ALDRID (*turning*). Good evening, Mrs. Hampton.

MRS. HAMPTON. Oh, good evening, Mr. Aldrid, I didn't see you. (MRS. ALDRID *laughs a bit nervously and moves across toward the center table.*) I hope you'll both excuse me for coming in without ringing.

ALDRID (*tossing the newspaper onto the desk*). Don't mention it. (*He reaches for the single chair, above his desk.*)

MRS. ALDRID. Saved me the trouble of answering the door.

MRS. HAMPTON. Well, I do hope I haven't intruded.

MRS. ALDRID. You haven't at all, dear, really. I've just gotten in from town.

MRS. HAMPTON. I've been in the city, too—I came out on the four fifty-three.

ALDRID (*placing the chair about midway between the center table and the archway*). Won't you take a chair, Mrs. Hampton?

MRS. HAMPTON. No, thank you, Mr. Aldrid, I can't stay a minute.

ALDRID. I'm sorry. (*He moves down to his desk again and picks up the newspaper.*)

MRS. ALDRID. Why not?

MRS. HAMPTON. Oh, I'm too upset.

MRS. ALDRID. Are you ill, dear?

MRS. HAMPTON. No, but I'd like to ask your advice about something.

MRS. ALDRID. Well, do sit down for a minute. (MRS. HAMPTON *hesitates, then sits; and* MRS. ALDRID *takes a chair from the back and, placing it above the center table and slightly to the left of it, sits also.*) What is it?

MRS. HAMPTON (*speaking directly to* MRS. ALDRID). I've lost some money.

[*There is a stillness; and then* ALDRID *lifts his eyes above the top of the paper and looks straight out. And his wife, still holding* MRS. HAMPTON's *eyes, rises slowly and quietly and moves forward to the center table, where she rests her left hand.*]

MRS. ALDRID (*finding it a bit difficult to speak*). Much?

MRS. HAMPTON. Quite a bit, yes.

ALDRID (*without moving*). Where did you lose it, Mrs. Hampton?

MRS. HAMPTON (*turning to him*). I haven't an idea — (MRS. ALDRID *relaxes slightly.*) — but I think it was in town.

ALDRID. How much was it?

MRS. HAMPTON. I'm almost afraid to tell you.

MRS. ALDRID. I suppose you don't know the exact amount, do you?

[MRS. HAMPTON *turns and looks at her.*]

MRS. HAMPTON. Four hundred dollars. (MRS. ALDRID *is frozen into stillness and stands looking blankly at her.*) Isn't that dreadful! Of course I know it'd only be an item to some people — but to *me* — I feel terrible about it.

[*She breaks down and cries.* ALDRID *turns and looks at her; then he lays the newspaper on the desk and strolls up toward the archway, looking significantly at his wife. But she has gotten hold of herself by this time and simply returns his look steadily, till he turns away and glances out into the hallway. Then she moves across and puts her hands on* MRS. HAMPTON's *shoulders.*]

MRS. ALDRID. Now don't cry, Mrs. Hampton, it isn't that bad.

MRS. HAMPTON. Oh, I think it's *dreadful* to lose all that money.

MRS. ALDRID. I know it is, dear. I don't wonder you feel the way you do.

MRS. HAMPTON. Eight *fifty*-dollar bills.

[MRS. ALDRID *raises her head slowly and looks straight out; and* ALDRID *steps forward eagerly from the archway where he has been watching.*]

ALDRID. Eight fifties?

MRS. HAMPTON. Yes.

ALDRID (*straightening up, and looking at his wife with an ingenuous smile*). Eight fifties.

[*But* MRS. ALDRID *simply turns her head and looks at him stonily; and the smile on his face gradually fades into an expression of puzzled curiosity.*]

MRS. HAMPTON. And brand-new ones, too! It's awful! (*She continues to cry.*)

ALDRID (*to his wife, voiceless, and indicating* MRS. HAMPTON *with a vaguely questioning gesture*). Why don't you tell her?

[*But* MRS. ALDRID *makes no move. And something in the icy steadiness of her eyes as she looks at him emphasizes the fact that she has no intention of telling anybody. He doesn't grasp the meaning of her attitude for a second; but when he does, his astonished resentment expresses itself in a slow raising of his left arm and an austere pointing of his finger at* MRS. HAMPTON. *His wife challenges the gesture for the fraction of a second; but then, having probably heard of the wrath of a quiet man, she chooses the better part of valor; and, with a little smile of pained amusement, leans over* MRS. HAMPTON *again.*]

MRS. ALDRID. Come now, Mrs. Hampton, you may not have lost it at all.

[*It requires a second or two for* ALDRID *to recover from the shock of his wife's behavior, and he stands looking at her in baffled amazement.*]

MRS. HAMPTON. Oh, but I *have*, Mrs. Aldrid.

MRS. ALDRID. I know, my dear, but you know sometimes we think we've lost a thing and we find out later that we haven't lost it at all.

[ALDRID *relaxes slowly; but still keeping his eyes upon his wife, moves forward to his desk, trying desperately to hit upon some reasonable interpretation of her conduct. He rests his hand on the back of the desk chair and stands thinking.*]

MRS. HAMPTON. But I've looked everywhere and it's lost, I tell you.

MRS. ALDRID. But you may find it again, honey.

MRS. HAMPTON. Oh, I don't think so.

MRS. ALDRID. Or someone else may find it.

MRS. HAMPTON. But that wouldn't do me any good.

MRS. ALDRID. It would if the person who found it were honest.

MRS. HAMPTON. I'm afraid very few people are honest if it costs them four hundred dollars.

MRS. ALDRID. Well now, it may be one of those very few who has found it.

MRS. HAMPTON. I don't expect ever to see it again.

ALDRID (*turning to the desk and picking up the newspaper*). Nonsense, Mrs. Hampton.

MRS. HAMPTON. I don't.

ALDRID (*sitting on the lower corner of the desk*). Now you wait and see.

[*He looks closely at a particular item in the paper, and* MRS. HAMPTON *touches her handkerchief to her eyes.*]

MRS. ALDRID (*quietly*). Of course you'll have to advertise.

MRS. HAMPTON. Yes, I suppose that's the only thing I can do. (*She turns to* ALDRID. *But it is only now that* ALDRID *realizes what his wife has said. And he raises his eyes slowly from the paper, as though he were listening to something, and turning suddenly, looks at her. But she is still looking away off.*) That's what I wanted to see Mr. Aldrid about — which would be the best paper for me to advertise in.

[*Gradually* ALDRID *becomes aware that* MRS. HAMPTON *has said something to him and is looking at him, and he shifts his eyes to her and looks at her blankly.*]

ALDRID (*suddenly coming out of his bewilderment, and getting up*). Oh — a — (*He leans for a second on the back of the desk chair, trying to think.*)

MRS. HAMPTON (*rising*). Now don't let me worry you, Mr. Aldrid.

ALDRID (*passing below her, like a person in a dream*). No, no, it isn't that — I was just — wondering —

MRS. HAMPTON (*turning to* MRS. ALDRID). If I'd thought it would bother you folks, I shouldn't have told you at all.

MRS. ALDRID. That's perfectly all right, dear.

[ALDRID *turns at the lower corner of the mantelpiece, and, resting his right elbow upon it, stands regarding his wife with a searching, curious expression.*]

MRS. HAMPTON. But I was so troubled when I got home, I simply *couldn't* stay in the house — I just *had* to come out and tell someone. And, my dear, I don't know how I'm *ever* going to tell Frank when he comes home tonight. Because he said to me this morning, when I told him I was going to town — he said: "Do you think I can trust you to deposit this money for me?" — And I said, "What do you think I am, a thief?" "Well," he said, "you're always losing things." "Well," I said, "there's no danger of my losing four hundred dollars." "Well," he said, "I hope not, or we'll have to get a guardian for you." (*Starting to cry again.*) And then I go straight into the city and lose it. (MRS. ALDRID *stands watching her coldly.*) And, mind you, to make *sure* that nothing would happen to it — I didn't even put it with my other money.

MRS. ALDRID. Where *did* you put it?

MRS. HAMPTON. In one of those little gold-mesh purses.

[ALDRID *stirs slightly at the mantelpiece, but his wife makes no move.*]

ALDRID. Mrs. Hampton.

MRS. HAMPTON (*turning toward him*). Yes?

ALDRID. Where did you first *miss* this money?

[MRS. ALDRID *listens.*]

MRS. HAMPTON. When I was going up the steps into the bank.

ALDRID. Which bank?

MRS. HAMPTON. The Franklin National.

MRS. ALDRID (*without turning*). Where's that?

ALDRID. Broad and Chestnut. Where had you been *before* that?

MRS. HAMPTON (*clasping her hands together nervously in an effort to remember as accurately as possible*). Why, when I came out of the station, after I got off the train —

ALDRID. Yes?

MRS. HAMPTON. I went over to Wanamaker's — to get some gloves.

MRS. ALDRID. Wanamaker's?

[MRS. HAMPTON *looks at her.*]

MRS. HAMPTON. Yes. (MRS. ALDRID *nods slowly, and pursing her lips, looks out, with a shade of relief.*) But they didn't have my size in what I wanted at Wanamaker's — so I crossed over to Blum's.

ALDRID (*simply*). Blum's glove counter?

MRS. HAMPTON. Yes.

[MRS. ALDRID *touches her hair, in an effort to be casual, and, turning smoothly toward the back of the room, wanders over to the archway, where she stands looking out into the hallway. Her husband has moved thoughtfully over to the left side of the center table and put down the newspaper.*]

ALDRID (*quietly picking up a book*). You hadn't missed this money up to that time? (*He stands the book on end and leans lightly on it.*)

MRS. HAMPTON. No, and I'm quite sure I *had* it up to that time, because I hadn't opened my pocketbook from the time I left the house, and the money was *in* the big pocketbook.

ALDRID. I see. And you went directly from there to the bank?

MRS. HAMPTON. Yes, directly.

ALDRID. Then you think it was somewhere between Blum's glove counter and the bank steps that you lost it?

MRS. HAMPTON. It must have been. I imagine I must have pulled it out without knowing it when I was paying for the gloves at Blum's.

ALDRID. Very likely.

MRS. HAMPTON (*turning to* MRS. ALDRID). Or else possibly someone opened my pocketbook and took out the little purse when I wasn't looking. (*She starts to cry again, and turns back to* MR. ALDRID.) You know they do that, Mr. Aldrid.

ALDRID (*abstractedly*). Yes, I know.

MRS. ALDRID. There wasn't a card or a paper of any kind in the purse, was there?

MRS. HAMPTON (*turning to her*). No, there wasn't a thing in it but the money.

MRS. ALDRID. That's too bad. No initials on it?

MRS. HAMPTON. No, I've always been *going* to have my initials put on it but — Oh, I don't know — I never seemed to get round to it.

MRS. ALDRID (*shaking her head a little regretfully*). That makes it bad.

MRS. HAMPTON. Dear me, I wish I had now.

MRS. ALDRID (*turning to her with a kind of forced sincerity*). Yes, because if someone finds it, and answers your advertisement, he'll naturally expect you to be able to identify it — definitely — that is, before you could reasonably expect him to return it to you, I mean.

MRS. HAMPTON. But then, I could describe the purse and the money.

MRS. ALDRID (*with an indulgent smile*). I know, my dear, but there may be a million purses exactly like it.

MRS. HAMPTON. That's true, too.

MRS. ALDRID. And as far as the money is concerned, why money is simply money — unless it's marked; and this isn't — (*Checking herself.*) — as you say.

MRS. HAMPTON (*oblivious of the slip*). No, it isn't.

MRS. ALDRID. So that really a person'd be more or less obliged to take your word for it, wouldn't he?

MRS. HAMPTON. I'm afraid he would.

MRS. ALDRID. And that's rather a lot for us to expect of people, isn't it?

MRS. HAMPTON. Too much, I'm afraid.

MRS. ALDRID. Especially when there's four hundred dollars in the bargain. (*She gives a mirthless little laugh.*)

MRS. HAMPTON. You're right — it's a poor prospect.

MRS. ALDRID. Of course, the only thing you *can* do is to advertise.

MRS. HAMPTON. Yes, I must, right away. (*She turns to* ALDRID.)

Which paper do you think it would be best for me to advertise in, Mr. Aldrid? (*He doesn't hear her, and* MRS. ALDRID *turns her head sharply and looks at him.*) Mr. Aldrid?

ALDRID (*coming suddenly out of his abstraction, and turning to her*). I beg your pardon, Mrs. Hampton, what did you —

MRS. ALDRID. She wants to know which paper you think it would be best for her to advertise in.

ALDRID (*directly to his wife*). None of them — (*She holds his eye for a second; then he shifts his look to* MRS. HAMPTON *and changes his tone.*) — until you hear from *me.*

MRS. ALDRID (*quickly, and laying her hand on* MRS. HAMPTON'S *arm*). He means he'll look up the circulations later.

ALDRID (*breaking the scene, and moving up toward the French door*). I'll telephone you after dinner, Mrs. Hampton.

MRS. HAMPTON. Well, that's very nice of you, Mr. Aldrid.

ALDRID. Don't mention it. (*In desperate irresolution he stands watching his wife.*)

MRS. HAMPTON (*to* MRS. ALDRID). And I really feel I owe you both a genuine apology for bothering you with my troubles.

MRS. ALDRID (*trailing after her*). That's what neighbors are for, dear.

MRS. HAMPTON. Good-by, Mr. Aldrid.

ALDRID (*coming a step or two out of the alcove*). Good-by, Mrs. Hampton.

MRS. HAMPTON. I'll be waiting to hear from you.

ALDRID. Right away, I'll call you.

MRS. HAMPTON. And be sure and ask for *me* when you telephone, won't you?

ALDRID. Yes, I shall.

MRS. HAMPTON. Thank you very much.

ALDRID. You're very welcome.

MRS. HAMPTON. I don't want Frank to know anything about this, if possible.

MRS. ALDRID (*following her*). No, there's no use annoying him.

[*Their voices die away.* ALDRID, *standing at the back of the room, watches his wife narrowly, out into the hallway; then he moves forward slowly, in a panic of indecision. Suddenly the impulse to recall* MRS. HAMPTON *whirls him around in a lightning-like movement toward the archway; but the closing of the front door arrests him, and he stops abruptly.* MRS. ALDRID *darts into view between the archway portieres, and, after a glance over her right shoulder into the hallway, stands regarding him with an amused expression.*]

MRS. ALDRID. Did you see that?

ALDRID (*in a repressed, ominous tone*). What?

MRS. ALDRID. She must have heard.

[ALDRID *turns and looks at her.*]

ALDRID. Have you told anybody?

MRS. ALDRID (*coming a little farther into the room*). No.

ALDRID. I suppose the walls have ears.

MRS. ALDRID. Not necessarily.

ALDRID. Then how would she know?

MRS. ALDRID. She must have heard me — there in the hallway.

ALDRID (*mercilessly*). When?

MRS. ALDRID. A few minutes ago — when I was telling you I'd found a purse.

ALDRID. How would she overhear you? She wasn't in the hallway.

MRS. ALDRID. *Wasn't* she?

ALDRID (*whipping the chair out of his way and moving forward in a restrained rage*). You know very well she wasn't. (MRS. ALDRID *crosses the back of the room, watching him a bit fearfully. He hesitates in front of the center table, as though uncertain which way to go.*) What are you trying to do, *kid* yourself, or me?

[*He goes unseeingly toward the right, and she comes forward at the left.*]

MRS. ALDRID (*picking up the apron from the sofa*). I suppose you didn't take notice of the fact that she came in without ringing, did you?

ALDRID. Well, what of it, what of it, what of it!

MRS. ALDRID (*taking his tone*). Nothing! Only just think it over while I'm getting your dinner. (*She starts toward the door at the left.*)

ALDRID (*leaning on the back of the desk chair*). You needn't get me any dinner.

[*She stops and looks back at him.*]

MRS. ALDRID. Why not?

ALDRID. Because I don't want any.

MRS. ALDRID. Don't you want anything at all?

ALDRID. Yes! (*He turns and moves across toward the back of the center table, indicating* MRS. HAMPTON *with a wide gesture.*) I want to know whether or not you intend to return that woman's property?

MRS. ALDRID. *Her* property?

ALDRID (*lifting his voice and striking the table with his right fist*). You *heard* me!

MRS. ALDRID (*trying to silence him*). Sh-sh!

ALDRID (*disregarding the gesture*). I want an answer, yes or no!

[*She flips the apron back onto the sofa and crosses very close to him.*]

MRS. ALDRID. What's the matter with you, Gene, are you blind?

[*He holds her eye stonily and moves his head slowly from side to side.*]

ALDRID. Not now. But I'm beginning to think I *have* been — terribly blind.

MRS. ALDRID (*turning away from him and taking a couple of steps forward and to the left*). Well, I'm glad something has happened to open your eyes.

[*She fumbles nervously with the lace at her left cuff. And he moves across to her side with an ominous deliberateness, and, taking hold of her right arm, turns her to him with a grip of iron. She looks up at him with a trace of fright.*]

ALDRID. If my eyes are not open after this, it isn't *your* fault. (*She attempts to move, but he pins her to his side.*) I want to know whether or not you intend to return that money?

MRS. ALDRID (*with a mingling of fear and conciliation*). When I find the owner, yes!

ALDRID (*breaking from her in wrath*). Ah! More *hedging!* (*He goes up to the back, then turns and comes forward again.*) God, how I *hate* that attitude!

MRS. ALDRID (*holding her arm as though he had hurt her, and talking through his line*). I'd like to hand over four hundred dollars to every Tom, Dick, and Harry that says he lost it! You must think I'm a —

ALDRID (*whirling fiercely upon her as he passes in front of the center table*). Please! (*She is instantly silenced, and he stands glaring at her for a second; then, dropping his voice, he continues across and up to the hallway.*) Don't drive me out of the house! (*He looks out into the hallway.*)

MRS. ALDRID. What do you think I am, some schoolgirl?

ALDRID (*turning*). No — I think you're a thief.

[*She is shocked into an astonished resentment, and looks across at him.*]

MRS. ALDRID. Do you, really.

ALDRID. More contemptible than the out-and-outer, for he, at least, doesn't try to justify himself.

MRS. ALDRID. And I'm not trying to justify *my*self, either.

ALDRID. You couldn't — there *is* no justification for *your* attitude.

MRS. ALDRID. There doesn't need to be any.

ALDRID. And there *isn't* — among *honest* people. (*He drifts forward and rests his hand on the back of the desk chair.*)

MRS. ALDRID. So you don't consider *me* honest?

[*He turns and looks at her, bitterly.*]

ALDRID. You're like a million other people in this world — honest as long as you don't *lose* anything by it. But as soon as you see where it's going to *cost* you a dollar — you begin to *hedge* — just as you've been doing in this.

MRS. ALDRID. I've been doing nothing of the kind.

ALDRID (*turning away*). You've been *tinkering* with honesty.

MRS. ALDRID (*beginning to whimper*). I never took a cent in my *life* that didn't belong to me!

ALDRID. There are *rafts* of people can say that — but they wouldn't walk back a block to return ten cents overchange that some clerk has given them. (*She sniffs contemptuously and turns away.*) Pat themselves on the back, as I've heard *you* do, when the conductor on the trolley car doesn't ask them for their carfare.

MRS. ALDRID. The trolley companies have enough.

ALDRID. There you are! (*He starts up toward the French door.*) That's the psychology of a thief!

[*He reaches the door and glances out, to see that no one has heard them, then closes it. And* MRS. ALDRID *stands fuming.*]

MRS. ALDRID (*as the door closes, and speaking low and rapidly*). Have I ever stolen anything from you? (*Evidently he doesn't hear her, and starts down toward the right of the center table. She turns and takes a step or two toward him.*) Have I?

[*He stops, on a line with her, and looks at her witheringly.*]

ALDRID. Now don't start *that,* please.

[*He continues on down to the right of the center table, and leans upon it; and* MRS. ALDRID, *keeping her eyes upon him, moves down to the left of the table.*]

MRS. ALDRID (*striking the table with her fist*). Answer me! Have I ever stolen anything from *you?*

[*But* ALDRID *is completely oblivious of her. He is occupied with his own thoughts. And there is a fractional pause. Then he moves forward a little and sits on the edge of the table. And there is a suggestion of weariness in his manner — as though the realization of having married an inferior woman were heavy upon him.*]

ALDRID (*with a complete change of tone*). Listen to me — (*He lays his left hand in the palm of his right and sits looking at the back of it, with a kind of vacant curiosity.*) A man's home, in the majority of cases, is founded on his belief in the *honesty* of his wife — you've stolen that from me tonight.

MRS. ALDRID. What?

[ALDRID *raises his eyes slowly and looks away off.*]

ALDRID. That *belief* — that I had in you — as an *honest* woman. (MRS. ALDRID *gives a slight shrug of her shoulders and crosses over in front of the center table to the desk, where she straightens the pad, then stands leaning on the back of the chair, listening sullenly.*) I remember seeing a line in a book somewhere one time that said:

"What a little thing makes the world go wrong!
A word too short — or a smile too long;

Then comes the mist — and the blinding rain,
And life is never the same again."

Your — *(He feels for the word.)* — *attitude* in this affair tonight — is that mist — and blinding rain — it has shown me that my *wife* is not *strictly honest* — for the sake of *being* so, and honesty is such a *passion* with *me* that as far as *you* are concerned life will never be the same again — because I could never absolutely *trust* you again. *(He gets up slowly, and moves around in front of the table.)* Never. *(He continues up to the French door, then stops and half turns to her.)* I'm sorry we found that out. *(He steps into the alcove and quietly pushes the door open; then, after glancing casually out, he leans against the side of the alcove and says, half to himself.)* I'm sorrier than if *I* had lost a *million* dollars.

[*There is a rather long stillness, and then* MRS. ALDRID, *who has been finding it difficult to encompass the seriousness of the situation, gradually abandons the effort.*]

MRS. ALDRID *(starting to move across the room)*. Well, Gene, if you hadn't been so *strictly honest* all your life, we might have *had* a *million* dollars now.

ALDRID *(without moving)*. Very true — but we'd have gotten it the way you're getting that four hundred.

MRS. ALDRID *(about to leave the room, and with something of a return to her former manner)*. And the way I'm going to hold onto it, incidentally. *(She starts to go out.)*

ALDRID *(with a rapid movement toward the telephone, which is on a small table halfway between the French door and the hallway)*. All right! Wait a minute — listen to this! *(She stops suddenly and turns to him. He snatches up the telephone and works the hook rapidly.)* I want you to hear this. *(She stands watching him fearfully, and there is a second's pause.)* Give me Wayne one-three-seven-d — Yes. *(She recognizes the number evidently, and takes a couple of frantic steps toward him; but her startled expression is met with a look of such deadly steadiness that she stops helplessly and turns away, waiting.)* Hello? Hello? *(He lowers the telephone again and there is another pause. Then suddenly he is answered.*) Hello? Mrs. Hampton? (MRS. ALDRID *turns, and their eyes meet.*) Is this Mrs. Hampton? – Mr. Aldrid. (*He shifts his position and takes a deep breath.*) I have some very good news for you.

MRS. ALDRID (*going a little closer to him and speaking low and breathlessly*). If you tell her I found that money I'll deny it!

ALDRID (*still holding her eye, and speaking with quiet emphasis into the telephone*). Your money has been found.

MRS. ALDRID (*venomously, and turning to the center table*). Oh, you silly fool!

ALDRID. Yes, really – *I* found it.

MRS. ALDRID (*searching frantically among her parcels on the center table*). Well, if you did you'll pay it.

ALDRID. I wanted to give you a scare.

MRS. ALDRID. For I'm very sure *I* won't. (*She glances quickly around on the floor and under the table.*) Where's my pocketbook! (*She hurries over to the desk and looks.*)

ALDRID. I know, but I imagine you must be rather careless, to drop that much money.

MRS. ALDRID (*excitedly coming back to the table*). Where's my pocketbook?

ALDRID. All right, Mrs. Hampton, come ahead – it's here for you. (*He hangs up and sets the telephone down casually.*)

MRS. ALDRID (*turning to him*). Listen! Have you seen anything of my pocketbook?

ALDRID (*quietly*). No.

MRS. ALDRID. I can't find it!

ALDRID. Where did you have it?

MRS. ALDRID. Right here among these parcels.

ALDRID (*disinterestedly, and moving down toward his desk*). *I* haven't seen anything of it.

MRS. ALDRID. My God, I wonder if I've lost that! (*Suddenly she stops dead and thinks – tapping the table, as though something has occurred to her.*) I wonder if *she* could have taken that.

[ALDRID *turns and looks at her.*]

ALDRID. Who?

MRS. ALDRID. Mrs. Hampton.

ALDRID. I'll ask her that when she comes over.

MRS. ALDRID. Don't you dare! (*He makes a little sound of bitter amusement and turns away, shaking his head from side to side.*) Well, it's gone!

ALDRID. Maybe you left it in the trolley car.

MRS. ALDRID. Oh, wouldn't that be awful! And that four hundred dollars is in it, too. (ALDRID *breaks into a dry little laugh and, thrusting his hands into his trousers' pockets, turns and goes up toward the back of the room and across toward the left.*) I don't see anything to laugh at! (*But he continues to laugh.*) And twenty-six dollars of my own! (*He throws his head back and laughs derisively.*) God, what's the matter with *me!*

ALDRID. Maybe you dropped it out there in the hallway.

MRS. ALDRID (*rushing toward the hallway*). Call up the Rapid Transit "Lost and Found" and see if a lady's pocketbook has been turned in! I'll look out here!

[*She vanishes into the hallway, and* ALDRID *stands thinking for a second; then he crosses up to the telephone.*]

ALDRID (*into the telephone*). Information, please. (*He looks toward the hallway.*) Do you see anything of it?

MRS. ALDRID (*calling back*). Not a sign!

ALDRID. Why don't you light that light? (*He stands looking out into the hallway until a light is turned on; then he turns suddenly and speaks into the telephone.*) Hello? Information? — Could you give me the number of the Rapid Transit "Lost and Found," please? — Yes — Kensington one-three-hundred. Thanks. Will you ask the operator to ring it, please?

[*He lowers the telephone and waits. And* MRS. ALDRID *appears at the archway, searching. He looks at her, and breaks into another slightly sardonic laugh. She darts a look at him.*]

MRS. ALDRID. Funny, isn't it!

[*She disappears into the hallway again; and immediately there is the sound of a chair being knocked over — as though she had flung it aside in her anger.* ALDRID *peers sharply toward the hallway, then shakes his head from side to side, slowly and conclusively. Then he shifts his position and sighs wearily.*]

ALDRID (*into the telephone again*). Hello? Information? (*He glances toward the hallway.*) Oh, this is "Lost and Found"? Why, I'd like to know whether or not a lady's pocketbook has been turned in there this evening?

MRS. ALDRID (*rushing in from the hallway*). Oh, it isn't out there! What do they say?

[*He silences her with a deft gesture and listens. And she stands watching him breathlessly. Suddenly he speaks into the telephone again.*]

ALDRID. This minute?

MRS. ALDRID. It *has* been turned in?

ALDRID. Yes.

MRS. ALDRID (*turning away*). Oh, thank God! (*She sinks onto the chair that* MRS. HAMPTON *occupied earlier.*)

ALDRID (*into the telephone*). No, my wife did.

MRS. ALDRID (*turning to him*). A regular lady's black leather pocketbook.

ALDRID (*into the telephone*). Well, can you wait just a minute? Please. (*To* MRS. ALDRID.) They want to know whether or not you can identify it.

MRS. ALDRID (*impatiently*). Oh, certainly I can. It's a regular lady's black leather pocketbook, with my initials E. A. on the outside.

ALDRID. Yes.

MRS. ALDRID (*illustrating with her hands*). There's a small gold-mesh purse inside, with four hundred dollars in it, and in the side pocket there are twenty-six dollars. Then there's —

ALDRID. Wait a minute. (*Into the telephone.*) Hello!

MRS. ALDRID. A silver vanity case and a bracelet with the —

ALDRID (*to his wife*). Wait a minute! (*Into the telephone again.*) A lady's black leather pocketbook with the initials E. A. on the outside. There's a gold-mesh — E. A. — No, no, no, no! — E. — Yes. That's right. — Why — (*He looks at her.*)

MRS. ALDRID. A gold-mesh purse —

ALDRID (*into the telephone*). A gold-mesh purse, with four hundred dollars in it. And, in the side pocket — there are twenty-six dollars — of her own.

[*She looks at him suddenly.*]

MRS. ALDRID. Five fives and a one.

ALDRID (*into the telephone*). In bills, yes. (*He looks at her, and she nods confirmation.*) Five fives and a one. One minute. (*To his wife.*) What else? Quick!

MRS. ALDRID (*becoming very nervous*). Why, a — there's a silver vanity case —

ALDRID. Yes.

MRS. ALDRID. And a gold bracelet, with the clasp broken. (*He makes a gesture of interruption, but she continues.*) And there's a tax receipt, and a —

ALDRID. Wait a minute, now, till I get that. (*Into the telephone.*) Hello!

MRS. ALDRID (*continuing on his line*). Sample of georgette crepe and a pale-pink silk handkerchief with the letter E embroidered in one corner —

ALDRID (*helplessly*). I can't remember all those. (*She stops suddenly; then he speaks into the telephone.*) Hello! — There's a silver vanity case and a bracelet —

MRS. ALDRID. Broken.

ALDRID (*into the telephone*). Broken! A broken bracelet. (*With a touch of annoyance.*) The bracelet is broken. Yes. And there is a bit of — (*He stops gradually and listens attentively — his eyes wandering to his wife's.*) I see.

MRS. ALDRID (*rising slowly, with a touch of apprehension.*) What is it?

[*He motions her to be still.*]

ALDRID. Why yes, that *is* rather funny.

MRS. ALDRID (*impatiently*). What does he say?

ALDRID (*into the telephone*). How about tomorrow afternoon? No, no, I'll call for it myself. If you will, please. Tha-ank you very much. Thanks. (*He sets the telephone down thoughtfully.*)

MRS. ALDRID. Is everything all right?

ALDRID. Yes.

MRS. ALDRID (*sighing with relief and moving over to the center table*). Oh, can you imagine if I'd lost that.

ALDRID (*moving slowly down toward his desk*). Everything but the money.

[*She looks at him quickly.*]

MRS. ALDRID. What'd you say?

ALDRID (*purposely avoiding her eyes*). He says that evidently the person that found your pocketbook took all the money out of it before turning it in.

[*Then he turns and looks at her; but she is too stunned to make the slightest movement — and just stands looking at him for a second or two.*]

MRS. ALDRID (*almost voiceless*). What!

ALDRID (*turning to the desk very casually*). That's what he says.

[MRS. ALDRID'S *face settles into a stony indignation.*]

MRS. ALDRID. Can you imagine anybody being that contemptible!

[ALDRID *turns and looks at her.*]

ALDRID. Please — (*He moves up toward the archway, still holding her eyes.*) — don't make me laugh — I'm not in the mood. (*He stands looking out into the hallway.*)

MRS. ALDRID. *You* won't laugh — when you have to pay that woman four hundred dollars out of your own pocket.

ALDRID. I would have had to do that, anyway — there didn't seem to be very much chance of getting it away from you.

MRS. ALDRID (*frantically*). Well, you're *not* going to give her four hundred dollars of your own?

ALDRID (*with quiet authority*). That'll do. And when she comes here, don't make it necessary for me to tell her who found her money. Now, be wise. (*He withdraws his eyes from her and looks out into the hallway. Suddenly he peers sharply, then steps forward quickly to his desk.*) Where's that gold-mesh purse of yours?

MRS. ALDRID. There in that drawer — what are you going to do?

[*He flips the drawer open and rummages among the papers.*]

ALDRID. Where is it?

MRS. ALDRID (*coming toward him*). Right where you're looking. What do you want it for?

ALDRID (*snatching up the purse*). Never mind. Is this it?

MRS. ALDRID. Yes. (*He slams the drawer shut.*) What are you going to do?

[*There is a sharp ring at the front door. He lays his hand on her arm and they stand perfectly still for a second, listening.*]

ALDRID (*quietly*). There she is. (*Turning and urging* MRS. ALDRID *across in front of the center table toward the left door.*) Go up to my money box and get me eight fifty-dollar bills — the newest you can find; and hurry! (*He turns quickly and crosses up above the center table toward the archway.*)

MRS. ALDRID (*recovering herself at the left door*). I'll do nothing of the kind!

ALDRID (*whirling upon her, and indicating the left door with an imperative gesture*). Quick! Now, you've lost enough tonight I think.

MRS. ALDRID (*defiantly*). I will *not!*

ALDRID. Very well, then. I shall be obliged to tell her the particulars.

[MRS. ALDRID *holds his eye for a second, then surrenders reluctantly.*]

MRS. ALDRID. Oh, I'll get them. But I never knew, Gene, that you were such a fool. (*She starts to leave the room.*)

ALDRID. Wait. (*She stops and turns.*) Wait a minute. (*He crosses toward her, passing above the center table.*) I'll get them myself.

MRS. ALDRID. Why can't *I* get them?

ALDRID (*looking steadily at her as he passes above her and goes out the door*). Because I'd rather get them myself.

[*She stands perfectly still, realizing the implication, until the doorbell has rung twice; then she crosses up back of the center table and goes out through the archway into the hall. Immediately she is out of sight,* ALDRID *steps through the door again at the left, and puts the little gold-mesh purse which he took from the desk drawer, and which he still has in his hand, on the lower corner of the mantelpiece. Then he crosses the room hurriedly, reaches down between the upper side of the desk and the wall, and picks up his wife's black leather pocketbook, which he deposited there at the opening of the play and which was concealed from view upon his entrance by the newspaper. At this point the voices of the two women become audible in the hallway.* ALDRID *opens the pocketbook, takes out the twenty-six dollars in bills from the side pocket and puts them in his own pocket, then lifts out* MRS. HAMPTON'S *mesh purse, and tosses the big leather pocketbook back onto the desk. Then he opens the mesh purse, looks at the four hundred dollars, closes it again, and turns toward the archway, twirling the purse on his finger, just as the women approach the entrance.*]

MRS. HAMPTON. I suppose I'm very impatient!

MRS. ALDRID. I don't wonder you are.

MRS. HAMPTON. But it seems so incredible that my own neighbor should be —

MRS. ALDRID (*entering*). Absolutely!

MRS. HAMPTON (*following her in, and almost hysterical*). I thought at first he must be joking!

MRS. ALDRID (*crossing toward the middle of the room, and extending her arm toward the purse*). There you are!

[MRS. HAMPTON *stops dead and clasps her hands against her breast. And* ALDRID *laughs and gives the purse an extra little twirl.*]

MRS. HAMPTON (*rushing toward him*). Oh, Mr. Aldrid!

ALDRID. Oh, you're a very careless person, Mrs. Hampton!

MRS. HAMPTON (*seizing the purse and trying nervously to open it*). Why, it doesn't seem possible!

MRS. ALDRID (*leaning on the center table, and trying to reflect the general tone of the scene*). It *is* a coincidence, isn't it?

MRS. HAMPTON (*turning to her*). Have you ever heard of anything so remarkable in all your *life!*

MRS. ALDRID. You must have been born under a lucky star.

MRS. HAMPTON (*turning to* ALDRID). Why didn't you tell me when I was over here a while ago?

ALDRID. Well, I was going to, but — (*He tries to laugh.*)

MRS. ALDRID (*touching her hair and looking away off*). I wanted him to — but he thought we'd better give you a little lesson.

[MRS. HAMPTON *turns and looks reproachfully at* ALDRID, *and he nods.*]

MRS. HAMPTON. Well, it *is* a lesson to me, I can assure you!

ALDRID. I hope you'll profit by it, Mrs. Hampton.

MRS. HAMPTON (*to* MRS. ALDRID). You know, I *never* expected to see this again! And then to think that of all the people that there are in this city — (*Turning back to* ALDRID.) — you should find it — and *return* it to me!

ALDRID. Why not?

MRS. ALDRID. It's your property, dear.

MRS. HAMPTON. Well, you know, they say, "Finders -- Keepers!"

MRS. ALDRID. Yes, that's what they *say*.

ALDRID (*turning slowly to his desk*). That's what they *do*, in the majority of cases.

[MRS. ALDRID *glances toward him.*]

MRS. HAMPTON (*moving toward* MRS. ALDRID). So that it really makes me *cry* — to think that there *are* honest people in the world, after all. (*She breaks down and cries on* MRS. ALDRID'S *shoulder.*)

MRS. ALDRID (*looking straight out*). There are a few of us left.

[ALDRID *turns and looks at her, and she looks right back at him.*]

ALDRID (*strolling up toward the back of the room*). One or two.

[*He crosses the room at the back, and* MRS. HAMPTON *straightens up, touching her handkerchief to her eyes.*]

MRS. HAMPTON (*crossing below the center table to the left*). And now, Mr. Aldrid, I must insist upon your taking a reward.

ALDRID (*moving forward at the left*). Don't you dare.

MRS. HAMPTON. Well, you *found* it!

ALDRID. Well, you *lost* it.

MRS. HAMPTON. Well then, I'm going to give you a present of some kind, anyway.

ALDRID (*smiling*). All right.

MRS. HAMPTON. Anything you say.

ALDRID. A pair of suspenders.

MRS. HAMPTON (*turning away*). Oh, it'll be something better than that, I can promise you. (*Starting across below the table toward the archway.*) But I must be going; Frank'll be home any minute. (*Pressing* MRS. ALDRID'S *arm, as she passes in front of her.*) I'll run over this evening.

MRS. ALDRID (*moving after her*). Yes, do.

MRS. HAMPTON (*turning at the archway*). I want to hear *all* the particulars. And, Mr. Aldrid, I don't know *how* to thank you.

ALDRID (*standing at the lower corner of the mantelpiece*). Don't mention it, Mrs. Hampton, we're very glad to have been able to return it to you.

MRS. HAMPTON (*going out*). Well, that's very nice of you, I *must* say.

MRS. ALDRID (*following her out*). Do come over this evening.

MRS. HAMPTON. Yes, I shall, right after dinner. Good-by.

MRS. ALDRID. Good-by, dear.

ALDRID (*quietly picking up his wife's gold-mesh purse from the corner of the mantelpiece*). Good-by, Mrs. Hampton.

MRS. HAMPTON (*out in the hallway*). I'm *so* grateful to you.

MRS. ALDRID. Not at all, darling.

MRS. HAMPTON. Good-by.

MRS. ALDRID. Good-by.

[*The front door closes.* ALDRID *proceeds slowly across the room, fumbling with the clasp of the little purse. As he passes below the center table,* MRS. ALDRID *sails in from the hallway and crosses directly to the sofa to get her apron. Her expression is set and sulky. Just as she is about to go out at the left door,* ALDRID *speaks to her.*]

ALDRID. How do you open this thing?

[*She stops near the door and looks back.*]

MRS. ALDRID (*icily*). What is it?

ALDRID (*without turning*). Your purse.

[MRS. ALDRID'S *expression becomes quizzical, and she moves a few steps nearer to him.*]

MRS. ALDRID. *My* purse?

ALDRID. Yes.

MRS. ALDRID. Where'd you get it?

ALDRID (*indicating the desk drawer with a nod*). In that drawer there.

[*She becomes more mystified, and unconsciously drifts closer to him.*]

MRS. ALDRID. I thought you gave it to her?

ALDRID (*still very casually, and without looking at her*). I gave her her own.

MRS. ALDRID. But hers is lost!

[*He turns and looks at her.*]

ALDRID. Not now; *I found* it.

MRS. ALDRID. But *her* purse was in *my* black leather pocketbook.

ALDRID (*quietly*). I know it was; but *I found* your black leather pocketbook.

[*She holds his eye for a second, bewildered.*]

MRS. ALDRID. Where?

ALDRID. In the hallway there, as I came in this evening.

[*He occupies himself again with the clasp, and* MRS. ALDRID *stands staring at him. Suddenly he clicks the purse shut, having adjusted the clasp, and looks at her; then, withdrawing his eyes, turns smoothly and tosses the purse onto the desk.*]

MRS. ALDRID. Then why did you call up the Rapid Transit?

ALDRID (*picking up the leather pocketbook*). I didn't.

MRS. ALDRID. You talked to somebody on the telephone.

ALDRID (*handing her the pocketbook*). I did not. (*He turns back to the desk.*)

MRS. ALDRID. You did, I heard you!

ALDRID (*picking up the gold purse again*). I had my finger on the hook.

[*She stands glaring at him, as he quietly opens the desk drawer and puts the purse in, then closes the drawer again.*]

MRS. ALDRID (*witheringly*). You're very clever. (*She opens the pocketbook and rummages hastily.*)

ALDRID (*picking up the blueprints*). And very honest, I hope.

MRS. ALDRID. Where's my twenty-six dollars?

ALDRID. Isn't it there?

MRS. ALDRID. No, it isn't.

ALDRID. What do you think of that!

MRS. ALDRID. Did you give her *that,* too?

ALDRID. No, I didn't.

MRS. ALDRID. Well, it's gone!

ALDRID. That's too bad.

MRS. ALDRID. *Somebody* must have taken it!

[*He turns to her.*]

ALDRID. I took it.

MRS. ALDRID. You!

ALDRID (*reaching into his pocket for the twenty-six dollars*). Yes.

MRS. ALDRID. What for?

ALDRID. Because I *found* it.

MRS. ALDRID. Well, I lost it!

ALDRID. And how do I *know* you did?

MRS. ALDRID. Because I *told* you that I did!

ALDRID. Can you identify it?

[MRS. ALDRID's *patience is being tried beyond endurance.*]

MRS. ALDRID. *Certainly* I can! I told you I had five five-dollar bills and —

ALDRID. But that isn't any identification.

MRS. ALDRID. Why isn't it?

ALDRID (*bearing with her innocence*). Why, because it isn't. (*He moves very slowly toward her, tapping the bills against his finger.*) Money is simply money, unless it's marked; and this isn't, for I've examined it very carefully. (*Suddenly she recognizes her own words; and, slamming the pocketbook shut, she whirls round, glaring at him, and sails toward the door at the left. But* ALDRID *is unruffled by the movement, and continues to follow her slowly, speaking in the same quiet, explanatory key.*) So that, really, a person would be more or less obliged to take your word for it, wouldn't he? (*The curtain begins to descend smoothly.*) And that's rather a lot for us to expect of people, don't you think? — considering that there are twenty-six dollars in the bargain. Of course, I'm perfectly willing to return it to you if you can absolutely identify it; but, under the circumstances, I'm afraid you'd have some difficulty persuading people that —

AFTER READING

1. "Honesty is the best policy," runs an old proverb. Is honesty a policy or is it a principle? What's the difference?

2. "It pays to be honest" is a slogan frequently heard. *Does* it pay to be honest? Mention some instances from your own experience to prove your point. Assuming that honesty does not always pay, is dishonesty ever justified?

3. Mrs. Hampton enters without ringing. Is there any plausible explanation for her act? Is Mrs. Aldrid justified in suspecting that she overheard the conversation with Mr. Aldrid?

4. How does Mrs. Aldrid feel when she learns that her "lost" pocketbook had been turned into the Lost and Found Department of the transit corporation minus all the money? What difference do you notice in her feelings as a loser and as a finder?

5. Mr. Aldrid tells Mrs. Hampton over the phone that he found the money. Is this a lie?

6. How does Mr. Aldrid show that he has lost faith in his wife's honesty?

7. Should Mrs. Hampton tell her husband of her loss?

CHALLENGES

1. Write the scene in which Mrs. Hampton visits the Aldrids after dinner to hear the particulars of how the money was found.

2. Relate a story, true or imaginary, about a valuable article which you found, and your efforts to locate the owner.

3. Assuming that you have found a valuable ring, compose an advertisement for insertion in the Lost and Found column of your local newspaper.

DRAMA WORKSHOP

A hint for playgoers: Live the play.

Once there was a Broadway show in which the action took place on a Pacific island during the rainy season. Throughout the play the rain fell in a steady heavy downpour. An interesting reaction occurred each day as the audience left. Standing in the street outside the theater one could hear exclamations of surprise when the playgoers discovered that the sky was clear. Everyone had expected to walk out into the rain. Why this surprise? Such was the wizardry of the theater that each member of the audience had identified himself completely with the setting of the play.

As you read or see a play, give yourself over to it completely. Remove all distracting elements — for instance, when reading, turn off the radio. Before you realize it, the barrier between you and the script, or you and the stage, will disappear. You'll be part of the dramatic conflict enacted in the pages of the book or on the stage of the theater. You'll be living the play!

A hint for actors: Know stage nomenclature.

The stage directions in *Finders Keepers* include references to right and left. Are stage directions determined from the standpoint of the audience or the actor?

If you want to take part in a play, you ought to know the terms in which directions are given. *Right* and *left* always refer to the actor's right and left. The *mid-section* of the stage is the center. *Downstage* refers to the half of the stage nearer the audience, *upstage,* to the half nearer the back wall. Test whether you know these terms by drawing a stage floor plan and locating the following: down center, up left, down right, up center.

OTHER PROBLEM PLAYS YOU WILL LIKE TO READ

Alma Mater by Paul Green (24). In a contest between loyalty to his ideals and to his fraternity, which is helping a football hero deceive the college authorities, the president of the Honor Council must make a choice.

Augustus in Search of a Father by Harold Chapin (38). A son tries not to deceive his father, who thinks he is honest and law-abiding, upon returning to England from a rather shady existence in America.

Back of the Yards by Kenneth Sawyer Goodman (36). Patience and persistence on the part of a priest and a sympathetic sergeant cause a change of heart in a boy who has been keeping bad company.

The Bishop's Candlesticks by Norman McKinnel (21). A tense episode from Victor Hugo's *Les Misérables* in which the kindly Bishop gives the convict Jean Valjean his beloved candlesticks.

Confessional by Percival Wilde (12). Although his family urges him to accept a substantial bribe by the president of the bank to give evidence that would clear him, an honest cashier does not succumb.

The Dust of the Road by Kenneth Sawyer Goodman (12). A stranger turns up at a farmhouse on Christmas Eve and by his own example persuades the farmer to return a large sum of money to its rightful owner.

The Forfeit by T. B. Rogers (12). A young office worker steals a ring from his employer to defray his losses on the stock market.

The Man on the Kerb by Alfred Sutro (34). A starving workman refuses to keep a purse his wife has stolen.

EMERGENCY, STAND BY!

BY TOM POWERS

ABOUT THE PLAY

Tom Powers, the author of *Emergency, Stand By!*, advises those who wish to perform his play: "This one I should do sitting in a chair with earphones on, if possible. If you can get hold of one of those sound-effect things, like another person's voice through a telephone, from off stage, rattling and squawking away in the pilot's ears, it would be very effective. No words are necessary, but careful rehearsals must teach the voice in the earphones to come in at the right moments. The parentheses in this monodrama are there to show what the ground man says. These speeches are effective, but it goes just as well without them. If this little play doesn't make 'em sit on the edge of their seats, it's your fault. But I'm sure it will."

Emergency, Stand By! is a monodrama. In other words it is a play written for only one actor. Ruth Draper and Cornelia Otis Skinner are two of the foremost contemporary exponents of the monodrama, and have given American theatergoers exciting experiences in plays similar to the one that follows.

ABOUT THE AUTHOR

The editors asked Tom Powers for his autobiography. This is what he wrote: "I occurred in Owensboro, Kentucky, longer ago than I like to admit, as the seventh son of respectable parents. I had to choose whether I would be the cleverest boy in my own home town, writing the school play, painting the scenery, composing the music and directing it while playing the best parts, or come to New York and vie with the cleverest boys from all the other home towns. I am still vying. I was not a promising pupil at the American Academy of Dramatic Arts, but they graduated me. I became a silent-picture cowboy; in fact it was I who cleared Staten Island of the Indians. After that, I acted in a lot of stock companies, and finally got to New York, and am still here. I was for twenty years in the New York Theatre Guild, have a trunk full of my unpublished works — books, plays, poetry; my walls are covered with my paintings. my neighbors know too well my music, and my wife is very patient. Thus you see my talents continue to flourish. I do a radio program every day for a very high-grade soap, act in other people's plays and occasionally in my own."

EMERGENCY, STAND BY!

BARTON, *a modern transport pilot, talking to Los Lunas Field by radio. Johnny, his copilot, sits beside him. The passengers are in the cabin behind them, as the plane goes tearing through the night, over New Mexico.*

Barton, in 241, calling Los Lunas . . . Barton, in 241, calling Los Lunas.

Los Lunas to Barton. Okay. Go ahead.)

Hello, Bugs. Barton, in 241, Guyinas to Los Lunas, over Guyinas River, 2500 feet, heavy stuff. Take this . . . there's a lot of it. Approaching Harville, I was directed by Bolivar Airport to make a landing at Harville Emergency Field. Landed just after dark, 9:32 – 9–3–2 – and boy, does that field need some work done on it! Picked up emergency case, appendicitis, Ethel Bevins. . . . B–E–V–I–N–S. Nobody with her; husband, Samuel Bevins, is in Los Lunas, already. Bolivar operator promised to get hold of him, and have him at your airport when we get in. Take this: Doctor, at Harville, says, advise Los Lunas Hospital prepare operate, immediately. Miss Harris, our stewardess, reports patient okay.

(*Okay.*)

Bolivar reports snow back there, and it don't look like May Day at Vassar, up here.

(*Yes, heavy snowstorm from north-northeast. . . . Ceiling dropping.*)

I got that. . . . Heavy snowstorm from north-northeast. . . . Well, hold it off ten minutes, Bugs, and I'll bring the patient in, before the first flake flutters.

(*What's that?*)

Never mind, skip it. It was poetry. So long. . . .

Well, Johnny, nice, neat little blizzard trying to sneak in between us and Los Lunas. Go back and tell the poor kid to keep her nerve up. Her husband's on his way out to the field, now. Tell Harris to be sure to put a pillow between her and her landing belt. Say, did you see what she had in her hand when we carried her in? Her baby's shoe. For good luck, she said.

Barton, in 241, calling Los Lunas. Barton, calling Los Lunas.

(*Okay . . . go ahead, Barton.*)

Say, were you right! . . . Here comes the snow, and here we go into it. Good-by ceiling. Climbing up to get above it . . . 3500 feet.

(*I tell you, Barton, you'd better turn back.*)

Listen, baby, we can't go back.

(*Don't think you ought to come in.*)

I know, but . . .

(*It's a blizzard.*)

Okay, but . . .

(*And it's heavy.*)

Listen, Toots, we've got to get this gal to the hospital soon.

(*What about the regulations?*)

Yeah? The guy that wrote those regulations meant them for transport ships. This one's just been converted into an ambulance.

(*It says on page 122 . . .*)

Yeah . . . and you know what it says on page 304: "In an emergency, the pilot makes all decisions."

(*There ain't no page 304.*)

Well, it would say it, if there was a page 304.

(*You can't come in, Barton.*)

No? . . . Well, come up here and stop me. Still climbing 4100 . . . no top yet.

(*Hey, Barton, Mr. Bevins is here.*)

Who did you say?

(*Bevins.*)

Her husband? . . . Swell! I guess he's worried sick. Say, get him in your radio tower, and let me talk to him. It might cheer the poor guy up.

(*He's in here now.*)

Oh, is he? Can he hear me?

(*Sure, go ahead.*)

Hello . . . Mr. Bevins. . . . Listen, this is Barton, the pilot, that's bringing your wife from Harville. We're up here, in the dark, coming along about 300 miles an hour. She was awful sick, Mr. Bevins, but she's doing all right. Dr. Schultz took your baby over to his house. Try not to worry, Mr. Bevins. Our stewardess is a trained nurse, and she's doing everything she can. I'll tell her you're waiting for her. And say, she brought along the baby's shoe, for luck, she said. Don't you worry. She's fine. Hey, Bugs, he'd better stay in the waiting room while we land, and you cut out your little side chats, and concentrate on your Uncle Dudley, for here I come.

(*Okay.*)

Oh, it's you, Miss Harris. . . . How is she? As bad as that, huh? Is Johnny with her? Well, we'll try to put the bus down without a jolt.

Oh, here's Johnny. You'd better go back, Miss Harris, and tell her her husband is at the airport, with an ambulance, waiting.

We must be just over Amsterdam, Johnny. . . . What's that? She sent me what? Well, I'll be durned! Yeah, I'll keep it here in my pocket until we land, and if I don't land easy on this snow, I hope this baby's shoe kicks me all over the town of Los Lunas. They've got good landing lights on that field. We can go in blind, on the radio beam, but I'll get a word of advice from Bugs, to help us in through this stuff.

Barton, calling Los Lunas. Barton, calling Los Lunas. Barton, calling Los Lunas. Barton, in 241, calling Los Lunas. . . . Calling Los Lunas. Better try somebody else. Barton, in 241, calling Bolivar Airport. . . . Calling Bolivar Airport. . . . Calling Los Lunas. Johnny, go in and tell the passengers to buckle on their safety belts while I keep trying.

Barton, in 241, calling Los Lunas. . . . Barton, in 241, calling Los Lunas. . . . Barton, in 241, calling Bolivar. . . . Barton, in 241, calling—practically anybody . . . Danny Kaye . . . Joe Stalin . . . Li'l Abner. . . . Barton, in 241, calling General Eisenhower. Hey, Los Lunas, how do you think I'm going to land on your cockeyed stubblefield if you don't help me a little?

(*Go ahead, go ahead.*)

Oh, is that you, Bugs? Hey, Bugs, Los Lunas . . . if you can hear me, set out some lights on the field. We'll be in before they can flicker a flick.

How is she, Johnny? Hot dog! No, I can't hear a thing, but I think he's getting me, all right. If you can hear me, Bugs, I ought to be just passing over Beacon 366. Going to switch onto the beam and fly in blind. Keep pinching your left ear for luck, and so long. . . . Keep your eye on the altimeter, Johnny. Here we go, onto the beam. There's the beam's pretty little voice. Gosh, Johnny, what did pilots do before they had these things? Listen to it. "Tit – tah – tit – tah."

We're left, off our course, Johnny . . . still left.

There, "Tah – ah," she says; if we can keep on that steady note, we can get her in. Read me the altitude as I drop down. I'll try to pick up those landing lights, but we couldn't hardly see the Goddess of Liberty tonight . . . not till she prodded us with her torch in the fusilage. 1450 feet. . . .

Oh, oh! we're off it, to the right.

Okay. She's singing steady again . . . 1300 . . . God pity the poor postman on a night like this. Yep . . . 1200 . . . we ought to be over the Reservoir by now, but I couldn't see Times Square. . . . Better try Bugs again.

Barton, calling Los Lunas. . . . Barton, calling Los Lunas . . . 1100. . . . Listen, Bugs, in case you can hear me . . . about over the Reservoir, on the beam . . . 1100 . . . going to drop down, to land . . . patient fine . . . keep the home lights burning. Here I come. . . .

We're off to the right, Johnny.

There we are, on it again. Here, Johnny . . . 1000 feet . . . open the little side glass and see if you can see those blinking lights. 900 . . . ugh . . . ugh! . . . It sure is a blizzard. How deep do you think the snow will be on the field? 800 . . . did you tell the passengers that it's all just a lot of fun, and that we love diving through this stuff? 700 . . . can't you see anything, Johnny? . . . Put your belt on. Do what I tell you. . . .

Do what I tell you. 600 . . . no use bumping your nose off if I don't make it. Put it on – that's right. 500 . . . can't you see the ground at all? I can't, either. We ought to be nearly over the beam . . . let's wait for it. She ought to cut out in a minute.

Yep! There she goes. We're right over the beam, at 500. That's swell! . . .

Tah! And there it is singing again. That makes it about perfect, and here we go down. Watch the altimeter, Johnny. There mustn't be any little hitch in this. Hey, pat that baby's shoe, in my pocket, for luck, will you? 400 . . . here we go. This is one of those tricks that you never know if you'll get a medal for, or have your license taken away. 300. . . .

We're left again. Here. Good Lord! This is no time to . . .

Gosh, there's the beam singing again! Attaboy! 220 . . . stick your head out, Johnny, and see if . . . 150 . . . see if I've gone blind, or if his lights are not on. 100 . . . for the Lord's sake, Johnny, can't you see anything? This is getting pretty . . . durned . . . uh uh! . . . never mind. There they are . . . I see 'em. Good old Bugs, he did hear me. He can cuss me all he wants to . . . 50 . . . feet . . . here we go. Right over the hangars, and down onto the . . . wait . . . easy now . . . down we . . . GO! . . . There you are, Johnny, taxi us in, will you, across the field? The snow's not too deep yet.

Well, Miss Harris, did she stand the landing all right? Swell; go back and tell her the baby's shoe brought us luck.

Well, Johnny, I'll switch onto Bugs and let him tell me what he thinks of me while you taxi us through the snow.

(*So, you made it, you crazy nut.*)

Yep, we made it. On the ground once more. Patient doing fine.

(*Main office wants you on the phone.*)

What? Main office wants me? Well, tell 'em to hold the phone, till Johnny gets us across the field. But before I find out whether I get a medal for this stunt or get fired, I've got a date with myself, to drink a little health . . . yeah, out of a lady's shoe.

AFTER READING

1. Should Barton have disobeyed the instructions from Los Lunas Airfield? Why? Is disobedience of a superior's orders ever justified? Mention some examples.

2. Find remarks by Barton which show his concern for the welfare of others.

3. Should Barton get a medal for his stunt, or should he be fired?

4. Show how *Emergency, Stand By!* follows the pattern of a regular drama. Refer to the "Open Letter" at the beginning of the book, which describes *exposition, rising action, climax,* and *denouement.* What is the climax of this play? What is the denouement?

5. Explain how the sound of a radio beam helps a pilot to keep his course.

CHALLENGES

1. Using the same situation, write a monodrama in which the speaker is Bugs, the control-tower operator at Los Lunas.

2. Imagine you are Mr. Samuel Bevins. Write a letter of appreciation to Barton for his exploit.

3. Compose the dialogue which occurs when Barton reports to the manager of the main office as ordered.

DRAMA WORKSHOP

A hint for playgoers: Check on empathy.

A tense moment on a football field: the home team must kick from behind its own goal line; a blocked kick means almost certain defeat. As you watch a situation such as this from your seat in the grandstand, you tend to move your foot upward as the player kicks, as if to help him send the ball down the field.

This kind of reaction is called *feeling-in* or *empathy.* Empathy consists in feeling the same muscular sensations that somebody else is experiencing. While watching a performance you unconsciously assume an actor's physical attitudes. If he smiles, you smile. If his face is distorted from pain or anger, your face reflects some of his feeling. If the actor who does Barton in *Emergency, Stand By!* is acting sensitively, you ought to feel some of the tense excitement and determination that Barton feels. Perhaps you may even find yourself leaning forward as if trying to peer through the ice-covered glass!

Empathy occurs in the audience only when an actor's performance is full of genuine feeling and understanding. Test the quality of a performance by checking on your own empathy.

A hint for actors: Good speech is essential.

Every actor speaks two languages. The first is a visible language: gesture and bodily movement. The second is an audible language: words and sound. With the aid of both an actor conveys emotion and meaning to his listeners. A radio actor is restricted to one language. He must make an impression on his unseen listeners by means of his voice and speech alone. Hence a pleasing voice and clear diction are paramount, in radio productions especially.

Many of us are careless about our speech. We fall into careless habits of enunciation and pronunciation, such as saying *gunna* for *going to, dint* for *didn't, strick* for *strict, liss* for *lists,* and the like. Our training in English classes helps greatly to improve our speech. Beyond this, however, the best way to correct such slovenly habits is to study under a competent teacher of speech. If you are not able to obtain such instruction, you can improve your speech by listening carefully to good speakers and by trying to emulate them. By all means have your voice recorded on a wire recorder or a phonograph record, if you can do so. Perhaps you'll be disappointed to hear how you sound, but with sustained attention and effort you should be able to clean up bad habits of articulation and make each word clearly understood as you say it.

OTHER MONODRAMAS YOU WILL LIKE TO READ

Before Breakfast by Eugene O'Neill (33). An unhappy wife drives her sensitive husband to an extraordinary decision by her persistent nagging.

First Person Singular by Florence Ryerson and Colin Clements (42). A group of twenty-one character sketches for platform and radio presentation, and also for reading to oneself. *Mike, Movie Mother,* and *Streamline* are well adapted for classroom use.

Life Studies by Tom Powers (42). A varied collection of one-character sketches, a few in verse. *Dark Glasses* is a general favorite.

Man with a Gun by Charles Vanda and Russ Johnson (9). An escaped criminal tries to kill his double-crossing confederate, but finds he is anticipated.

More Life Studies by Tom Powers (42). More favorites from Mr. Powers's repertory.

The One Woman Show by Marjorie Moffett (42). Girls will find that *Bargain Basement* and *A Philadelphia Mother Visits School* are good material for high-school audiences.

The Bottle Imp

BY ROBERT LOUIS STEVENSON

ADAPTED FOR RADIO BY ROMANCE C. KOOPMAN

ABOUT THE PLAY

Young people enjoy fairy tales in which genii do superhuman things. Even for adults an interest in such characters does not wane, as the success of various comic strips based on Superman's exploits proves. Perhaps many of us are willing to believe such stories because secretly we would like to have some of the world's riches at our beck and call. If you have any such liking yourself, you will not want to put this play down until you have finished it.

Robert Louis Stevenson, the famous author of *Treasure Island,* wrote the original short story which is adapted here as a radio play. The author died in 1894, before the radio and television and other marvels of our era were discovered. Today atomic energy in a little bottle, when released, could accomplish some of the superhuman deeds ascribed to the bottle imp in the story. The days of magic are not by any means over, but now it is Science which is the bottle imp rather than an imaginary genie.

ABOUT THE AUTHOR

Robert Louis Stevenson (1850–1894) is known all over the world for his novels, short stories, and poems for children. Who has not thrilled to *Treasure Island, Dr. Jekyll and Mr. Hyde, Kidnapped,* and some of the finest short stories in modern times like "The Sire de Maletroit's Door" and "Markheim"? In his brief lifetime Stevenson also wrote several plays, and his novels reveal his talent for dramatic construction. *The Bottle Imp* was originally a short story or tale, most of which Romance C. Koopman has preserved faithfully in her radio adaptation. Stevenson maintained that fiction enables man to escape from the commonplace realities into a world of spiritual freedom. Perhaps the author thought so little of the daily realities because for years he battled with ill health, traveling in many lands to find a climate which would enable him to live in comfort. Like the sailor in his story, he was familiar with faraway places, and in fact spent the last years of his life on an island in the Pacific.

THE BOTTLE IMP

Characters

ANNOUNCER	KOKUA
NARRATOR	MAN
LOPAKA	LAWYER
KEAWE	HAOLE
OLD MAN	SERVANT
WOMAN	YOUNG MAN
CHANG	SECOND OLD MAN

BO'SUN

ANNOUNCER. *The Bottle Imp!*

MUSIC. *Background.*

NARRATOR (*low confidential*). He said that it all began one day when he and his friend had left their ship to walk along the streets of San Francisco. . . .

MUSIC. *Up — sprightly — fading for . . .*

LOPAKA (*panting*). Wait, Keawe! Don't walk on! That wasn't a hill we just climbed. That was a mountain!

KEAWE. It was a hill, Lopaka . . . a hill with a view! Look! To the left of us, the ocean spreading as far as we can see . . . spreading home to Hawaii. To the right of us, the largest, most beautiful homes in all San Francisco!

LOPAKA. And beside you, the tiredest sailor that ever spent a day's leave climbing hills.

KEAWE. You've no imagination, Lopaka, that's your trouble. Here we are, two sailors with a month's pay in our pockets, and what are we doing? We're walking along the sidewalks and peering into the windows of the richest people in all America.

LOPAKA. I'd rather be sitting in their chairs.

KEAWE. So would I, if I owned them. But this is the next best thing. Look at that house right across from us. Have you ever seen anything like it? Steps that shine like silver . . . windows that glitter like diamonds . . .

LOPAKA. And an old bearded gentleman frowning at us from the doorway. Very pretty, Keawe.

KEAWE. He probably hasn't anything else to do all day but frown at people like us. Oh, to have nothing to do all day but sit in your fine house and watch the sea and the people!

LOPAKA. We could be sitting in an inn right now, with our feet on a table . . .

KEAWE. Sh! Look! The old man's calling us!

OLD MAN (*fade on — calling*). If you, young gentlemen, wish!

KEAWE (*calling*). Just a minute! We'll come closer. (*Whispering.*) Let's find out what he wants, Lopaka. Come on.

LOPAKA (*low*). From the sour look on his face, he'll ask us what we've been staring at. Don't rush so, Keawe!

OLD MAN (*fade on*). I noticed that you were interested in my little house. I wondered if you'd like to see it closer?

KEAWE. Thank you! We've never seen anything quite like it before. I'd think you'd be happy all day long just living in it.

OLD MAN (*sighing*). Yes indeed. I suppose you'd like to own one like it.

KEAWE (*laughing*). Who wouldn't? If they could.

OLD MAN (*slyly*). There's no reason why you shouldn't. You have some money, I suppose?

KEAWE. Fifty dollars. And that's more than my friend here can say!

OLD MAN. Fifty dollars. Well . . . it's too bad you don't have more, but I'll let you have it for that.

KEAWE. The house?

OLD MAN. No. The bottle.

KEAWE (*laughing*). Fifty dollars for a bottle! That's a good one.

OLD MAN. No! This is no joke! It may seem rich to you, but everything I have, this house and its gardens, all of them, came out of a little bottle no bigger than a pint. Would you like to see it?

KEAWE. I would at that! If I believed you.

OLD MAN. Wait one moment, young gentleman! (*Fade.*) I'll get it for you.

LOPAKA. Keawe, let's go! This man is crazy!

KEAWE. Maybe not. The world is full of strange things we might not hear of in Hawaii!

LOPAKA. If he's not crazy, so much the worse. We ought to . . .

KEAWE. Sh! He's coming back.

OLD MAN (*fade on*). I've brought the bottle, young gentlemen! Sit down on that bench there. I'll show it to you.

KEAWE. All right. Sit down, Lopaka! Nothing's going to hurt you.

OLD MAN. Here! This is the bottle.

KEAWE. Whew! What an odd-looking one! Like an opal. What is that inside it, that flickers like a flame?

OLD MAN. That is the imp.

LOPAKA (*whispering*). Come on, Keawe, let's get out of here!

KEAWE. No! Wait! What imp is there that could live in a glass bottle?

OLD MAN. The glass in this bottle was tempered in the flames of hell. If any man buys the bottle, the imp within it is at his command. He can have anything . . . money, fame, whole cities. . . . When he sells it, the power goes.

KEAWE. I shouldn't think you'd want to sell it.

OLD MAN. I have everything I want. I'm growing old.

KEAWE. Why don't you ask the imp to let you live forever?

OLD MAN. That's the only thing the imp can't do.

KEAWE. I'd think you'd try to get more than fifty dollars for the bottle, even so.

OLD MAN. I'd like to, for the good of the buyer, not because I need the money.

KEAWE (*amused*). You're a strange one.

OLD MAN. No. There are two things about this bottle that you must know. Once it's yours, you can never be rid of it except by selling it. And it can only be sold for less than it was bought for. I paid ninety dollars for it, but were I to sell it for more than eighty-nine dollars and ninety-nine cents, the bottle would come right back to me.

KEAWE. I shouldn't think you'd worry about that.

OLD MAN. But I do, for you see any man who dies still owning the bottle will burn in hell forever.

KEAWE (*whistling*). No wonder you want to be rid of it. I wouldn't touch it, not even for fifty dollars!

LOPAKA. That's the first sensible thing you've said, Keawe. Now let's be on our way.

OLD MAN (*desperately*). Don't you want riches? Don't you want a fine house like mine?

KEAWE. Not if it costs me my immortal soul!

OLD MAN. But it needn't! You can buy the bottle from me, get all you want from it, and then sell it again as I'm doing.

LOPAKA. We've got to get away from here, Keawe!

KEAWE. We're in no danger, Lopaka! We haven't bought the bottle. And besides, how do we know that what this old man says is true, eh?

OLD MAN. You can prove it! Look! The bottle is glass, isn't it? And glass breaks, ordinary glass, that is, yet I can throw this on the walk, so . . .

SOUND. *Hollow ring of glass on pavement.*

OLD MAN. And it doesn't break. It bounces right back into my hand.

KEAWE. Which doesn't mean that the bottle can do all these wonderful things you told us about.

OLD MAN. I'll make a bargain with you. Give me your fifty dollars, take the bottle, and wish your fifty dollars back in your pocket. If it doesn't happen, I pledge you my honor I'll call off the bargain and give you back your money myself.

LOPAKA. Don't risk it, Keawe!

KEAWE. You're not deceiving me, old man?

OLD MAN. By the God that rules Mauna Loa, it is so.

KEAWE. Very well.

SOUND. *Clinking of coins.*

KEAWE. This should be fun, Lopaka. Here's my money, old man. Give me the bottle. Thank you. Now . . . imp of the bottle, I want my fifty dollars back.

LOPAKA. You're a fool, Keawe. You've lost your month's pay for a piece of glass.

KEAWE. No! Look, Lopaka

SOUND. *Clinking of coins.*

KEAWE. My fifty dollars . . . back in my pocket just as he said. It is a remarkable bottle, at that!

OLD MAN. And I wish you luck with it!

KEAWE. Oh no. Here, take it back. I've enjoyed our talk, and all that, but I don't want to fool around with anything like this for long.

OLD MAN. You've bought it for less than I paid for it. It's yours now, and that's the end of it as far as I'm concerned. I'm expecting guests soon, and I'll thank you not to stay too long in the garden. (*Fade.*) Good day, young gentlemen.

LOPAKA. Now you've done it, Keawe! Why didn't you leave when I said to?

KEAWE. How did I know he was going to trick me into buying the bottle? Well, he can't do it. Come on, Lopaka, we're going to go, and leave him the bottle. I won't take it.

LOPAKA. What are you going to do with it?

SOUND. *Bottle.*

KEAWE. Leave it on the bench here. There. Now hurry, let's be out of sight before the old man sees we've left the bottle.

LOPAKA (*as if walking fast*). All right. Only maybe now you'll listen to me when I try to keep you out of trouble.

KEAWE. Don't talk like an old woman. Think of the stories we can tell to our friends on board ship. Think of the . . .

LOPAKA. What's the matter?

KEAWE. Look back at the house. Is the bottle still on the bench?

LOPAKA. Just a minute . . . no! The old man must have taken it away!

KEAWE. No he didn't. And I've just remembered that the old man said once the bottle belonged to a man, he could lose it only by selling it.

LOPAKA. Then where is the bottle?

KEAWE (*scared*). In my coat pocket.

MUSIC. *Surge up — fade for . . .*

SOUND. *Conversation in background.*

LOPAKA (*calling*). Bring us two rums, please. (*On mike.*) Sit down, Keawe, we've got to talk this thing over. Is the bottle still in your pocket? Sh! Here's the man with the rum.

SOUND. *Clink of glasses and money.*

KEAWE. It is. You know, Lopaka, I'm beginning to be glad we talked with that old man. There are lots of things I want, and if what he said is true, and the bottle will grant my wishes, I'm going to be a happy man!

LOPAKA. What would you wish for?

KEAWE. A house first, on the islands. I'd want seventeen rooms, and three porches, all overlooking Kona Bay. And an avenue lined with palms leading to a paved courtyard with a fountain spraying colored water. . . .

LOPAKA. You'd better wish for enough money to keep it up, Keawe!

KEAWE. Of course. I'd want enough money so I'd never need work again.

LOPAKA. Why don't you try it? You have the bottle.

KEAWE. No, I don't want to take the chance until I'm sure of the bottle.

LOPAKA. The best way to be sure is to make your wish.

KEAWE. No. There's one more test. I'm going to try to sell the bottle for more than fifty dollars. If it comes back to me then, I'll believe the old man, and use the bottle for the things I want.

LOPAKA. And if you get them, you can always get rid of the bottle for less than you paid. It's a good idea . . . let's try it.

KEAWE. Have you finished your rum? All right, let's go. We'll sell the bottle for sixty dollars, and then go back to the inn and see what happens. . . .

MUSIC. *Sneak in — bring up — fade out for . . .*

SOUND. *Feet climbing stairs.*

KEAWE. If my bottle comes back, Lopaka, this'll be the last time I climb rickety inn stairs to get to my room!

LOPAKA. Even if the bottle doesn't come back, you're sixty dollars richer for it.

KEAWE. I thought for awhile that the storekeeper wouldn't pay what I asked. He was a wary old cuss.

LOPAKA. He'd have been warier if he'd known what kind of a bottle it's supposed to be!

KEAWE. Well, the bottle hasn't come back yet, anyway. . . . Whew . . . that was a climb.

SOUND. *Steps out — door opens.*

LOPAKA. Look . . . someone's shoved a letter under our door, Keawe. It's for you.

KEAWE. Wait'll I get my breath. Sit down.

LOPAKA. You're a cool one! Don't even want to see a letter from home.

KEAWE. From Hawaii? Give it to me!

LOPAKA. Here it is.

KEAWE. Yes sir, a letter from home. . . .

SOUND. *Paper tearing.*

LOPAKA. Who's it from? Anyone I know?

KEAWE (*low*). Lopaka . . . my uncle has died.

LOPAKA. Oh say, that's tough going . . . I'm sorry.

KEAWE. It's not that, Lopaka. I've never seen this uncle. But it seems that he had no heirs but me . . . and he's left me all his fortune.

LOPAKA. Whew!

KEAWE. Enough money so that I won't need to work ever again, the lawyer says. And . . . a piece of land overlooking Kona Bay. It's just what I've always wanted. . . . I'm sorry Uncle had to die, but it means I've everything. . . . Say! What's up? Aren't you going to congratulate me on my good fortune? What are you staring at in the corner there?

LOPAKA. Keawe . . . the bottle is back. It's on the chest in the corner. And as you spoke, the flame in it flared up until the whole thing was a brilliant crimson.

KEAWE. Where . . . I don't . . . oh . . . and this letter brings me the things I said I'd wish for when we were talking this afternoon.

LOPAKA. Then it's true, Keawe.

KEAWE. It is. And I have everything I want and must sell the bottle quickly, for less than I paid. I don't want it near me any longer.

LOPAKA (*rapidly*). Keawe, I'll buy it from you. I'll take the chance. I can get me a little schooner, and set up my own business sailing about the islands. I'll buy it from you for forty-nine dollars and ninety-nine cents, and sell it for a penny less when I have my schooner.

KEAWE. You'll be able to find plenty of buyers, Lopaka. Give me the money and take the bottle.

SOUND. *Clink of coins.*

LOPAKA. All right. Here. What are you going to do now?

KEAWE. I'm going back to the islands, to build my house on Kona Bay . . . to live in ease and luxury . . . (*Joyously.*) to be repected and admired for my wealth and power. . . .

MUSIC. *Sneak in, over his words — then change into Hawaiian melody — fading to background.*

SOUND. *Conversation.*

WOMAN (*gushing*). Oh, Mr. Keawe, your party is delightful . . . there's no place on the island so grand as the Great House . . . such gardens . . . such pictures . . . oh me . . . your house lacks but one thing . . .

KEAWE. And that is, madame?

WOMAN (*coyly*). A wife.

KEAWE. So it does, madame.

WOMAN. You must look around for yourself a little, Mr. Keawe. Many women would like to be mistress of the Great House.

KEAWE. I don't doubt it, madame. But when I meet the one who is to be mistress of my house, I shall know her.

MUSIC. *Sneak in over words — fade for . . .*

SOUND. *Horses cantering.*

KEAWE (*calling*). Wait, Chang!

SOUND. *Horses halt.*

CHANG. Master wishes to stop?

KEAWE. Yes. You know everyone on the island, Chang. Who is that girl there by the sea?

CHANG. She who has just come from a swim? She is Kokua, daughter of Kiano.

KEAWE (*softly*). There is something about her . . . (*Normal.*) Ride on home, Chang. Don't wait dinner for me. I don't know when I'll be home.

CHANG. Very well, master.

SOUND. *One horse galloping off.*

KEAWE (*calling softly*). Kokua! Kokua!

KOKUA (*fade on*). Who's there? Who's calling?

KEAWE. It is I . . . here by my horse.

KOKUA. But who are you?

KEAWE. I am Keawe.

KOKUA. Keawe of the Great House?

KEAWE. Yes.

KOKUA. My father has spoken of you. Yet, it's silly of me, how did you know who I am?

KEAWE. Does it matter?

KOKUA. Why . . . I . . . I . . .

KEAWE. Here is the plain truth, Kokua. I have met you here by the roadside. I see your eyes and my heart has gone to you as swift as a bird.

KOKUA. Keawe has said the same to many young girls.

KEAWE. By the gods of the islands, I have not, Kokua. And so now, if you want none of me, say so, and I will go to my own place. But if you find me no worse than any other young man, say so too, and I will turn aside to your father's house, and tomorrow I will ask him for your hand.

KOKUA. My father's house lies this way . . .

MUSIC. *Up and out for . . .*

KEAWE (*jubilant*). Chang! Chang! Where are you?

CHANG (*fade on*). I am here, master.

KEAWE. Help me off with my things, Chang. We are going to be busy, you and I, these next few days. We must fit the Great House for a bride.

CHANG. Master is to be married?

KEAWE. To Kokua, daughter of Kiano. I spoke to her father last night. Life may be no better, Chang. This is the mountaintop. Here I am on my high place! Here . . .

CHANG. Master! Look at your arm.

KEAWE. My arm? A speck of something on it . . . rub it off, will you?

CHANG. Oh no, master! I won't touch it . . . come no closer to me!

KEAWE. Chang! I am your master!

CHANG. But the speck on your arm, master, is the Chinese evil.

KEAWE. Leprosy? Oh no, Chang . . . no . . . don't stare at me so! Go away . . . let me alone!

CHANG (*fade off*). I will wait your bidding.

KEAWE. Now it all ends. Very willingly could I leave Hawaii, the home of my fathers. Very lightly could I leave my house, the many-windowed, here upon the mountains. Very bravely could I go to Molokai, to Kalaupapa by the cliffs, to live with the smitten and to sleep there far from my fathers. But what wrong have I done . . . what sin lies upon my soul that I should have encountered Kokua coming cool from the sea water in the evening? Her may I never wed; her may I look upon no longer; her may I no more handle with my loving hand. It is for this . . . it is for you, O Kokua, that I pour my lamentations. . . . It is . . . but the bottle? If I could buy it back again . . . if I could ask the imp to cure me . . . it must be so. Would I beard the devil once only to get me a house, and not face him again to win Kokua? (*Calls.*) Chang! Chang!

CHANG (*fade on*). Master calls?

KEAWE. Where was Lopaka when I heard from him last?

CHANG. Singapore, master.

KEAWE. Pack all my things, and find me passage to Singapore! I must buy from him the bottle I was so pleased to be rid of!

MUSIC. *Surge up.*

SOUND. *Steamship whistle.*

MUSIC. *Give it a Chinese turn — fade for . . .*

MAN (*Chinese accent*). Mr. Lopaka is not in. He has left for long trip to the Indies.

KEAWE. Is there no way I can reach him?

MAN. Perhaps through his lawyer. (*Fade.*) I will give you his name . . .

MUSIC. *Up briefly — still Chinese — fade quickly for . . .*

LAWYER. Mr. Lopaka didn't leave us much in the way of an address. His route was undetermined. Was it important?

KEAWE. He purchased from me a certain piece of goods which I am very anxious to possess.

LAWYER. Don't say it! It's an evil, ugly business. Lopaka sold the affair. However, if you call at the house of Mr. Haole, you may be able to trace it. (*Fade.*) His address is . . .

MUSIC. *Up briefly — fade to low background through . . .*

KEAWE. Mr. Haole?

HAOLE (*jolly*). None other. And what can I do for you?

KEAWE. I am tracing an article sold by Mr. Lopaka to . . .

HAOLE. Sh! Yes, of course. (*Low.*) I haven't got it any longer, but . . . (*Fade.*) the man I sold it to . . .

MUSIC. *Up briefly.*

KEAWE (*fade on*). . . . and Mr. Haole sent me to you.

MAN (*whispering*). It has passed from my hands. (*Fade.*) Go to this man . . . see if he still has it.

MUSIC. *Up briefly and out sharply on unresolved chord.*

SERVANT. A Mr. Keawe to see you, sir.

YOUNG MAN (*dully*). Very well. Be seated, Mr. Keawe.

KEAWE. I'll take but a minute. I have come to buy the bottle.

YOUNG MAN (*horrified*). To what?

KEAWE. To buy the bottle. There's no need pretending you don't know what I mean.

YOUNG MAN. No. No need — no need at all.

KEAWE. Very well, then let's settle it. What is the price?

YOUNG MAN (*dully*). Oh. You don't know, then.

KEAWE. I am only asking you to tell me the price so that I can pay you.

YOUNG MAN. I bought the bottle for two cents.

KEAWE. Why, then, the price now is . . . one cent.

YOUNG MAN. I can't sell it for less.

KEAWE. And I won't be able to sell it at all. Very well, let's have it.

YOUNG MAN. You're going to buy?

KEAWE. Rather than die in loneliness without Kokua, I'll chance the fires of hell!

MUSIC. *Surge up — with unresolved chord — and hold in background.*

KEAWE. O bottle imp, make me once more a clean man, and let the Chinese evil depart hence, that I may wed Kokua!

MUSIC. *Resolve chord — fade out for . . .*

KOKUA. Chang, did your master Keawe say when he would come for his dinner?

CHANG. No, Mistress Kokua.

KOKUA (*sighing*). Was he always like this, Chang? So moody, so gruff . . . gone for so long in the evenings?

CHANG. No, mistress. It was after his trip to Singapore that he changed.

KOKUA. That was when we were married. Oh, Chang, do you think he is sorry? Has he tired of me? (*Weeps.*)

CHANG. There is something lying heavy on his heart, mistress. What it is . . .

SOUND. *Door opens.*

KEAWE (*angrily*). Is there no one in this house to help me with my horse? Must I stable it myself? What are you loitering around for, Chang? There's work to be done.

CHANG (*fade off*). Right away, sir.

KEAWE. And you, Kokua. Must you weep and snivel so that your husband has no cheer about him at all?

KOKUA (*through sobs*). O my husband, I have tried . . . if I only knew what were troubling you, and could share it with you! That would make it easier for us both!

KEAWE (*sarcastically*). Do you think so, little Kokua?

KOKUA. I can't feel that I have your love unless I share all things with you.

KEAWE. And if I told you that I had sold my soul to the devil for you, what would you think then?

KOKUA. Oh, Keawe!

KEAWE. Listen to my story, and see who should weep around this house. (*Fade.*) It was a . . .

MUSIC. *Up briefly — out for . . .*

KEAWE (*fade on*). . . . and so now, much as I delight in you, my mind is always on the bottle that I can never sell.

KOKUA (*gaily*). Oh, Keawe, Keawe! Why didn't you tell me all this before? You are worrying because you bought the bottle for a cent.

KEAWE (*interrupting*). You haven't understood a word, Kokua! I can't sell the bottle! I must keep it till I die.

KOKUA. All the world is not Hawaii, my Keawe. In France there is a coin called the centime. It takes five of them to make a cent.

KEAWE. Are you sure, Kokua?

KOKUA. I have seen the coin myself. We'll go to the French islands as fast as ships can bear us. There we have four centimes, three centimes, two centimes, one centime . . .

KEAWE. Four possible sales!

KOKUA. Let's leave immediately, Keawe, and in a week we'll be happily at rest!

MUSIC. *Up gaily — changing to sad — fading for . . .*

KEAWE. Shall we go back into the house, Kokua?

KOKUA. If you don't mind, Keawe, I'll stay out in the moonlight a while longer. Sometimes, when I look at the sea, it seems almost as though we were back in Hawaii.

KEAWE. That's why I want to go in the house. We've been gone too long, Kokua, and it's time we went home.

KOKUA. But we haven't sold the bottle! We can't leave yet, Keawe!

KEAWE. We've tried for six months — we thought it would take only a week. It seems pretty clear to me that we're not going to be able to sell it.

KOKUA. But we can't give up, Keawe. Think what it means.

KEAWE. I made the bargain, Kokua. I'll stick by it, but I want to end my days near the hills of my fathers, not in a strange land.

KOKUA. Keawe, you can't . . . I won't let you!

KEAWE. Don't weep, child. . . . Look you, I'll go in the house and wait for you. There's an old man by that tree, and it wouldn't be wise to let him hear us. (*Fade.*) We'll talk more when you come in.

KOKUA. Keawe! (*Weeps.*)

SECOND OLD MAN (*fade on*). Can I help you, young lady? I'm a stranger on these islands, but if there's anything I can do . . .

KOKUA. No. Thank you, but . . . Wait! There is something . . . a bottle that I want very dearly. He won't sell it to me, but he'd sell it to you, I'm certain. He'd be very eager to sell it to you.

OLD MAN. But I have no need of a bottle.

KOKUA. You don't understand. He'll sell you the bottle for four centimes, not a centime more. I'll give you the four centimes, and then buy the bottle from you for three centimes.

OLD MAN. For such a cheap bottle, you seem to be going to a good deal of trouble.

KOKUA. Never mind. It's a private matter. Will you do it for me?

OLD MAN. I don't like it . . . but I'll do it . . . if you'll promise to buy the bottle from me.

KOKUA. I do . . . by all the gods you hold dear. Take this money, now . . . bring the bottle back to me immediately. . . .

MUSIC. *Up and over — fade for . . .*

OLD MAN (*fade in — in a hurry*). Young lady . . . here . . . quickly. I have the bottle. Give me my three centimes. The man I bought it from is coming out to see you now. He nearly followed me.

KOKUA. Good man! Here's the money. . . . Now go, so that Keawe doesn't find you! I'll hide the bottle in my cloak. Thank you. You don't know what you've done.

OLD MAN (*fade off*). Look out . . . here he comes . . .

KEAWE (*fade on — calling*). Kokua! Kokua! Oh, my darling Kokua, do you know what has happened?

KOKUA. Tell me at once!

KEAWE. I have sold the bottle!

KOKUA. To whom? Tell me!

KEAWE (*laughing*). An old fool came and bought it while you were out here. . . . A worthy old man he seemed, too. But no one can judge by appearances. For why did the old reprobate require the bottle?

KOKUA (*humbly*). My husband, his purpose may have been good.

KEAWE (*laughing*). Fiddle . . . dee . . . dee. . . . An old rogue, I tell you, and an old ass to boot. For the bottle was hard enough to sell at four centimes, and at three it will be quite impossible. The margin was not broad enough, the thing begins to smell of scorching . . . brrr.

KOKUA. O my husband, is it not a terrible thing to save oneself by the eternal ruin of another? It seems to me I could not laugh. I would be humbled. I would be filled with melancholy. I would pray for the poor holder.

KEAWE (*angrily*). You may be filled with melancholy if you please. It is not the mind of a good wife. If you thought at all of me, you would sit shamed. (*Changing his tone.*) Come let's take a ride . . . the day is beautiful.

KOKUA. My husband, I am ill. I am out of heart. Excuse me, I can take no pleasure.

KEAWE (*again angrily*). This is your truth, and this your affection. Your husband is just saved from eternal ruin, which he encountered for the love of you . . . and you can take no pleasure . . . Kokua, you have a disloyal heart . . . I'll go out alone . . .

KOKUA. Very well, my husband. (*Fade.*) You'll find me waiting for you when you return.

MUSIC. *Up and — fade on note of intoxication.*

KEAWE (*tipsy*). Come along then, my fine sailing friend. I was a sailor once myself, and I like to help a friend. We'll go in my house, it's this one, right here.

BO'SUN (*laughing*). You were a sailor, says you, and lives in a house like this. Belay me!

KEAWE. Much good it does me to have a house, though. My wife sits home and sulks. Why, tonight, before I met you, I'd just had the most wonderful piece of luck, and would she help me celebrate it? She would not.

BO'SUN. Tha's women for you, every time.

KEAWE. Yep. She sits here at home . . . Oh! We better go quietly now, for fear she'll see us . . . sh!

BO'SUN. Is she still up, do you think?

KEAWE. There's a light by this window. I'll look in . . . sh, now! (*Gasp.*)

BO'SUN. Is she there?

KEAWE. The bottle. She has the bottle.

BO'SUN. Bottle? (*Happily.*) Good!

KEAWE (*sobered from shock*). She bought the bottle to save me. She sent the old man to do the errand for her.

BO'SUN. What are you talking about? If there's a bottle, let's have it.

KEAWE. This is a bottle with an imp of the devil in it. It'll bring you anything you ask for . . .

BO'SUN. I've heard tell of that. Lots of folks around here heard about it, only I don't believe it.

KEAWE. It's true. I owned the bottle till tonight, and sold it to an old man, so I could be rid of the devil in it, and die at peace. Only my wife in the kindness of her heart has bought it from him, and sits there now, staring at it . . . silently.

BO'SUN. Well, let's go in and surprise her, huh? Cheer her up.

KEAWE. No. Look, I'll give you two centimes with which to buy that bottle from her.

BO'SUN. You mean you want me to buy the bottle?

KEAWE. Yes. Go into the house. I'll wait where I can watch. Now, take these two centimes and offer her them for the bottle, which, if I am not mistaken, she will give you instantly. Bring it to me here, and I will buy it back from you for one centime; for that is the law with this bottle, that it still must be sold for a less sum. But whatever you do, never breathe a word to her that you have come from me.

BO'SUN. Mate, I wonder are you making a fool of me?

KEAWE. It will do you no harm if I am.

BO'SUN. That is so, mate.

KEAWE. And if you doubt me, you can try. As soon as you have the bottle, wish to have your pocket full of money, or a bottle of the best rum, or what you please, and you will see the virtue of the thing.

BO'SUN. Very well, Keawe, I will try; but if you are having your fun with me, I will take my fun out of you with a belaying pin. . .

KEAWE. Then go, quickly!

BO'SUN (*fade off. Singing*).

SOUND. *Knock on door — door opens.*

KOKUA (*off*). Who is it that comes at this hour of night?

BO'SUN. Nev' mind what. I've come to buy that precious bottle of yours, and I've got the two centimes to pay for it right here.

KOKUA. Are you serious?

BO'SUN. Are you going to give me the bottle, or ain't cha? I won't stand here forever.

KOKUA. I don't understand it, but I'll let you have it. Here! It must be the mercy of a kind god . . .

SOUND. *Door closes.*

BO'SUN (*board fade*). Come on . . . let's try it!

SOUND. *Drunken singing fading in* BO'SUN.

KEAWE. You have it, I see that.

BO'SUN. Hands off! Take a step near me and I'll smash your mouth. You thought you could make a cat's-paw of me, did you?

KEAWE. What do you mean?

BO'SUN. Mean? This is a pretty good bottle, this is; that's what I mean. How I got it for two centimes I can't make out, but I'm sure you shall not have it for one.

KEAWE (*gasping*). You mean you won't sell?

BO'SUN. No sir, but I'll give you a drink of the rum if you like.

KEAWE (*excitedly*). But I tell you the man who has that bottle goes to hell.

BO'SUN. I reckon I'm going anyway, and this bottle's the best thing to go with I've struck yet. No sir, this is my bottle now, and you can go and fish for another.

KEAWE. Can this be true? For your own sake, I beseech you, sell it to me.

BO'SUN. I don't value any of your talk. You thought I was a flat, now you can do without your old bottle. (*Fade off singing.*)

KEAWE (*calling*). Kokua! (*Fade — calling.*) Kokua! We're saved!

MUSIC. *Surge up and under for . . .*

NARRATOR (*low confidential*). So they lived a life of peace and plenty on the islands of Hawaii. Or so the story was told to me.

MUSIC. *Up and out.*

AFTER READING

1. What do you think finally became of the sailor who bought the bottle?

2. Do you at any time believe in the power of the imp? At what point in the story?

3. What examples of self-sacrifice do you notice?

4. What part does coincidence perform in the play?

5. Does this story gain anything by being laid in the South Seas? Would it be just as believable in, for example, western Europe?

6. Read the original story of the same title by Robert Louis Stevenson. In what important respects does the radio version differ from the original story? Which do you prefer? Why?

7. How do Lopaka and Keawe differ in personality? Refer to lines in the play to justify your statements.

8. What kind of movie would *The Bottle Imp* make? Support your point of view with sound reasons.

9. What leads normally intelligent people to believe in the magical powers of certain objects, such as a horseshoe or a rabbit's foot?

CHALLENGES

1. Lopaka at one time had the bottle imp. Why do you think he sold it? Write a conversation he has with Keawe in which he relates his experiences with the bottle and the manner in which he disposed of it.

2. How do you think the man from San Francisco obtained the bottle? Write an imaginary scene indicating how he purchased it.

3. Can you think of a different ending? Try writing one.

4. The sailor writes a letter to Keawe asking him to take back the bottle. Write the letter.

DRAMA WORKSHOP

A hint for radio listeners: The announcer is important!

Radio announcers are selected with care. Major networks employ only those who have had several years' experience with small local stations. Experience is necessary because an announcer performs a variety of duties. Besides announcing the station's call letters, he reads commercial announcements and news scripts, describes athletic contests and important current events, acts as master of ceremonies, conducts radio interviews, and even participates in skits and dramatic presentations if occasion demands.

If you are thinking of becoming an announcer, you ought to equip yourself by obtaining a college education. Your training should include instruction in dramatics, journalism, and foreign languages. It goes without saying that your voice must have a pleasing quality and your diction must reflect good American speech. In addition you ought to have a good appearance, for many radio shows are also presented before "live" audiences.

A radio announcer plays an important part in the success of a program. Listen carefully to an announcer who is generally recognized as top-notch and use him as a model for reading the announcer's roles in radio plays.

A hint for radio actors: Know the director's hand signals.

During the performance of a radio play a director gives instructions to the actors by means of silent hand signals. An actor must know and obey them instantly. The more common signals are the following:

- *Get ready to begin:* pointing upward toward the ceiling with an index finger
- *Begin:* pointing with an index finger at the person who is to speak
- *Stand closer to the microphone:* moving the palm of the hand toward the face
- *Get away from the microphone:* moving the hand away from the face, palm outward
- *Increase volume:* raising the hands, palms up
- *Decrease volume:* lowering the hands, palms down
- *Slow down:* pulling clenched hands away from one another as if stretching a rubber band
- *Speed up:* turning an index finger in the clockwise direction
- *Stop:* drawing an index finger across the throat
- *O.K.:* forming a circle by touching the tips of thumb and index finger

OTHER RADIO PLAYS YOU WILL LIKE TO READ

Cartwheel by Vick Knight (13). An improperly minted silver dollar has a strange history.

Daniel Webster and the Sea Serpent by Stephen Vincent Benét and Sheldon Stark (9). Daniel Webster finds Samanthy, the sea serpent, useful in Washington.

The Devil and Daniel Webster by Stephen Vincent Benét and Charles Jackson (17). Daniel Webster acts as defense attorney for a man who has sold his soul to the devil.

The Half-Pint Flask by Richard Sale and Margaret Lewerth (9). The theft of a glass flask from the grave of one of the natives leads to mysterious voodoo practice until the flask is recovered.

J. Smith and Wife by Charles Tazewell (40). J. Smith and his wife at first are refused entrance to Heaven, but their application is reviewed with good success.

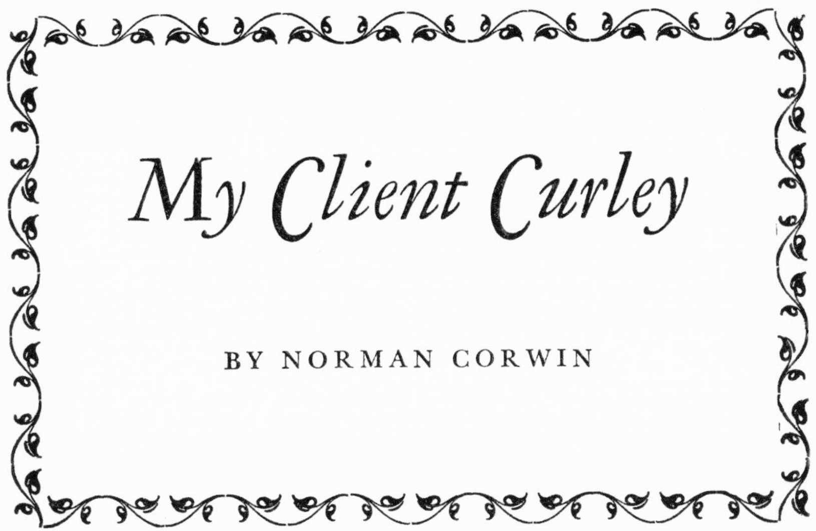

My Client Curley

BY NORMAN CORWIN

ABOUT THE PLAY

You'll probably want to produce *My Client Curley* in your class, first because it's a rattling good story, abounding in humorous touches and original situations, and second because it's easy to present, having few technical problems and no difficult characterizations. Mr. Corwin's script is based on an unpublished short story by Lucille Fletcher Herrmann. With Mrs. Herrmann's consent, Mr. Corwin modified the narrative in many particulars. In the original story Curley's entire life is lived in Hollywood, where he achieves stardom, and a fortune into the bargain, as a result of his unusual dancing talent. Mr. Corwin enlarged the original story, gave it a different setting, and injected satire of certain features of American life. (A vocabulary note giving definitions of specialized or difficult words in the play follows the text.)

Many plays have been written about dogs, cats, lions, bluebirds,

---

and other animals and birds, but *My Client Curley* is probably the only play ever written about a caterpillar — one which loves swing music and Beethoven at that!

ABOUT THE AUTHOR

Norman Corwin is generally acknowledged as one of our most original radio playwrights. He was born in Boston in 1910. After some time in the newspaper business, he joined the Columbia Broadcasting Company as a director-producer and introduced a new type of radio program with his series "Words without Music." During World War II he won a prize for his dramatization of the Bill of Rights, *We Hold These Truths,* and was commissioned to write a radio play to celebrate V–E Day, *On a Note of Triumph,* which has since been often rebroadcast. His radio plays have been collected in the following volumes: *Thirteen by Corwin, More by Corwin,* and *Untitled and Other Plays.* He was the first radio writer to be honored by the American Academy of Arts and Letters. Carl Van Doren, noted critic and historian, has said of Norman Corwin, "He is to American radio what Marlowe was to the Elizabethan stage."

MY CLIENT CURLEY

Characters

ANNOUNCER	KNELL
AGENT	MAN
FATSO	WOMAN
STINKY	SPOKESMAN
BIDDER	CONDUCTOR
CHILD	MUSICIAN
GIRL	A. P. REPRESENTATIVE
DISNEY	ELEANOR ROOSEVELT
FIRST LEPIDOPTERIST	PHILATELIST
SECOND LEPIDOPTERIST	POLICE ANNOUNCER
THIRD LEPIDOPTERIST	WINCHELL
EDITORIAL WRITER	FIND-CURLEYITE
DEFENDER	WAITER

SHIPPER

VOICES of the following newspapers and magazines: *Times, Post, Brooklyn Eagle, World-Telegram, News, Grdfico, Le Temps,* Shanghai paper, *Variety, Life*

ANNOUNCER. Ladies and gentlemen: In the following play, any similarity to caterpillars, living or dead, is purely coincidental.

MUSIC: *Symphonic treatment of "Yes, Sir, That's My Baby" up and out, under . . .*

AGENT. There are some things a man doesn't like to talk about because they're . . . (*Breaks off.*) Well, I'll just tell this story about my client Curley, and then I'll go back to the agent business and try to forget it. But if I should get a lump in my throat while I'm telling it, I hope you'll understand, because this whole thing was so recent I still feel pretty upset about it.

To make a long story short, I'm out walking one day in the suburbs where I live, when my attention is attracted by two kids sitting on the side of the road and one of them is playing a harmonica.

Harmonica in, well off mike, after "the side of the road."

They're bent over, watching something on the ground, and I, being curious, go over to see what it is.

Fade in harmonica, playing "Yes, Sir, That's My Baby."

AGENT. Hiya, boys, what you got there?

Harmonica stops abruptly.

FATSO. We got a trained caterpillar.

AGENT. What's trained about it?

STINKY. He dances.

AGENT (*laughing*). I don't believe it.

STINKY. He sure does!

FATSO (*the business brains*). Give us a nickel and we'll show you.

AGENT (*good-naturedly*). Oh, a racket, eh? All right, I'm a sucker. Here's two nickels.

FATSO. Thanks, Mister. Okay, play, Stinky.

Harmonica begins tune.

AGENT (*fascinated. After a moment*). Well, what do you know! (*To* STINKY.) Now stop.

Harmonica out.

AGENT. I'll be darned! Stops right when you do.

FATSO (*proudly*). Sure. That's the way Stinky trained him, didn't ya, Stinky?

STINKY. Aw, it was nothin'.

AGENT (*still incredulous*). Play some more, Stinky.

Harmonica starts and plays through briefly to finish.

AGENT (*laughing with delight*). Lies right down when you're finished!

STINKY. Sure, he's talented, ain't he? (*To* CURLEY, *affectionately.*) Come on up on my finger, Curley. Th—a-at's a boy!

AGENT. Does Curley dance to any kind of music?

FATSO. Nope. Only "Yes, Sir, That's My Baby."

AGENT. You mean to tell me he dances to only *one* tune?

STINKY. That's right. I tried lots more, but I guess he only likes that one.

AGENT. Well, why is that, do you suppose?

STINKY. Feller I know says he got a real musical ear.

FATSO. I guess that's what those two branches are on his head, huh? Musical ears.

AGENT. No, that's his antennae.

STINKY. Antenna? (*Laughs.*) He ain't no radio set! (*Vastly amused by his own joke, he laughs again.*)

FATSO (*joins in laughter*).

AGENT. Say!

FATSO. What?

AGENT. I wonder if he's got any snake blood in him? You know there are some snakes who dance.

FATSO. No kiddin'?

AGENT. Here, let me take your harmonica a minute.

STINKY. Okay. Sure.

AGENT. Curley may be related to one of them Asiatic snakes or something. Lemme play it a minute.

Harmonica plays "Hoochie Koochie" (danse de ventre).

AGENT (*stopping*). Nope. Won't budge. I guess it's an American caterpillar, all right.

STINKY. Oh, sure.

AGENT (*all business*). Look, fellers, I'll make you a proposition. How would you like to sell Curley?

FATSO (*the commercial-minded*). How much?

STINKY (*the sustaining-minded*). Wait a minute. I own Curley, and I don't wanna sell him.

AGENT. Why not, Stinky?

STINKY (*ashamed to confess he loves the thing*). Well, because I — well — just *because!*

FATSO (*interpreting*). Know why he don't wanna sell?

AGENT. Why?

FATSO. On account of he's stuck on him.

STINKY. Aw, shut up, Fatso!

AGENT. You mean you like Curley so much you don't want to part with him?

STINKY. I just don't want to sell him, that's all. Not even for a dollar. (*Afterthought.*) Not even for two dollars!

AGENT. Well, of course I don't think anybody'd ever offer you *that* much money.

STINKY. I don't care. He's my pet, and I want to keep him. I trained him from a pup.

AGENT. Now look, kiddo, I think you're a very bright and sensitive boy, and because of that, I'm going to make you an immediate cash payment of *five dollars* for Curley!

FATSO. Hey! *Five bucks!* Holy smackerels! Whadda ya say, Stinky? Huh?

STINKY (*almost in tears*). Well — gosh — I dunno.

FATSO. Take it, I'm tellin' ya! Now you can buy a bike!

STINKY (*deserted by* FATSO *and now a martyr to his affection for Curley*). Well, that sure is a lot of money — but, y'see — I *like* Curley, and I guess Curley likes me, too; and when we're alone I talk to him, and he understands me. (*Warming up; finding reasons to support his refusal to sell.*) Curley likes me around. He's very intelligent, even though he don't look so smart.

AGENT. Oh, he looks smart, all right.

STINKY (*deadly serious*). You know — if somebody took him away from me — Curley would die.

AGENT. Think so?

STINKY. Sure. He's only human, ain't he? He would absolutely die.

AGENT. Listen to me, Stinky. I'm going to talk to you man to man. This caterpillar you've got is very valuable. He's worth a lot of money — 'way more than five dollars, maybe.

FATSO. No kiddin'?

AGENT. Now this is what we're gonna do. Stinky, you're gonna *stay* with Curley and I'm gonna manage both of you. Curley will be my client!

FATSO. What's that mean?

STINKY. What's a client?

AGENT. Well, you wouldn't understand very well. That's something I'll have to explain to your parents, because I've got to get their signatures on a long-term contract with options. You're a minor under the law, you see.

STINKY (*apprehensive of the terminology*). I didn't do anything wrong, did I?

MUSIC. *Transitional cue, orchestra with harmonica.*

AGENT. That was how it began. I get Curley under my management, and take him and Stinky with me. The first thing I do is start out after some publicity, and *say* – do those reporters eat it up! Front page, with pictures! Pictures of Curley and pictures of Stinky and pictures of me; pictures of my client dancing on a leaf, curling around the mayor's finger, climbing up a pretty model's leg, sitting in a tiny box at the opera. And *headlines!* Headlines, like in the *Times* . . .

TIMES. Swing Caterpillar Sways to Strains of "Yes, Sir, That's My Baby"; Fred Astaire of Insect World Demonstrates Almost Human Sense of Rhythm.

MUSIC: *Motif.*

AGENT. The *Post* . . .

POST. Curley in Custody of Stinky, Young Svengali of Caterpillars.

MUSIC: *Motif.*

AGENT. The *Brooklyn Eagle* . . .

BROOKLYN EAGLE. Insect Phenomenon Learned to Truck in Truck Garden, Manager Avers.

MUSIC: *Motif.*

AGENT. The *World-Telegram* . . .

WORLD-TELEGRAM. The Curley Crawl Becomes New National Dance Sensation.

MUSIC: *Motif.*

AGENT. The *Daily News* . . .

NEWS. BUG CUTS RUG! Story on page 2.

MUSIC: *Finale treatment of motif.*

AGENT. And sure enough, with all that publicity, things really begin to happen. First, Bill Robinson introduces the Curley Capers at the Cotton Club!

MUSIC: *Effect of solo tap dancing.*

AGENT. Then Raymond Scott writes a song called "The Caterpillar Creep."

MUSIC: *"Caterpillar Creep."*

AGENT. Then half a dozen agencies bid for the rights to syndicate a comic strip.

BIDDER. Four hundred twenty-nine papers, five days a week, making a grand total of . . .

AGENT. Other companies pay me royalties for Curley balloons and spaghetti and dolls and toys and picturebooks and decorations on the outside of drinking glasses.

CHILD (*whining*). Maw, buy me the glass with Curley's picture on it!

AGENT. And to make a long story short, I get a vaudeville offer; the money begins to roll in; I hire an expensive suite and a secretary . . .

GIRL. Curley Enterprises. Good afternoon!

AGENT. I buy Stinky a bike and a new suit of clothes.

STINKY. Gee, thanks!

AGENT. The publicity begins to pile up, and at the height of the excitement, I get a wire from Hollywood!

DISNEY (*on filter*). Offer ten thousand for Curley appearance in feature-length cartoon. Propose using live character for first time among cartoon characters. Appreciate immediate answer. Would like to rush story and production. Cordially, Walt Disney.

AGENT. Mm. Oh — er — Miss Neilson!

GIRL. Yes?

AGENT. Take a wire to Walt Disney, Hollywood, California.

GIRL. Yes, sir.

GIRL. Curley price one hundred thousand.

GIRL. Is that all?

AGENT. Do you think I should ask for more?

GIRL. No, I mean is there any more to the wire?

Phone rings. Receiver off.

GIRL. Curley Enterprises. . . . Just a moment, please. (*To* AGENT.) *Time Magazine* on the line. Will you take it on the table phone?

AGENT (*going off*). All right.

SOUND *of phone receiver off, and following conversation is background all the way through to end of scene.*

AGENT. Hello? Yes? This is him. . . . Yes. . . . Well, you see . . . yuh. . . . Uhuh. . . . No, I discovered him in the boy's possession. . . . That's right. . . . No. . . . No. . . . Yes, sure. . . . No, he hasn't yet. . . . Right. . . . I keep him right here. . . . Stinky looks after him most of the time. . . . Yes. . . . What? . . . No. . . . Oh, no. . . . I beg your pardon. . . . Oh, by all means. . . . From the very first, yes . . . that's right . . . that's right. . . . Hm? . . . Not yet. . . . Probably not for another week or two. . . . Absolutely. . . . Well, we tried all kinds of tunes . . . no, sir . . . which . . . which . . . are you referring to? . . . No. . . . I don't. . . . Hm? . . . Yes. . . .

Second phone rings; perspective with the GIRL.

GIRL. Curley Enterprises. . . . Well, he's busy on another line. Who? . . . Oh yes. He wanted me to tell you to order a special airmail daily shipment of willow leaves from Florida. (*Third phone rings.*) Wait a minute, will you? (*Fourth phone rings; alternates with third. Finally the flustered* GIRL *can stand it no longer, and she shouts to the* AGENT.) You better hire some more secretaries!

MUSIC: *Sock cue. Rides over ringing phones and conversation.*

AGENT. Well, things are going in great shape and Curley is making us a bundle of dough, when all of a sudden I get three visitors I didn't figure on.

FIRST LEPIDOPTERIST. We have been reading about your wonderful specimen in the papers, and we have come to ask permission to examine it.

AGENT. Examine it? What for?

SECOND LEPIDOPTERIST. We are lepidopterists.

AGENT. Lepidopterists? But Curley's a caterpillar, not a leopard.

THIRD LEPIDOPTERIST. Ah no, my dear man — lepidopterology is a branch of entomology dealing with the insect order of which your — er — shall we say client — is a member.

AGENT. Well, I'm sure Curley doesn't want to be examined by nobody.

FIRST LEPIDOPTERIST. Oh, come, come! If this caterpillar is as remarkable as the newspapers say, then you certainly owe science the courtesy of permitting an examination.

SECOND LEPIDOPTERIST. Exactly.

THIRD LEPIDOPTERIST. It would be nothing short of criminal to withhold such knowledge from science.

AGENT (*grudgingly*). Well — if you want to put it that way, I suppose —

FIRST LEPIDOPTERIST. It will take no more than two minutes.

AGENT. Oh — I suppose it's all right. Come with me, please.

Steps, as of group passing from one room to another. Door opens, closes.

AGENT. Hello, Stinky.

STINKY. Hello.

AGENT. This is Master Stinky, gentlemen — discoverer and trainer of my client. He guards Curley all the time.

ALL (*ad lib greetings*).

AGENT. Well, there he is in that box. Please be careful how you handle him.

SECOND LEPIDOPTERIST. Aaahhh — here you are!

THIRD LEPIDOPTERIST. My! Muscular little fellow, isn't he?

FIRST LEPIDOPTERIST. Mm-hm. (*Examining.*) Normal mandible . . . unusually conspicuous first maxillae . . .

SECOND LEPIDOPTERIST. I say, watch out there, Doctor, he's trying to bite you!

THIRD LEPIDOPTERIST. Ha! Never been attacked by a caterpillar before! Astounding!

FIRST LEPIDOPTERIST. See here, Doctor — just notice this remarkable elongation of the abdominal feet.

SECOND LEPIDOPTERIST. Yes, quite. And doesn't this feature make you think of the *Aglais antiopa?*

THIRD LEPIDOPTERIST. Incredible!

FIRST LEPIDOPTERIST. Look here! Isn't *this* remarkable! I've never seen such ocelli except in the *Melanargia galathea.* And the chitinization . . . !

AGENT. No kidding?

SECOND LEPIDOPTERIST (*to the* AGENT). Well, sir! Congratulations!

This is a remarkable specimen, even before we test its reactions to musical stimuli.

AGENT. Gosh, thanks.

THIRD LEPIDOPTERIST. It is of the ordinary genus *Papilio rutulus,* mind you, but it has the most extraordinary features. . . .

AGENT. Thanks very much.

FIRST LEPIDOPTERIST. But — ahum — we feel that the specimen would be much more valuable to society if you, instead of exhibiting it for commercial purposes, were to — uh — lend or donate it to the Museum of Natural History, where it could be further studied by the leading entomologists of the world.

AGENT. But I . . .

SECOND LEPIDOPTERIST. Yes, and when it dies, we can dissect it, and . . .

STINKY (*terrified by the thought*). No! No! They're not gonna take him away! (*Crying.*) Don't let them take Curley! (*Keeps protesting and crying under . . .*)

THIRD LEPIDOPTERIST. Don't cry, my boy, we're not going to hurt him.

FIRST LEPIDOPTERIST (*ignoring the commotion*). An insect like this occurs probably once in a million years — and surely, for the sake of a few dollars, you're not going to risk injuring him by overwork!

AGENT (*rising above mercenary motives*). Are you accusing me of sacrificing Curley's health for *profits?* (*Scornfully.*) Why, that's ridiculous! Curley is . . .

Knocking on door. All noise stops, including STINKY's *protestation.*

AGENT. Yes — come in.

Door opens.

GIRL. Just got another wire from the coast! Disney's raised his offer to twenty thousand!

AGENT (*heatedly*). Twenty! Tell him a hundred thousand or nothing!

MUSIC: *Sock cue up, then down behind . . .*

AGENT. Well, the papers get hold of the lepidopterists' story, and there's another pile of publicity. It gets to be a moral issue, with preachers delivering sermons, and all like that. I'm attacked editorially for exploiting caterpillar labor.

EDITORIAL (*fade on*). . . . of the shameless exploitation of a little unsuspecting insect, by a mercenary agent who has turned to his own greedy personal advantage a natural phenomenon which belongs nowhere else but in a museum. The public at large is to be condemned for encouraging this veritable slave-trader to continue . . . (*Fading.*) . . . his career of rank exhibitionism, unabashed and in the full glare of wide publicity . . .

AGENT. But on the other hand, I am defended as an individualist who refuses to submit to regimentation!

DEFENDER. A man owns a clever bug. He has the right to manage that bug. There is no *question* about his status as manager of that bug. Yet he is asked to release his client for scientific purposes. He refuses. He has a right to refuse. Nobody denies that right. Yet in certain quarters he is attacked merely because he insists upon his constitutional guarantees. We say it is consoling to find a man, in this day of reckless encroachment upon the individual, who will stand up and fight for his rights. We wish him well. We stand behind him, foursquare, our feet firmly implanted in the soil from which his bug has sprung, to support his defiance . . . (*Fading.*) . . . of those who would turn back the progress . . .

AGENT. The American Legion and the Daughters of the American Revolution send Curley an engraved silver-plated twig and a miniature flag to put on top of his box. The foreign correspondents get busy and cable stories to their papers. In Madrid, the Spanish *Gráfico* comes out with a dirty dig.

GRÁFICO. *Más los norteamericanos no deben olvidar que la danza española es la mejor de todas y que si la oruga del Señor Stinky tuviese un poquitin de buen oído para la música, reconoceria los irresistibles ritmos de la jota, y no se limitaria a tocar* "Yes, Sir, That's My Baby." *Es un insulto a los paises latinos que esse insecto . . .*

AGENT. How do you like that for nerve? That's the Latin mind for ya! But darned if the Curley motif ain't reflected, as they say, in the latest Paris fashions. Caterpillar doodads on hats and coats and scarfs and all like that. *Le Temps* — that's a newspaper in Paris — comes out with a swell plug.

LE TEMPS. *Tous ceux qui aiment la nature, de même que ceux qui s'intéressent aux aspects les plus subtiles de la danse et de la musique, se réjouiront avec notre république sœur, les Etats-Unis, de la découverte faite récemment par un garçon qui s'appelle Stinky . . . la découverte d'une chenille dansante que le monde connaît affectueusement sous le nom de Curley. Et c'est remarquable de constater que cet insecte ne consent á danser que si l'on joue l'air justement célèbre: "Oui, monsieur, C'est Mon Bébé"!*

AGENT. And you know what? My clipping service sends me some encouraging comment from Shanghai, which I get my laundryman to translate.

CHINESE.

六月上海電

聲音之道與性情通
其感人亦微矣哉故一曲
雍門鬼神歆泣成連海上
禽鳥移人從未有不定中
聲而可言正樂不嫺妙技
而可說知音者也音樂名
家士丁記君無所不能復
樂所不精允文允武担任
各劇無不盡量拍演亦
現身術界不可多得之全

AGENT. The Maharajah of Lahore sends Curley some willow leaves from the sacred willow trees of the temple.

STINKY. Gee, look, a package from a place named Lakeshore with a lot of funny-looking stamps.

AGENT. Lahore, not Lakeshore.

STINKY. C'n I have the stamps?

AGENT. Yeah — here y'are. . . . I sign Curley up for a superspecial movie short, and it sweeps the box office of the country in spite of terrible weather, including blizzards and rainstorms. *Variety* reports:

VARIETY. Bliz and Driz Fail to Fizzle Biz as Bug Biffs B.O. from N.Y. to L.A.

AGENT. *Life Magazine* runs a Margaret Bourke-White picture of Curley on the cover, with the caption:

LIFE. Curley.

AGENT. CBS does a pickup direct from Curley's box, bringing the sound of Curley eating dinner.

KNELL. This is Jack Knell speaking to you from the headquarters of Curley Enterprises, where we have a microphone buried among willow leaves, to pick up the sound of the world's leading insect dancer, busy . . . (*Fading.*) . . . eating dinner after a hard day's work of exhibiting his talents to the press. . . .

AGENT. The *New Yorker* comes out with a cartoon showing Martha Graham nibbling willow leaves.

MAN (*laughing*). Did you see this cartoon in the *New Yorker*?

WOMAN. Lemme see. (*Silence.*) Well, what's funny about that?

MAN. For heaven's sake, don't you get the point?

WOMAN. No.

MAN. Well, don't you know who Martha Graham is?

WOMAN. Yes.

MAN. And you know who Curley is, of course?

WOMAN. The caterpillar.

MAN. Yes. . . . Well, now . . . (*Fading.*) . . . you see, Curley lives on willow leaves, and . . .

AGENT. Walt Disney raises his bid to fifty thousand, but I still hold out for a hundred thousand; Grover Whalen invites Curley to do an English country dance on the cover of the Magna Carta at the World's Fair; and, to make a long story short, everything's going along hunky-dory until one day some *more* public-spirited guys get ahold of Curley—only this time they're not scientists, but musicians.

SPOKESMAN (*fading on*). And therefore, in the interests of music, we of the committee feel that you would be rendering an invaluable service to musical knowledge if you would permit us to test the effect of *classical* music on your client.

AGENT. But what good will that do anybody?

SPOKESMAN. Why, it may open up an entirely new field of psychology in relation to music. The world knows very little about musical instincts of animals, and nothing at all about insects'. Now . . .

AGENT. But you're wasting your time. Curley dances to only one tune.

SPOKESMAN. Have you *tried* other tunes?

AGENT. Why, sure. Tell him what you've played, Stinky.

STINKY. I played "It Ain't Gonna Rain No More," "My Country, 'Tis of Thee," "The Beer Barrel Polka," "Shine On, Harvest Moon," "The Music Goes Round and . . . "

SPOKESMAN. Ah, but no *classical* music!

AGENT. Sure we did. I myself played "Ah, Sweet Mystery of Life," by Victor Herbert.

SPOKESMAN (*condescendingly*). But you haven't tried any symphonies, have you?

AGENT (*straight*). Disney's trying to get us for a Silly Symphony right now. His latest offer . . .

SPOKESMAN. No, I'm afraid you don't understand. Let me explain what we propose to do. (*Fading.*) We get Curley in a studio with an orchestra and go through a careful series of tests, using selected symphonic music of dancelike tempo. Now, by the choice of representative works, we can quickly establish . . .

Rap of baton.

CONDUCTOR. All right! I know you're tired, gentlemen; we've now been through sixty-seven pieces already. But let's try a few more, and then we'll quit until tomorrow.

MUSICIAN. Has the caterpillar moved at all?

CONDUCTOR. So far he hasn't budged once, but maybe we'll get him with the "Habañera" from *Carmen*.

Baton rapping for attention.

MUSIC: *"Habañera" for about twelve measures. Then:*

CONDUCTOR (*perfunctorily; this is the sixty-eighth time he's had to stop almost at the beginning*). Stop . . . stop.

MUSIC: *Out.*

CONDUCTOR. All right, try Number 69 — *Rosamunde* ballet.

MUSIC: *Same business as before.*

CONDUCTOR. Stop.

MUSIC: *Out.*

CONDUCTOR. Next, Number 70 — Strauss's "Perpetuum Mobile."

MUSIC: *Same business as before. Fade under:*

AGENT. For two and a half days this went on, and finally, after the two-hundred-second try, something happened that really made the papers sit up and take notice all over again. The Associated Press next day carried this story.

Fade in news printer. Establish, and take down for . . .

ASSOCIATED PRESS. Curley, the terpsichorean caterpillar, today staggered scientists and musicians when he suddenly went into a stately dance upon hearing the second movement of Beethoven's Eighth Symphony. The movement, marked Allegretto Scherzando, was the two-hundred-third musical sampling performed in an effort to determine whether the super-caterpillar could, or would, dance to anything besides the song "Yes, Sir, That's My Baby." The insect further astonished observers by dancing in a contrapuntal manner to an arrangement of melodies from both the song and the movement.

Scientists are unable to explain the phenomenon. (*Fade in Allegretto Scherzando movement after "unable."*) The management of the caterpillar announced meanwhile that Curley will appear as the lead in a ballet entitled "Extravaganza for Insects Only" by William Saroyan, and that Curley will also be seen soon in a dance recital at Carnegie Hall.

MUSIC: *Up full and down, under . . .*

AGENT. Well, then things really begin to break for us. Mrs. Roosevelt writes about it in her column, "My Day."

ELEANOR. It is not often that a creature smaller than one's little finger can completely captivate the imagination of millions. Yet such is the remarkable truth about the caterpillar named Curley, and only today I was telling the President that . . . (*Fading.*) . . . it has been many years since the country has become so interested in . . .

AGENT. There's talk among stamp collectors of issuing a special Curley stamp.

PHILATELIST. And since the Curley stamp would be the only insect subject in existence, its value to philately would naturally . . . (*Fading.*) . . . assume prodigious proportions . . .

AGENT. Scientific societies offer to investigate Curley's genius – and would you believe that the annual convention of the American Lepidopterological and Entomological Academy even invites Stinky to lecture before it.

STINKY (*echo – hesitantly; scared; obviously no speechmaker*). Er – so I says to my mother, "Ma, can I have a penny? I want to buy a piece of candy," so my mother says yes, so she gives me the penny – er – so on my way to the store, I see a caterpillar – uh – crossing the road – er – um – so I stopped to watch it, see? So then (*Fading.*) I picked it up, and then I started to whistle a song – uh – and it happened to be – er – "Yes, Sir, That's My Baby."

AGENT. And all this time the money keeps coming in. We're getting along fine, although it costs a lot to keep up my expensive offices and staff of secretaries, but I'm figuring on getting the big dough – the hundred thousand from Disney, and then retiring, see? Well, to make a long story short, there are a couple of exchanges of telegrams and phone calls, with me holding out for my price, and then one night Disney wires.

DISNEY (*filter*). Will meet your price of hundred thousand. Please fly out with Curley next plane.

AGENT. Wow! Am I excited! I rush into the next room, where Stinky and Curley are sleeping.

Door.

AGENT. Stinky! Wake up! We're rich! We're practically millionaires!

STINKY (*sleepily*). What's the matter?

AGENT (*excitedly*). Come on, kid! Get your clothes on! Hurry! You're gonna take a long airplane ride with me and Curley! And, boy, I'm gonna buy Curley the juiciest willow leaf he ever ate in his life! . . . Now lemme tell the news to Curley. (*As if opening Curley's box.*) Here you are, little fella, here you . . . (*Freezes, then panicky.*) Where is he? Why isn't he in his box? Where's Curley? *Curley!*

STINKY (*refusing to believe*). I put him to bed all right. Ain't he in his box?

AGENT. Quick! Look all around the room. Under the carpet, under the bed, on the walls – everywhere – And be careful where you walk!

STINKY (*half calling, half crying*). Curley! Come back! Curley! Where are you, Curley?

AGENT. Curley! Curley, listen . . . (*Sings "Yes, Sir," in a croaking, terror-stricken voice.*)

STINKY (*joins in the general desultory singing, interspersed with cries for Curley*).

AGENT. Curley! I love you! Where are you?

STINKY. Curley, don't leave us!

AGENT. A hundred thousand bucks, Curley! (*Sings vehemently; breaks off when he gets an idea.*) Here, Stinky! Take this flashlight and look for him along the corridor and ask the manager to let you look at the bottom of the elevator shaft. Meanwhile I'll phone the police!

STINKY. (*Goes off half singing, half crying.*)

Phone receiver jiggles.

AGENT. Operator! Operator! Get me the police headquarters! Operator!

Siren.

POLICE RADIO (*filter*). Calling all cars. Calling all cars. Be on the lookout for a dancing caterpillar. Be on the lookout for a dancing caterpillar. C-A—T-E—R-P-I—L-L—A-R – caterpillar. That is all!

Code.

WINCHELL. Flash! The Federal Bureau of Investigation will neither deny nor confirm rumors that Curley, the hundred-thousand-dollar caterpillar, was *kidnaped!*

Single Chime.

ANNOUNCER. Ladies and gentlemen, we have been requested by the civic authorities to make the following announcement. Whenever you hear the song "Yes, Sir, That's My Baby" will you please watch very carefully, wherever you may be, for a dancing caterpillar in your vicinity. This announcement is (*Fading.*) in reference to Curley, the famous caterpillar whose recent career has . . .

AGENT. The whole country searches in vain; nobody's seen Curley.

The police throw out a dragnet. Posses are formed. Radio stations play "Yes, Sir, That's My Baby" at intervals throughout the day, and ask all listeners to be on the lookout; Curley fans from all over send in money for a Find-Curley Fund.

FIND-CURLEYITE (*orating — slight echo*). And I am privileged, as president of the Find-Curley Club, to announce to the members that the Find-Curley Fund has reached the impressive and staggering total of twelve thousand, three hundred eighty-five dollars and fourteen cents, with the entire South yet to be heard from!

CAST (*great applause*).

FIND-CURLEYITE. And I am positive that every mother's son of you — yes, and every father's daughter — will pledge his or her heart and hand to the one main and permanent objective — that Curley may be found!

CAST (*even greater applause*).

AGENT. But nobody finds Curley. And now that he's gone, I begin to realize how much I love that bug. I begin to understand why it was Stinky couldn't bear to sell him to me, 'way back in those happy days. I can't bear thinking of willow leaves. I find myself hating all birds and looking suspiciously at cats. And I take to drinking. . . .

Light background of sound.

WAITER. What will it be for you, sir?

AGENT. A triple zombie.

WAITER. Are you sure you . . .

AGENT. *A triple zombie!*

WAITER. Yes, sir. . . .

Background sound out.

AGENT. And even Stinky tries to drink his way out of his grief. . . .

Background sound in.

WAITER. And what will it be for you, young man?

STINKY. A cup of coffee — and make it *black!*

WAITER. Are you sure you want . . .

STINKY. *Black coffee!*

WAITER. Yes, sir.

Background sound out.

AGENT. Meanwhile, sympathizers from all over the world, including Scandinavian countries, send me caterpillars, hoping maybe they have found Curley and are eligible for a reward offered by the Find-Curley Fund!

SHIPPER. Mister, here's another barrel of caterpillars from Australia. Where shall I put it?

AGENT. Give it to the zoo.

SHIPPER. Which zoo, mister?

AGENT. Any zoo, any zoo — so long as you get it out of here!

SHIPPER. Okay, mister.

Door closes.

AGENT. Days go by. Weeks go by. I send Stinky home.

STINKY (*tearfully*). Good-by.

AGENT. Good-by, Stinky. Well, at least you got a nice suit of clothes on you, and a fine automobile and a chauffeur to drive you home.

STINKY. I would rather have Curley back again.

AGENT. Yes, I know. Well — good-by.

STINKY. G'by.

AGENT. G'by.

STINKY. G'by. (*Pause.*)

AGENT. And then one day I'm sitting in my place, playing sadly on the piano with one finger, as is my want.

MUSIC: *One-finger plunking of "Yes, Sir" on piano.*

AGENT. All of a sudden, out from under the music rack creeps — Curley!

MUSIC: *Piano stops.*

AGENT. Only he's changed. He's different. He's not dancing any more. He — he's a — a *butterfly!*

MUSIC: *Orchestra sneaks in with Beethoven movement, softly.*

AGENT (*to* CURLEY, *tenderly*). Curley! Hello, Curley . . . you're a big boy now, ain't you? . . . (*Low, narrating.*) He flutters his wings a little when I say that, and I stroke his antennae, which are now very long and beautiful. I see he's getting restless for the outdoors, where he no doubt hears the call of his mate, so I sing a farewell to him.

MUSIC: *Orchestra stops.*

AGENT (*sings softly "Yes, Sir"*). He flutters around my head, and then flies over to a picture of Stinky on the bureau, and then flutters back to me . . . and after one long look at me, he flies out of the window, never more to come back again.

MUSIC: *Sneak in slow reprise combining both the Beethoven and "Yes, Sir" themes, and hold under . . .*

AGENT. To make a long story short, I sit down, and I feel like crying. In fact, I do cry. (*Pause.*) Yes, who would ever think that a grown man would ever cry about a caterpillar? But I did, and I'm not ashamed to admit it.

MUSIC: *Up briefly, then down again for . . .*

AGENT. Well . . . that's the story of my client Curley.

MUSIC: *Up to finish.*

VOCABULARY NOTE

There are a number of unusual words in *My Client Curley,* some of which you will want to remember and some of which are technical terms of passing interest only. Among the latter are *maxillae* (jawbones), *chitinization* (the process of making an insect's "skin" into a hard and horny shell), *Aglais antiopa* (a large yellow-and-blue butterfly), *Melanargia galathea* (the marbled white European butterfly), *ocelli* (little eyes), *Papilio rutulus* (a species of swallowtail butterfly), and *lepidoptera* (butterflies and moths). What impression is Mr. Corwin trying to create by using these specialized words?

Among the words which you should know are the following: *mandible,* a jaw; *mercenary,* acting merely for profit; *unabashed,* not disconcerted or confused; *regimentation,* the process of organizing people into groups in which all must act the same way; *encroachment,* the act of intruding or trespassing upon; *contrapuntal,* according to the rules of counterpoint in music; *philately,* the collecting and study of postage stamps; *reprise,* a repetition or encore. Margaret Bourke-White is a famous photographer; Martha Graham is a well-known dancer.

AFTER READING

1. The author describes Fatso as "commercial-minded" and Stinky as "sustaining-minded." What is meant by these descriptions? In what ways is Fatso less likable than Stinky?

2. Why couldn't Stinky sign a contract with the Agent?

3. The *Post* headline refers to Stinky as a "Young Svengali of Caterpillars." What does this mean? (If you don't know, you can find an explanation in a large dictionary under the entry *Trilby,* or in *The Oxford Companion to English Literature,* or *The Reader's Digest of Books.*)

4. Mr. Corwin injects a little humor into the newspaper headlines by alliteration and puns. Find instances of each. (Alliteration is a succession of words beginning with the same sound.)

5. Why are two phone calls carried on simultaneously? What effect is the author trying to produce on the listener?

6. The Agent is indignant when the First Lepidopterist insinuates that Curley's health may be impaired by overwork. (The Agent protests: "Are you accusing me of sacrificing Curley's health for *profits?* Why, that's ridiculous!") What makes the Agent's protestation funny?

7. *Variety* is a theatrical weekly famous for its treatment of our language. Translate the *Variety* headline into acceptable English.

8. Can you find any instances of satire in the play? (Satire is a sort of humor in which public events or the follies of mankind are ridiculed.)

CHALLENGES

1. Write a letter to your favorite radio station criticizing, either favorably or unfavorably, a recent dramatic program.

2. Read *Thirteen by Corwin* or *More by Corwin,* or both, and review them for your classmates. Which plays in these volumes do you like best? Why?

3. There's an excellent short story about a caterpillar that you will like to read. It's entitled *The Death of Red Peril* and can be found in *Mostly Canallers,* a collection of short stories by Walter Edmonds. Red Peril was a stubby red caterpillar with a sort of wart

near his tail. He could outrace every caterpillar along the Erie Canal. His owner trained him like a race horse and matched him against Leopard Pillar, Buffalo Big Blue, Fenwick's Night Mail, and many other caterpillars, but there wasn't one the equal of Red Peril. At least not until he met the Horned Demon of Rome. And then — but you'd better read the story for yourself. Report on it to your class and discuss its possibilities as the basis for a radio play.

DRAMA WORKSHOP

A hint for radio listeners: Notice the transitions.

In radio broadcasting six types of transitional devices — or "bridges" — are used to indicate the end of one scene and the beginning of another.

Music is the most common and readily adaptable method of establishing a new scene or mood. *Voice-fading,* which consists of allowing the final words of a line to drift farther and farther away until they are inaudible, is also very common. After the voice fades out, a new scene starts. *Sound effects* also indicate a change of place or time. For example, the rapping of a baton, the screech of a siren, and the closing of a door are among the sounds Corwin uses in *My Client Curley* to indicate a change of locale. *An announcement* by a narrator can effect a scene transition and inform the audience of intervening events. *Silence* or "dead air" of a few seconds' duration is another means of changing scenes. *Combinations* of the foregoing are possible as, for instance in *My Client Curley,* orchestral music riding over ringing phones and conversation.

One test of good radio production is the naturalness and appropriateness of its transitions. A good performance does not disrupt the attention or break the mood of the listeners by abrupt or confusing transitions.

A hint for radio actors: Know radio language.

Radio script writers and directors have coined many words to express their ideas about production. These terms are clear and unmistakable to radio people, but to those who have had little or no experience with radio studios they may be confusing or incomprehensible. Here are brief explanations of radio terms appearing in *My Client Curley* and other radio plays in this volume.

Ad lib: to improvise speech, to speak impromptu. It comes from the Latin phrase *ad libitum,* meaning *freely.* *Cross fade:* gradually dissolving one sound and increasing another. *Fade in:* to increase the volume of sound by gradually moving closer to the mirophone. The engineer can obtain the same effect by adjusting the volume control. *Fade out:* to diminish the volume of sound by gradually moving away from the microphone. As in *fading in,* the engineer can produce a similar effect by a dial adjustment. *Motif:* a recurrent theme, usually a musical phrase. *P.A.:* a public address system. *Ride over*: to drown out, to be heard above all other sounds. *Segue:* a musical transition or bridge. The music moves from one key or tempo to another without interruption. (The pronunciation used by radio people is "seg-way.") *Sock cue:* a sudden and energetic musical effect.

OTHER RADIO PLAYS YOU WILL LIKE TO READ

One Special for Doc by Milton Geiger (17). An old pharmacist dissuades a young man from suicide by a clever ruse.

Seven Waves Away by Richard Sale and Margaret Lewerth (9). The struggle for existence in an overcrowded lifeboat leads to an inhuman dumping of the women and children.

Sorry, Wrong Number, by Lucille Fletcher (17). A helpless invalid learns, by an accidental mix-up of phone calls, of a plot to murder her.

The Nosebag

BY LOUIS MacNEICE

ABOUT THE PLAY

You'll enjoy *The Nosebag.* The original story is a simple and delightful folk tale which has been popular for generations in eastern Europe and is still told by peasants around their hearth fires. When it was presented over the British Broadcasting Company network a few years ago, it was an instant success. The listening public liked its freshness, imagination, and cleverness. Mr. MacNeice did not have a copy of the original tale at hand when he prepared his radio script. He relied solely on his creative ability and childhood memory, and the result is a funnier account than the original. If you wish to compare, read *The Soldier and Death* by Arthur Ransome or another version of the same story by Leonard A. Magnus in his book *Russian Fairy Tales.* A third account is entitled *The Soldier and the Demons* by Ida Zeitlin in *Skazki,* a collection of tales and legends of old Russia.

The play contains a few unfamiliar words but you'll be able to

---

guess their meanings from the context. You might like to know that *gnädige Frau* is a German expression meaning *my good woman,* that a *boyar* is a Russian aristocrat who ranks just below a ruling prince, and that a *tocsin* is an alarm bell.

ABOUT THE AUTHOR

Louis MacNeice is one of England's most distinguished contemporary poets. Born in Ireland, he was educated in one of England's great public schools and later at Merton College, Oxford. For ten years he taught classical languages and literature in English universities before joining the British Broadcasting Company as a feature writer and producer. A few years ago he started to write radio plays, and quickly achieved a notable reputation because of his craftsmanship and originality. He is the author of fifteen books of poetry, plays, and criticism. His publications include *Poems, The Agamemnon of Aeschylus, Letters from Iceland* (with W. H. Auden), *The Poetry of William Butler Yeats, Christopher Columbus,* and *Springboard.*

THE NOSEBAG

Characters

ANNOUNCER
SOLDIER
FIRST BEGGAR
SECOND BEGGAR
THIRD BEGGAR
FIRST PEASANT
SECOND PEASANT
LANDLORD
MARYA
CHAMBERLAIN
TSAR
DEVIL CAPTAIN
FIRST DEVIL
SECOND DEVIL
THIRD DEVIL
FOURTH DEVIL
LITTLE DEVIL
FIRST SMITH
SECOND SMITH
WIFE
DOCTOR
MAIDSERVANT
DEATH
OLD WOMAN
SENTRY
ROBBER SOUL
FEMALE SOUL
CROOK SOUL
OFFICER
GATESMAN

ANNOUNCER. *The Nosebag!* The program that follows is a traditional Russian folk tale. The story itself is fantastic, but the hero is a true Russian peasant. We hope you will all find something in *The Nosebag.*

Introductory music.

SOLDIER. Damn the sergeant! Damn the officer! Damn the Colonel! Damn the General! Who do they think they are to do such a thing to me? After twenty-five years of service. Out on my neck and the wind is cold and the steppes are wide and the years are empty. A discharged soldier that nobody wants. Twenty-five years of service to God and the Great Tsar. And now discharged . . . discharged! And nothing to show for it all but three dry biscuits. Three . . . dry . . . biscuits. Well. It's a long road; I'd best be moving. Left — left — left right left; left — left —

FIRST BEGGAR. Soldier! Soldier! Stop!

SOLDIER. What's up, father? (*Pause.*) No, I've got no money.

FIRST BEGGAR. No money, soldier. Food! I have sixty years of age and little breath in my body. Hunger is always with me and —

SOLDIER. Hunger? Take him away. And take this biscuit too.

FIRST BEGGAR. May the good God bless you, soldier.

SOLDIER. Aye, may the good God bless me. Two . . . dry . . . biscuits. Left — left — left right —

SECOND BEGGAR. Soldier!

SOLDIER. What do *you* want?

SECOND BEGGAR. Food, soldier, for the love of God. I have seventy years of age and —

SOLDIER. No flesh on your bones, eh. This won't help you much but —

SECOND BEGGAR. A biscut! A biscuit! May the good God reward you.

SOLDIER. In the next life maybe. One . . . dry . . . biscuit. Well, well, a Russian soldier cannot drown in water or burn in fire. This is a long road but who knows whether —

THIRD BEGGAR. Soldier!

(*The* THIRD BEGGAR *speaks with a serenity lacking in his predecessors.*)

SOLDIER. A third old rag-and-bones!

THIRD BEGGAR. Soldier, forgive me for stopping you. I am an old man — older than you can guess — I have not eaten today, yesterday I dined on birch bark —

SOLDIER. I've done that in my time. I know what you'd like. See this? Not so fast, graybeard. Suppose we break it in two?

THIRD BEGGAR. Just as you will, soldier.

SOLDIER. Seems more sense to halve it. All the same . . .

THIRD BEGGAR. All the same?

SOLDIER. Your brother beggars got a biscuit each; it don't seem fair that – Here!

THIRD BEGGAR. All for me?

SOLDIER. Aye, beggar. I never liked biscuits anyway.

THIRD BEGGAR. I thank you, soldier. Now it is my turn. Tell me how I can help you.

SOLDIER. You! Help me! God bless you, beggar, you couldn't help a fly.

THIRD BEGGAR. You think not? Have faith. What would you like?

SOLDIER. Nothing, old fellow, nothing. Leastways, maybe, for a keepsake – you haven't a pack of cards, have you?

THIRD BEGGAR. Cards? Here.

SOLDIER. Upon my soul, brand-new!

THIRD BEGGAR. Whomsoever you play with using these cards, you will win.

SOLDIER. Eh?

THIRD BEGGAR. And here . . . is something else.

SOLDIER. What's that? A nosebag!

THIRD BEGGAR. A nosebag.

SOLDIER. A nosebag! What in the name of –

THIRD BEGGAR. Soldier, mark what I say. You have been good to me, I will be good to you.

SOLDIER. Aye, but a nosebag without a horse –

THIRD BEGGAR. You can have horses and all if you want. As you go on by this road, whatever you see that you fancy, be it beast, bird, or fish – just you hold out this bag and open the mouth of it so, and call out "Beast or bird! Jump in here in my nosebag." And mark my words, they will.

SOLDIER. Ha! Ha! Ha! Ha! Ha! That's a good story if ever I –

THIRD BEGGAR. A good story is a true story. You do not know who I am, soldier –

SOLDIER. Who *are* you?

THIRD BEGGAR. I leave you to guess, soldier. But make a good use of my gifts. Farewell now. God bless you.

A balalaika fades up, introducing an inn crowded with noisy peasants.

FIRST PEASANT. Come on, landlord. Vodka on credit.

LANDLORD. Nothing on credit, friend. Not in these days.

FIRST PEASANT. Stingy old cheeseparing —

MARYA. No, he's right. In these days a body has got to —

FIRST PEASANT. A body has got to have vodka.

SECOND PEASANT. Aye, that's right. Folks won't come to no good unless —

LANDLORD. Folks won't come to no good unless they work, I tell you.

SECOND PEASANT. A body can't work without drink. And food too, o'course. When I remember the old days —

ALL. A-a-ah!

FIRST PEASANT. Rivers of brown beer!

SECOND PEASANT. Armies of roast geese!

SOLDIER (*entering*). Who wants roast geese?

LANDLORD. Come in, soldier. Sit down. But if you want drink, you must pay.

SOLDIER. I said, "Who wants roast goose"?

MARYA. Who wants it! Hark ye, soldier, you look like a stranger here and a joke's a joke but —

SOLDIER. See what I've got in my hand?

MARYA. A nosebag. What about it?

SOLDIER. Well, it looks full, don't it? Guess what I've got inside.

SECOND PEASANT. *I* know . . . Hay!

VOICES. That's right. Hay.

SOLDIER. Well, look here. One! Two!! Three!!!

LANDLORD. The saints preserve us! Geese!

ALL. Geese! Geese! Geese!

SOLDIER. Three wild geese. Landlord, take 'em. The first you can roast for my supper, the second you can change for vodka —

SECOND PEASANT. Ooh, won't he be drunk!

SOLDIER. And the third you can keep as payment.

LANDLORD. Upon my soul —

SOLDIER. Is that fair or isn't it?

LANDLORD. Fair? Of course it's fair, sir. Now, sir, if you'd like to sit here, sir —

SOLDIER. You needn't sir me and I won't sit here. Give me that big table and lay a place for all.

MARYA. What do you mean?

SOLDIER. When I have luck I share it. Sit you down, folks.

FIRST PEASANT. Me?

SECOND PEASANT. Me?

SOLDIER. All of you.

Cheers.

SECOND PEASANT. All of us except Marya. She has to do the cooking.

MARYA. Aye, and it'll take time.

SECOND PEASANT. All the more time for drinking.

SOLDIER. Aye, and for music. Landlord!

LANDLORD. Yes, sir?

SOLDIER. Give us some music, can't you?

LANDLORD. Music, sir, but —

SOLDIER (*authoritatively*). Music!

The balalaika strikes up.

SOLDIER. That's more like it. (*A pause, then he puts an idle question.*) What's that big house yonder out of the window?

The balalaika breaks off abruptly; the PEASANTS *whisper.*

SOLDIER. Why has the music stopped?

LANDLORD. Because of what you said, sir.

MARYA. The music always stops when a body mentions that.

SOLDIER. Mentions what?

SECOND PEASANT. The house outside the window.

SOLDIER. Why! A man can mention a house.

LANDLORD. Aye, sir, but that is the Tsar's palace.

SOLDIER. Pah! A man can mention a palace.

LANDLORD. Aye, sir, but this is a haunted palace.

The PEASANTS *murmur endorsement.*

SOLDIER. Haunted?

LANDLORD. Aye, soldier, by devils.

FIRST PEASANT. Aye, a regular pack of 'em. Every shape and size and —

MARYA. See them windows, soldier? Ain't a whole pane of glass in 'em.

FIRST PEASANT. They meets there every night. Horrible goings-on.

SOLDIER. They do?

LANDLORD. They do indeed, sir. Every night at midnight in they comes a-growling and screeching – you can hear 'em from over here.

MARYA. Playing cards and dicing and –

SOLDIER. What does the Tsar do?

LANDLORD. Tsar? He ain't put his foot in there for over a dozen years.

SECOND PEASANT. That's right. No one can spend a night in that there palace and live.

SOLDIER. Is that so? Where can I find this Tsar?

The PEASANTS *express alarm.*

LANDLORD. He lives in the next parish, but what do you –

SOLDIER. Never you mind. Fill up your glasses, friends. (*Decisively.*) I shall call on your Tsar tomorrow.

Court music leads to the Court – and to tomorrow.

CHAMBERLAIN (*approaching*). Your Most Imperial Majesty.

TSAR. Yes, yes, what the deuce is it now?

CHAMBERLAIN. A discharged soldier is waiting without at the gate.

TSAR. A discharged soldier? Go and discharge him again.

CHAMBERLAIN. But your Imperial –

TSAR. I will *not* have my mornings disturbed by men of the people. There *is* such a thing as autocracy. Why, in my father's time –

SOLDIER (*entering*). Good morning. Are you the Tsar?

TSAR. What!

CHAMBERLAIN. Who let that man in here?

SOLDIER. I let myself in, master. I've got business with –

TSAR. Call in the guard and clap this fellow in gaol.

SOLDIER. In gaol, eh? (*Slyly.*) Why not the haunted palace?

TSAR. The haunted – What do you want, you scum, with the haunted palace?

SOLDIER (*dead-pan*). I want to see them devils.

TSAR. Why? They'd tear you to pieces, man.

SOLDIER. You think so?

TSAR. I know so. Other people have tried this game before. And not just trash like you. Well-set-up young fellows with blue blood in their veins, but it was all the same. When we sent round in the morning all we found was their bones. (*With gusto.*) And the ivory floors were red with their blood.

SOLDIER. Red? Why not blue?

TSAR. I believe it *was* blue. But as I was saying —

SOLDIER. What will you give me if I get rid of them devils?

TSAR. Give you? What did we offer 'em last time?

CHAMBERLAIN. I do not remember, your Majesty. It was a large sum.

SOLDIER. Well, give me a large sum. Now where's the key?

CHAMBERLAIN. What do you mean, boor? His majesty has not as yet consented to —

TSAR. Give him the key, give him the key. There you are, soldier. Let yourself in tonight and we'll fetch you out tomorrow.

CHAMBERLAIN (*smoothly*). His Majesty means your bones.

Ghost music creeps up and continues while the SOLDIER *walks round inspecting.*

SOLDIER. So this is the haunted palace. Fancy carvings. Ivory. Marble. Must have cost a bit. Draughty though — and don't it smell? That'll be all this muck on the floors. Devils done that, I reckon. Bones, feathers — (*He laughs but not happily.*) — might be a barnyard. Lucky the moon shines in, I can find me a place to sit. (*He speaks slowly, settling himself.*) Time for a nice smoke before it comes on to midnight.

MUSIC *and wind. A clock begins striking midnight, then is drowned in jabbering and screeching.*

DEVIL CAPTAIN. Devils! You all here?

VOICES. Aye, aye, Captain.

DEVIL CAPTAIN. Good. Orders for tonight are simple. Palace to be haunted from end to end as usual. Every devil to be on his worst behavior. Is that in disorder?

VOICES. Aye, sir.

DEVIL CAPTAIN. Right. In you go!

MUSIC *swells up, as the* DEVILS *cheer.*

FIRST DEVIL. Hugger and mugger, pell and mell,
Here we come the devils from Hell.

SECOND DEVIL. Fire and brimstone, bug and nit,
Here we come from the burning pit.

THIRD DEVIL. Horn and dewclaw, blood and malice,
Here we come to the Tsar's palace.

FOURTH DEVIL. Cloven hoof and burning bill,
This big devil is out to kill.

LITTLE DEVIL. Shining tusk and twining tail,
This little devil is . . . is . . . is . . .
Oh, I do want a rhyme!

DEVIL CAPTAIN. Devils! Halt! (*The music ends.*) This is no time for rhymes. What do I see at the far end of the hall?

FIRST DEVIL. A man!

SECOND DEVIL. A man!

THIRD DEVIL. A man!

FOURTH DEVIL. A man!

LITTLE DEVIL. A live one!

DEVIL CAPTAIN. Ahoy there, man!

SOLDIER (*distant*). Ahoy there, devils!

DEVIL CAPTAIN. Come up here.

SOLDIER (*distant*). Com-ing.

FOURTH DEVIL. Ph-e-ew! Now for some fun.

SECOND DEVIL. Not seen one of these in a twelvemonth.

LITTLE DEVIL. Aw, why did I leave my pitchfork at home?

The DEVILS *growl in anticipation.*

DEVIL CAPTAIN. Silence there. I'll handle this business. No one to act till I give the order. I want no biting, scratching, pronging, eating-up, or other molestation until such time as —

SOLDIER (*joining them*). Hullo there, Scaly.

DEVIL CAPTAIN. Welcome, soldier, to our little party. What can we do to amuse you?

SOLDIER. I'm amused already. Ha! Ha! Ha! Such a funny-looking bunch I never in my life — Ha! Ha! Ha! —

The DEVILS *hiss at him.*

DEVIL CAPTAIN. I beg your pardon. I merely wanted to know what are your favorite pastimes. Dancing? Skittles? Knucklebones? Cards?

SOLDIER. Cards.

DEVIL CAPTAIN. Excellent. Now take a seat here at this table and — Who's got a pack?

SOLDIER. I have.

DEVIL CAPTAIN. A new pack, eh?

SOLDIER. Somebody gave it me. Want me to deal?

DEVIL CAPTAIN. Go ahead.

The DEVILS *scratch on the table and jabber.*

DEVILS. Yub-a-yub-a-yub-a-yub-a-yub-a-yub-a-yub . . .

SOLDIER. Now then. Turn 'em up.

FIRST DEVIL. Seven of hearts.

SECOND DEVIL. Four of clubs.

THIRD DEVIL. Knave of clubs.

FOURTH DEVIL. Ten of diamonds.

DEVIL CAPTAIN. Queen of spades.

SOLDIER. Ace of diamonds.

DEVILS. Urrr-urrr-urrr-urrr-urrr . . .

SOLDIER (*very calmly*). Your gold, please. Your deal, Scaly.

DEVIL CAPTAIN. Thank you.

LITTLE DEVIL. Hee-hee-hee. Now we'll see some play.

Short passage of music to cover another round.

SOLDIER. Your gold, please.

Ditto.

SOLDIER. Your gold, please.

Ditto.

SOLDIER. Your gold, please.

The music ends. The DEVILS *are very angry.*

DEVILS. Urrr-urrr-urrr-urrr-urrr . . .

DEVIL CAPTAIN. Extraordinary, quite extraordinary. Skraglitch!

LITTLE DEVIL. Here, sir.

DEVIL CAPTAIN. Run back to Hell and fetch some more money.

LITTLE DEVIL. Yes, sir. How much, sir?

DEVIL CAPTAIN. Every ounce you can carry. And don't go dropping it in space.

LITTLE DEVIL. No, sir, I won't, sir.

DEVIL CAPTAIN. Well, soldier, your luck's been quite phenomenal. (*The* DEVILS *growl.*) But, as I always say, he who laughs last – Ah, Skraglitch! Put it down here.

LITTLE DEVIL. Pretty good time, eh, Captain? I didn't drop none either.

DEVIL CAPTAIN. Put the money down and stop talking. Now then, friends, whose deal is it?

The DEVILS *scratch the table and jabber as before. Short passage of music.*

SOLDIER. Your gold, please. (*The music ends abruptly. This is too much.*) What, are you all cleaned out? Looks as if the game is over.

DEVIL CAPTAIN. On the contrary, soldier, the game is about to begin. Devils! Where are your pitchforks?

Hubbub.

LITTLE DEVIL. Aw, why did I leave mine at home!

DEVIL CAPTAIN. Now then, before we destroy him – Aren't you afraid, soldier?

SOLDIER. Afraid? What of? A Russian soldier cannot drown in –

DEVIL CAPTAIN. Yes, yes, yes, I know that proverb: A Russian soldier can't burn in water. (*The* DEVILS *laugh.*) But, Russian soldier or no Russian soldier, you've cheated at cards and you're going to pay for it.

The DEVILS *growl, warming up.*

SOLDIER. Stand back, devils. See this?

DEVILS. A nosebag?

LITTLE DEVIL. A dirty old, empty old nosebag.

SOLDIER. Dirty. Maybe. Empty? We'll see about that.

More growling.

SOLDIER (*with sudden authority*). Devils – in the name of God – in with you into my nosebag!

Screams. Music.

SOLDIER. That's right. One – two – three – four – five – six – seven – eight – nine – ten – eleven – twelve – thirteen . . .

His voice is drowned in music – which passes away like the night.

CHAMBERLAIN. Your Imperial Majesty, your morning vodka.

TSAR. Morning already! What's going on in the world?

CHAMBERLAIN. Nothing new, your Majesty. Except the soldier, of course.

TSAR. Soldier?

CHAMBERLAIN. The one that slept last night in the haunted palace.

TSAR. Oh, yes, yes – Have they fetched his bones yet?

CHAMBERLAIN. No, your Imperial –

SOLDIER. I'm not a doctor. What the devil can *I* – Eh! 'What the *devil'?* Where's that contract gone to?

WIFE. What contract? Why are you searching in the mattress?

SOLDIER. Here it is, here it is! Leave me alone, my love, time is short.

WIFE. But, husband –

SOLDIER. Leave me alone, I say.

WIFE. But I must nurse Ivan.

SOLDIER. I will see to Ivan. Go. Go out of the room.

WIFE (*submitting to a forlorn hope*). Very well then.

The door closes.

SOLDIER. Now then. Quickly. Where's that cheat of a devil?

DEVIL CAPTAIN (*popping up*). Cheat! . . . Who says that I am a cheat?

SOLDIER. All right. You prove you're not. See this contract?

DEVIL CAPTAIN (*ungraciously*). What do you want me to do?

SOLDIER. Look over there. In the cot.

Pause while the DEVIL *moves over. His voice sounds farther off.*

DEVIL CAPTAIN (*matter-of-fact*). Hm! Your son looks ill.

SOLDIER. The plague, Devil, the plague!

DEVIL CAPTAIN. Want me to cure him?

SOLDIER. Can you?

DEVIL CAPTAIN. That remains to be seen. I have something here in my pocket. This glass. Fill it with water. (*A sound of bubbling water.*) Thank you. Now then, we hold this glass over the patient's bed. Come here and stand by me. Look in this glass and tell me what you can see.

SOLDIER. See, Devil? . . . Nothing. Nothing but bubbles, that is.

DEVIL CAPTAIN. Those bubbles will soon settle. Keep on looking. Well?

SOLDIER. Bubbles, only bubbles.

DEVIL CAPTAIN. Go on. Go on looking.

SOLDIER. Ah!

DEVIL CAPTAIN. Yes?

SOLDIER. I see . . . I see . . . I see my son in his cot.

DEVIL CAPTAIN. Yes?

SOLDIER. And I see the figure of a woman standing beside him.

DEVIL CAPTAIN. Know who that is, soldier? That is Death.

SOLDIER. Death!

DEVIL CAPTAIN. Of course. Where is she standing?

SOLDIER. Where?

DEVIL CAPTAIN. At his head or his feet?

SOLDIER. His feet.

DEVIL CAPTAIN. That's all we need to know. If Death stands at his feet, your boy will survive.

SOLDIER. Thank God!

DEVIL CAPTAIN. Now if she were at his head – Ha! Ha! – nothing could save him, soldier. Here, take this water and pour it over the child.

CHILD. Ouch!

DEVIL CAPTAIN. You see? He has come to.

SOLDIER. Ah, God be praised for this –

DEVIL CAPTAIN. *God* be praised, eh? Well, anything else you want?

SOLDIER. No, Devil. Unless . . .

DEVIL CAPTAIN. Unless what?

SOLDIER. Would you give me that glass of yours?

DEVIL CAPTAIN. Oh no! Oh no you don't.

SOLDIER. Go on, Devil. If you give me that glass, I'll release you from this here contract.

DEVIL CAPTAIN. Ah, that's different. Hand me the contract and I'll – Thank you. (*A noise of tearing parchment.*) Good-by, soldier. You know how to use the glass?

SOLDIER. Aye. From this day on *I'm* setting up for a doctor.

Funeral music creeps in, leads to the CHAMBERLAIN'S *sickbed.*

CHAMBERLAIN. Where's that doctor? Where's that doctor? Didn't you take him my message?

MAIDSERVANT. I'm sorry, master. He says if you've got the plague, he's attending no more cases.

CHAMBERLAIN. The damned German! Isn't there –

MAIDSERVANT. He says, master, that all that remains for you is to say your prayers and die. But if you was to ask *me* . . .

CHAMBERLAIN. What? Go on, I'm asking you.

MAIDSERVANT. I'd say my prayers and send for that discharged soldier.

CHAMBERLAIN (*with distaste*). The discharged soldier? Why?

MAIDSERVANT. Folks do say that he has a cure for the plague. He's cured a few already. Boyars, generals, and that. Does it all with a glass.

SOLDIER (*entering*). Aye. With a glass. Like this.

MAIDSERVANT. Well! Talk of the devil!

SOLDIER. No you don't; don't talk of the devil to me. (*Cheerily.*) Now then, Chamberlain, want to be cured?

CHAMBERLAIN. What's that medicine?

SOLDIER. Water, only water. And I hold it above you so. Now come here, you, and tell me what you can see.

MAIDSERVANT. See? . . . I can see bubbles.

SOLDIER. Go on looking. Now?

MAIDSERVANT. I see the master lying on his bed.

CHAMBERLAIN. Hmph! You don't have to look in a glass to —

SOLDIER. Hsh! Anything else?

MAIDSERVANT. Aye. A kind of a woman —

SOLDIER. That's not a woman; that's Death.

The CHAMBERLAIN *moans with horror.*

MAIDSERVANT. Death?

SOLDIER. At his head or his feet?

MAIDSERVANT. At his, er — now, now, now, I can't see if you joggle the glass — She's standing right at his feet.

SOLDIER. Here's a cold douche for you, Chamberlain.

CHAMBERLAIN. Ow! What do you mean by —

SOLDIER. I'll send you the bill in the morning.

Funeral music, as before.

DOCTOR. A boil! So? The plague! Call the lawyers and I'll make my will.

SOLDIER (*entering*). Your will will keep, Herr Doktor. Want to be cured?

DOCTOR. Who let *you* in, quack?

SOLDIER. "Want to be cured?" I said.

DOCTOR. No one can cure this plague. I am a doctor, I know.

SOLDIER (*sardonically, moving off*). Well, if you know . . .

DOCTOR. Where are you going?

SOLDIER. Well, I thought as I'm not welcome —

DOCTOR. What is this cure of yours?

SOLDIER. It's simple, Herr Doktor, but it's costly.

DOCTOR. What is your fee?

SOLDIER. If I cure you, as I can, you must resign to me — (*He pauses to get his effect.*) — your post as the Tsar's physician.

DOCTOR. As the Tsar's — but no, no, no! I will not give up my post. Besides, it is ridiculous. You as the Tsar's physician! No, no, no! A million times no. A thousand times no. A hundred times no. Ten times no . . .

Funeral music as before.

CHAMBERLAIN. Send for the Tsar's physician. The Tsar is ill unto death.

SOLDIER. You need not send, Chamberlain. News travels fast these days; I travel faster. Just fill me this glass with water and —

TSAR. Who's that? The discharged soldier?

SOLDIER. The Tsar's physician, your Imperial Majesty.

TSAR. Thank God you are here. You can cure me?

CHAMBERLAIN. He cured *me,* your Majesty.

TSAR. That's nothing to do with it.

CHAMBERLAIN. He has also cured hundreds of boyars, dozens of generals, and —

TSAR. Hold your tongue. Have you filled his glass with water?

CHAMBERLAIN. Yes, your Imperial —

TSAR. Well, then, let him get on with it.

SOLDIER. Chamberlain, stand by me. Look in this glass and look very carefully. What do you see?

CHAMBERLAIN. Bubbles.

SOLDIER (*smugly echoing him*). Bubbles.

CHAMBERLAIN. A figure.

SOLDIER. A figure.

CHAMBERLAIN. The Tsar in his bed.

SOLDIER. The Tsar in his bed.

CHAMBERLAIN. And another figure.

SOLDIER. Death.

CHAMBERLAIN. Death! Dear me, is that —

SOLDIER. Death standing at his feet.

CHAMBERLAIN. But no, soldier, no.

SOLDIER (*shocked*). What!

CHAMBERLAIN. Look in your own glass. It's Death standing at his head.

SOLDIER. At his what? . . . What! . . . (*Resigning himself.*) Aye. Death standing at his head.

Pause.

TSAR. Come on, come on; I'm not cured yet.

SOLDIER (*quietly*). You never will be, your Imperial Majesty.

TSAR. What's that? What do you mean, man?

SOLDIER. You have three hours left to live.

TSAR. You liar!

SOLDIER. No, your Imperial —

TSAR. Did you not cure the boyars?

SOLDIER. Aye.

TSAR. And the generals?

SOLDIER. Aye.

TSAR. And my Chamberlain here?

CHAMBERLAIN. Aye — Yes, I mean.

TSAR. And you refuse to cure me!

SOLDIER. I do not refuse, I —

TSAR. You are a traitor. I'll have you beheaded at once.

CHAMBERLAIN. Shall I pass on the order, your Majesty?

TSAR. Yes. Behead him at once and —

A female voice cuts in — very rarefied and formal.

DEATH. I only bargained for one. Now it seems there'll be two.

TSAR. What's that? Who's talking?

DEATH. One by the plague and one by the block.

CHAMBERLAIN. *Cherchez la femme,* your Majesty, *cherchez la* —

SOLDIER. Hsh, you! Look in this glass, can't you? There's the one that's doing the talking. Death! Hi, Death! That you?

DEATH. Aye, soldier. Greetings.

SOLDIER. You are waiting to take the Tsar?

DEATH. I am, soldier.

SOLDIER. Supposing now . . . supposing . . .

DEATH. Supposing what?

SOLDIER. You are a person of honor. You only bargained for one. Well now . . .

DEATH. Yes?

SOLDIER (*taking the plunge*). Instead of the Tsar, why don't you take me?

DEATH. You, soldier?

SOLDIER. What's the odds? He's going to behead me anyway. Give the old pig his life and take me instead.

DEATH. Do you want it that way?

TSAR. We do!

SOLDIER. Nobody asked you. Aye. I want it that way. But give me just three hours more. Then I'll have time to get home and say farewell to my family.

DEATH. So be it, soldier. I release my claims on the Tsar and you shall have three hours more. I shall be there at your bedside.

MUSIC *punctuates the following.*

SOLDIER. Farewell, my friends. . . . Farewell, Ivan my son. . . . Farewell, my beloved wife. . . .

DEATH. Your time is up, soldier.

The music ends; the SOLDIER'S *time is up.*

SOLDIER (*feebly*). That you, Death? Where are you?

DEATH. Your eyes are dim. You have only three minutes left to live in the bright world. So hurry, soldier, I'm waiting. What are you doing, rummaging under the pillow?

SOLDIER. Looking for something. A locket.

DEATH. A locket? Hm. Always the same story. Well, find it quickly and —

SOLDIER. Here she is.

DEATH. That's not a locket.

SOLDIER. What is it then?

DEATH. Why that thing's a . . .

SOLDIER. What?

DEATH. Why, that's just an old nosebag.

SOLDIER. You sure about that?

DEATH. Of course I am. Enough of this nonsense; I've got other engagements —

SOLDIER. One thing at a time, Mistress Death. If this is a nosebag — jump into it.

Musical effect, representing the nosebag trick.

PEASANT. Hey, soldier. What have you got in that nosebag?

SOLDIER. Never you mind. Is this the way to the forest?

PEASANT. Yonder's the forest ahead of you. That bag of yours looks heavy.

SOLDIER. It *is* heavy, my brother.

PEASANT. It's cold in that forest, soldier.

SOLDIER. Cold? (*Gleefully.*) The colder the better.

MUSIC *and wind. Here is the forest.*

SOLDIER (*grunting from his efforts*). Now then — the bitter aspen — the very top of it — the topmost twig — fasten her well. (*Triumphantly.*) Good-by, nosebag. Good-by, Death. Looks as if from now on folks won't die any more.

The forest music recedes slowly into Ancient History.

TSAR. Extraordinary thing, Chamberlain. Nobody's died here lately. Noticed that in your rounds?

CHAMBERLAIN. How could I not, your Majesty? The bishop says it's a scandal.

TSAR. No more burial fees, eh?

CHAMBERLAIN. No, your Majesty; it's serious.

Passage of music: the Non-Dying Era progresses.

CHAMBERLAIN. Your Majesty, this really is serious.

TSAR. What's it now, Chamberlain?

CHAMBERLAIN. The census has just come in.

TSAR. Yes? What of it?

CHAMBERLAIN. It proves beyond a doubt that your kingdom is overpopulated.

TSAR. Is it? Why?

CHAMBERLAIN. Because, your Majesty, none of us ever die.

TSAR. When was the last death?

CHAMBERLAIN. Oh, years ago, your Majesty.

TSAR. Years? You mean decades!

CHAMBERLAIN. Your Majesty is always right. I ought to have said decades.

Another passage of music.

SOLDIER. Well, well, well, lovely weather today! Just the right day to have taken this trip to the city. Beautiful blue sky, everyone ought to be happy. But they're not, you know, they're not.

Look at that old woman blowing about in the wind – and there's hardly a wind to speak of – just like she was a straw. My word, that's an old woman. It's almost time she died.

OLD WOMAN (*croaking with age and misery*). You took the words out of my mouth, discharged soldier. Almost time I died! That time has come and gone. Long, long years ago. And ever since then my life – if you call it life – is an agony. And you know whose fault that is. The day that you put Death in the nosebag, I had no more than an hour to live in the white world. All I want is rest and it's you who's kept it from me.

SOLDIER. I'm sorry, mother.

OLD WOMAN. Sorry! Do you know what you've done, soldier? You've committed an unforgivable sin. And there's other folk like me. Have you ever thought about that?

SOLDIER. No, I can't say I –

OLD WOMAN. Then you'd better think now. And if you can undo what you've done – maybe you can't –

Suddenly converted, he interrupts her.

SOLDIER. No? . . . Maybe I can.

Back to the forest. Wind and music.

SOLDIER (*shouting*). Death! Death! . . . Where's that bitter aspen? Ah, here we are. Death! Hey, Death, are you alive?

DEATH (*distant and very feeble*). Aye, soldier – just.

SOLDIER (*shouting up to the aspen top*). Good. I've come to take you home with me.

The forest slowly recedes again.

WIFE. Husband! Husband! Why are you going to bed? The sun's still up and –

SOLDIER. I've got business to do.

WIFE. Business? In bed?

SOLDIER. That's what I said. Give me a kiss and go.

WIFE. Oh very well. Here's your kiss. I'll bring your supper in later.

The door closes.

SOLDIER. Supper? Ha! Ha! Now then, where's that nosebag? Patience, Death, I'm just about to unbuckle it.

DEATH (*muffled*). Thank you, soldier, thank you.

SOLDIER. But only on one condition.

DEATH (*muffled*). What's that?

SOLDIER. That, before you take anyone else, you take me.

DEATH (*muffled*). Why?

SOLDIER. I have had a sinful life and a long one. I reckon death will be best for me. (*Pause.*) Is that understood?

DEATH (*muffled*). Yes.

SOLDIER. Good. Then I'll let you out.

Musical effect: the nosebag trick in reverse.

SOLDIER. Hey! Where are you off to?

DEATH. Catch me if you can.

SOLDIER. But you promised –

DEATH. I promised nothing. Do you think that I want to have any more truck with *you?*

SOLDIER (*pleadingly*). But Death, Death –

DEATH. It's no good begging my pardon. If people play tricks on me I can play tricks on them. You'll never see me again. Good-by now, and ill luck to you.

The door bangs.

SOLDIER. Never see her again? That means I can never die. The beasts will die and the trees and everyone else but me. And I am a sinful man . . . sinful . . . sinful. . . . But there's an idea. They have a place for sin. I know what I'll do; I'll take me off to Hell. Just as I am. I'll pay for my sins alive. And I only hope it will be warm.

A tocsin is heard in the far, far distance. It grows louder. Hell is in a state of alarm.

DEVIL CAPTAIN. Sergeant!

FOURTH DEVIL. Sir?

DEVIL CAPTAIN. Who gave orders for that?

FOURTH DEVIL. For what, sir?

DEVIL CAPTAIN. For the tocsin.

FOURTH DEVIL. You did, sir.

DEVIL CAPTAIN. *I* did?

FOURTH DEVIL. Yes, sir. Two and twenty years ago. Remember, sir? The soldier with the nosebag.

DEVIL CAPTAIN. *That* fellow! You don't say *he* is –

FOURTH DEVIL. Yes, sir. He was seen at 00 hours approaching the West Gate. He ought to be there by now.

DEVIL CAPTAIN. The sentries got their instructions?

FOURTH DEVIL. Yes, sir. But if I was you, sir —

DEVIL CAPTAIN. You're quite right, Sergeant. I'll go along myself.

The tocsin reaches a peak, then fades away.

SOLDIER. But I tell you, devil, I'm guilty. I'm a guilty soul to be tortured.

SENTRY. Can't help that. You're alive.

SOLDIER. Alive? Maybe, but —

SENTRY. We don't take in no live 'uns. Besides, *you've* got a nosebag.

SOLDIER. What's that got to do with it?

SENTRY. It's a standing order of ours. Any soldiers with nosebags —

DEVIL CAPTAIN (*arriving*). What's the trouble here, sentry?

SENTRY. *He* is, Captain.

SOLDIER. Scaly! We meet again.

DEVIL CAPTAIN. Oh no we don't. Get away from the gates. Off with you into space. We've got no room for you here.

SOLDIER. But, Scaly, I've come to be tortured.

DEVIL CAPTAIN. Tortured? Ha! Ha! Ha! You'll be a lot more tortured drifting around in space. Rents are high in Hell. Think that we'd let a practical joker like you —

SOLDIER. Any little corner — I'm not particular —

DEVIL CAPTAIN. You go away somewhere else. And in double-quick time, do you hear?

SOLDIER. Somewhere else? Where?

DEVIL CAPTAIN. They say there's a place called Heaven —

SOLDIER. Heaven? They wouldn't look at me. Unless . . . unless . . . Scaly, do me a favor. And then I'll leave you in peace.

DEVIL CAPTAIN. What is it?

SOLDIER. Give me two hundred souls. Black ones out of the Pit. To take with me up to the gates of Paradise. Then perhaps they'll forgive me my sins and —

SENTRY. Well, of all the nerve!

DEVIL CAPTAIN. Shut up, sentry. Anything to get rid of him. Two hundred souls, did you say? If you'll take yourself off at once — and promise not to come back — I'll throw in an extra fifty.

SOLDIER. That a deal?

DEVIL CAPTAIN. Two hundred and fifty souls from the Pit. Take 'em away and be blessed to you!

Ethereal music mounts with the souls through space.

ROBBER SOUL. Well, well, well, ain't it cool up here? Anyone got a spare sheepskin?

FEMALE SOUL. What I want to know is: How much higher are we going?

CROOK SOUL. Soldier, hey, soldier! The lady here –

ROBBER SOUL. Lady? Ha! Ha! Ha!

CROOK SOUL. The lady here would like to know where you're taking us.

SOLDIER. Why! Didn't the devils tell you? I'm taking you all to Paradise.

The BAD SOULS *murmur in astonishment.*

ROBBER SOUL. Paradise!

FEMALE SOUL. Wings, you mean? And harps? What luck that I've kept my complexion.

ROBBER SOUL. Kept your complexion? Where?

The BAD SOULS *break into coarse laughter.*

SOLDIER. Stop laughing, you fools. Look yonder.

CROOK SOUL. Hm! What's that? The sun's so bright in my eyes I can't exactly –

SOLDIER. The sun's below you, brother. That's the Gate.

THE SOULS. The Gate! . . . The Gate of Paradise!

SOLDIER. That it is, so you'd better behave decent.

CROOK SOUL. Decent? And why not? When in Rome, as I said when I cheated the Grand Tartar – But one point, soldier – do we have to pass through the customs?

SOLDIER. Why do you ask that?

CROOK SOUL. Well, they're only trifles of course, but as I was leaving Hell –

FEMALE SOUL. Look, darlings, look! I can see the pearly ramparts.

ROBBER SOUL. Yus, and I can see some fellows up there with spears. Watching us too, they are. Don't look too good to me.

A pause while we switch to Paradise.

OFFICER. Gatesman.

GATESMAN. Yes, sir.

OFFICER. What's that crowd down there? They on their way here?

GATESMAN. Yes, sir. Two hundred and fifty guilty souls from Hell and one live soldier with nosebag from – er – Earth.

OFFICER. Oh, indeed?

GATESMAN. What shall I do, sir? Give 'em the rightabout turn?

OFFICER. No. Let 'em come in. Two hundred and fifty's a nice round number.

GATESMAN. Two hundred and fifty-one, sir.

OFFICER. Two hundred and fifty I said. Can't have that soldier in here.

GATESMAN. Right, sir. I understand. They're coming up now, sir.

OFFICER. Good. Give the order to the Gates.

GATESMAN. Yes, sir. (*He turns and shouts out the formula.*) Gates! Gates of Paradise! Stand by to admit two hundred and fifty souls. Gates! Unbolt! Swing on your hinges! Open!

MUSIC *opens the gates.*

SOLDIER. Here, you.

ROBBER SOUL. Me?

SOLDIER. Quick. Take hold of this nosebag. As you go in, say to me – get this right – say to me "Soldier, jump into the nosebag."

ROBBER SOUL. All right, all right, let go of it.

SOLDIER. But don't forget – this is my only chance – so don't forget, promise me, don't forget.

The GATESMAN'S *voice rings out.*

GATESMAN. Gates! Gates of Paradise! Stand by to close! Swing on your hinges. Close!

MUSIC *closes the gates. Silence. The* SOLDIER *is alone.*

SOLDIER. So he forgot, the pig! And took my nosebag with him. Well, that's the way things are. These gates will never open again for me. And Hell's out of it too and Death she won't come near me. Nothing for it, I reckon. Can't stay hanging round here; it's cold in space tonight. I can fancy a worse thing now than a place on a Russian stove and music maybe and a pipe of tobacco. I think I'll go back to Earth.

A balalaika steals in, then peasant chatter. He has been here before.

MARYA. Landlord! Remember that soldier many years gone come in here once with three wild geese in a nosebag?

LANDLORD. The one that drove the devils out of the Tsar's palace?

MARYA. That's him, landlord. He's here again.

Incredulous exclamations all round.

LANDLORD. What! I heard he'd died.

SOLDIER (*himself again*). No, landlord, no such luck. Here's my last ruble; bring me some vodka.

LANDLORD. Marya, a bottle of vodka.

SOLDIER. Well, what's the news round here since I've been gone?

LANDLORD. News! Where've you been? The country's gone to war.

SOLDIER. War?

LANDLORD. Aye. They'll soon be calling on you.

SOLDIER. Not on me. I am a man of sin.

LANDLORD. Sin? Don't make me laugh. You're a soldier, ain't you?

SOLDIER. I was a soldier once. Then they discharged me.

LANDLORD. How much service did you have?

SOLDIER. Twenty-five years.

LANDLORD. Not much.

MARYA. The vodka, masters.

LANDLORD. Thank you. Fill up the soldier's double.

MARYA. He looks as if he can do with it.

SOLDIER. You're right, woman. Here's to —

LANDLORD. Not yet, soldier, not yet. *I'm* going to give you a toast. You've had twenty-five years of service? Well, you're going to have more. Campaigns like you never dreamed of. You had a magic nosebag, I see you've lost it. Well, that don't matter, you've got something better. You've got a —

SOLDIER. I've got a terrible thirst. Give me your toast.

LANDLORD. You've got a fighting heart and a fighting arm. Well, now you're going to fight with 'em. That's what you're going to do, all through the centuries, you are. Tartars, Swedes, French, Teutons —

SOLDIER. That will all come when it comes. Give me your toast.

LANDLORD. All right, soldier. Here's to our Motherland.

SOLDIER. Here's . . . to our Motherland!

AFTER READING

1. *The Nosebag* is a dramatization of a folk tale entitled *The Soldier and Death* or *The Soldier and the Demons.* Which of these titles do you prefer? Why?

2. The Soldier does not mention the reasons for his dismissal from the army after twenty-five years of service, although he blames his sergeant, commanding officer, colonel, and general for dismissing him. Why do you suppose he was dismissed?

3. The First Beggar says, "You do not know who I am, soldier." Do *you* know? Who were the other beggars?

4. When a palace or a house is haunted in the old tales, a reason is usually given. None is offered here. Why do you think the palace was haunted by devils?

5. Do you know of any other famous legend in which the leading character makes a compact with the Devil? Hint: A famous opera is based on such a legend. If you know the plot, summarize it briefly for the class.

6. Why did Death, the Devil Captain, and the Officer in charge of the Gates of Paradise refuse to have anything to do with the Soldier when he tried to deliver himself into their hands?

CHALLENGES

1. Write a scene or a group of scenes leading to the Soldier's dismissal from the army.

2. Relatively few fairy tales and legends have been made into radio scripts. Here's a dare! Select a story of any of the many collections of fairy tales and write a radio play based on it. After class discussion, get a group of boys and girls together for rehearsals and present the play to the class or the school assembly.

DRAMA WORKSHOP

A hint for radio listeners: Fantasy must be realistic.

In our introductory "Open Letter" the editors pointed out that radio is particularly adapted to fantasy. *The Nosebag* is a case in point. This play would be difficult to present on a stage, not only because of the supernatural characters but also because of the numerous scenes, some of which are laid, most improbably, in Hell and outside the Gates of Paradise.

Although a fantasy resembles a fairy tale, it must be entirely believable. In other words, even though the events of a fantasy couldn't possibly happen, they must be plausible. Sounds like a contradiction, doesn't it? A clever writer makes us believe in fantastic occurrences by combining them with matter-of-fact dialogue, wit, and touches of realism. All the persons in *The Nosebag,* even the supernatural characters, have human failings. As an instance of this down-to-earth technique, notice the Devil Captain's instructions to his devils: "Orders for tonight are simple. Palace to be haunted from end to end as usual. Every devil to be on his worst behavior. Is that in disorder?" Bits of humor and realism such as this make supernatural persons and events credible. The next time you hear or read a fantasy, watch for this combination of realism, humor, and imaginativeness.

A hint for radio actors: Guard against overacting.

Beginning radio actors have a tendency to overact. Their characterizations are often exaggerated, especially when they portray elderly people or use dialect. An actor who has this fault should remember that suggestion is more powerful than unrestrained expression. A good actor rarely depicts emotions as vividly as they occur in real life; he allows the listeners to use their imagination. For example, if you are playing the Soldier in *The Nosebag,* you need only suggest his deep, powerful, and naturally rough voice. There is no need for blustering.

Tone down your acting, particularly when portraying old persons. Young players unfortunately seem to think that every old man is feeble and has a quavering, high-pitched voice. Similarly, be restrained when using dialect. A trace of dialect may give a truer suggestion of a character than an exaggerated or a grotesque imitation.

OTHER RADIO PLAYS YOU WILL LIKE TO READ

Air Raid by Archibald MacLeish (13). One of the classic radio plays in verse, it gives an impression of an air raid upon a city.

The Face by Arthur Laurents (25). The experiences of a soldier in undergoing plastic surgery for a serious injury to his face, and his final return to his civilian life.

The Fall of the City by Archibald MacLeish (23). A small town surrenders to a conqueror when their desire for a master to order their lives overrules other counsels.

The Ghost of Benjamin Sweet by Pauline Gibson and Frederick Gilsworth (9). A ghost who has been falling down on the job redeems himself by killing a man and going on a jaunt with *his* ghost.

Little Johnny Appleseed by Bernard C. Schoenfeld (17). A folk tale about Johnny Chapman, known as Johnny Appleseed, who in the early part of the nineteenth century distributed apple seeds over one hundred thousand square miles of America.

ACKNOWLEDGMENTS

The editors thank sincerely all those whose co-operation and help have made this anthology possible. We are indebted to Mr. Evan Lodge, Supervisor of English, Board of Education, Cleveland, Ohio, for constructive criticism; to Mrs. Henry Finnegan for typing the manuscript; and to Dr. Jewel Friedman, New Utrecht High School, Brooklyn, New York, for helpful suggestions.

A NOTE ON THE DEVELOPMENT OF THE ONE-ACT PLAY

One-act plays are known to more people today than ever before in the many centuries during which they have been written, read, and performed. Television, radio, movie adaptations, the legitimate theater, school and Little Theater productions — these together bring one-act plays before the sight and hearing of an audience numbering in the millions. In 1916 only a few hundred spectators attended the première of James M. Barrie's *The Old Lady Shows Her Medals.* Today it is possible for as many as twenty million people to hear the same play during a single radio performance. In the modern age the one-act play has also become popular reading fare. Many plays appear regularly in magazines and general anthologies, and collections of them are published in book form annually.

This wide currency of the one-act play can be explained in part by its development, particularly in the last half-century, as a dramatic art and as popular entertainment. It is sometimes thought — wrongly — that the one-act play came into being as a "curtain raiser" to full-length plays, that is, as something to warm up the audience before the presentation of the evening's main attraction. Actually, the one-act play is more than a thousand years old and was first performed when full-length or formal plays were not commonly known to audiences in Europe.

During the Middle Ages in Europe the plays that were popular with the people were one-act plays. Brief dramas, known as Miracle and Mystery plays, were performed from wagons that passed through the towns; throngs of townsmen gathered on both sides of the roads or were seated in temporary bleachers. These plays dealt entirely with religious subjects, usually with Biblical stories, but sometimes, as in the famous play *Everyman,* with moral struggles between Good and Evil in ordinary human beings. *Everyman* has been produced in recent years and has proved to be a stirring drama even in this time.

In the late Middle Ages, in England especially, professional theaters began to appear with plays performed by theatrical companies before paying audiences. One-act plays were part of the repertoire offered by these companies, one of the first to become well known being John Hayward's *The Four P's.* About the time of Shakespeare (who, incidentally, did not write one-act plays himself) there appeared the first puppet shows. Little plays, starring such now familiar characters as Pierrot and Harlequin, were devised and produced by puppeteers in Italy and France in the sixteenth century. The child of today who stares with amazement at a one-act puppet play is often watching an art that has been passed down, father to son, for more than four centuries.

Despite its long tradition, however, it was not until about seventy-five years ago that the one-act play attracted the serious attention of important playwrights. After the sixteenth century one-act plays were written, it is true, but they were mostly regarded as minor entertainment — indeed, as "curtain raisers." Then beginning with Lord Tennyson's *The Falcon,* written in 1878, the literary value of the plays increased. One important reason for the growing interest in one-act plays was the founding of small theaters that specialized in presenting this form of drama. Such theaters as the Little Theater of Antoine in Paris, which opened in 1877, were the forerunners of the "Little Theater movement" that was so prominent in America during the 1920's.

Among the important playwrights who turned to writing one-act plays during the past half-century were Maurice Maeterlinck, the Belgian, and Anton Chekhov, who wrote his great play *The Swan Song* for the first Russian Little Theater. In 1899 the Irish Literary Theatre was founded. This was a fortunate event for the advancement of the one-act play, for it was from this organization that there later developed the world-famed Abbey Theatre of Dublin. The Abbey Theatre gave to the English-speaking stage not only famous actors (among them, Barry Fitzgerald of the movies) but also accomplished one-act play authors, such as John Synge, St. John Ervine, Padraic Colum, and Lord Dunsany.

As a result of a tour in the United States in 1911 the Irish Players, as they were known, gave an impetus to the founding of Little Theaters in this country. The Little Theaters were formed by amateurs who enjoyed the drama and wanted to participate in it directly; for the most part, the participants did not seek professional careers as actors or directors. Within one of these groups, for example, the director might be in private life an accountant and the scene designer an advertising artist. Very often all the members took a turn in the acting. It was soon found that persons with promising dramatic talent were attracted to the Little Theaters, for here they discovered not only a ready opportunity to display their abilities but also a fertile field in which to experiment with new ideas and new techniques that would hardly be accepted by the convention-bound commercial theaters.

By 1916 there were almost fifty Little Theaters in the United States. Several playing companies were formed in New York City that were later to contribute significantly to the growth of American drama. One was the Washington Square Players, which eventually became the Theatre Guild of the present day. Another was the Provincetown Playhouse, which moved from Provincetown, Massachusetts, to New York City. This was the theater that produced the first plays of America's greatest living playwright, Eugene O'Neill. O'Neill's first plays were, significantly enough, one-act plays, for the Little Theaters vastly stimulated the writing of this form of drama. The Little Theaters found that one-act plays were less costly to produce than full-length plays. Furthermore, an evening's entertainment comprised of several plays engaged more writers, actors, and directors than would the performance of a single full-length play.

Beginning with World War I, also, there developed a growing interest in the writing and acting of one-act plays in many American colleges. At Harvard, for instance, Professor George Baker taught many leading dramatists of our time, among them Eugene O'Neill and Philip Barry, in his course called "47 Workshop," which was established in 1911. In 1920 there appeared the first collection of one-act plays for use as a high-school textbook; since then there has been at least one such collection each year. Not long afterward radio broadcasting added to the swelling enthusiasm for the one-act play. Established playwrights hastened to write for radio, and the studios themselves developed new writers, such as Norman Corwin, Arch Oboler, and Archibald MacLeish. With the present-day expansion of television the one-act play has found still another outlet.

Today the writer of one-act plays has as many fields to work in as his talents permit. Schools, churches, Little Theaters, and various social organizations find the inexpensive and easily manageable production of one-act plays particularly suited to their limited facilities. Radio and television likewise are particularly adapted to one-act play production, because for the most part these media require dramas that are brief in time and restricted in setting. Both radio and television playwrights will no doubt learn new techniques as the years advance, but it is certain that – like the stage dramatists of past and present – they will create one-act plays of continuing enjoyment and lasting value.

BIBLIOGRAPHY

1. Barrie, James M., *Echoes of the War,* Scribner, 1918
2. ——, *Half Hours,* Scribner, 1914
3. Clark, Barrett H., *Representative One-Act Plays by British and Irish Authors,* Little, Brown, 1935
4. ——, and Cook, Thomas R., *One-Act Plays,* Heath, 1929
5. Cohen, Helen Louise, *The Junior Play Book,* Harcourt, Brace, 1923
6. ——, *More One-Act Plays by Modern Authors,* Harcourt, Brace, 1927
7. ——, *One-Act Plays by Modern Authors,* Harcourt, Brace, 1921
8. Cook, George C., and Shay, Frank, *Provincetown Plays,* Appleton-Century-Crofts, 1921
9. Coulter, Douglas, *Columbia Workshop Plays,* McGraw-Hill, 1939
10. Dickinson, Thomas H., *Chief Contemporary Dramatists,* First Series, Houghton Mifflin, 1915
11. Eliot, Samuel A., Jr., *Little Theatre Classics,* Little, Brown, 1918
12. Goldstone, George A., *One-Act Plays,* Allyn and Bacon, 1926
13. Griffith, Francis J., and Mersand, Joseph, *One-Act Plays for Today,* Globe, 1945
14. Kelly, George E., *The Flattering Word,* Little, Brown, 1925
15. Knickerbocker, Edwin Van B., *Short Plays,* Holt, 1931
16. ——, *Twelve Plays,* Holt, 1924
17. Lass, Abraham H., and others, *Plays from Radio,* Houghton Mifflin, 1948
18. Leonard, Sterling A., *The Atlantic Book of Modern Plays,* Little, Brown, 1934
19. Leverton, Garrett H., *Plays for the College Theatre,* Samuel French, 1932
20. Lewis, Benjamin Roland, *Contemporary One-Act Plays,* Scribner, 1922
21. Marriott, J. W., *One-Act Plays of Today,* Third Series, Harrap, London, 1927
22. ——, *One-Act Plays of Today,* Dodd, Mead, 1929
23. Mayorga, Margaret, *The Best One-Act Plays of 1937,* Dodd, Mead, 1938
24. ——, *The Best One-Act Plays of 1938,* Dodd, Mead, 1939
25. ——, *The Best One-Act Plays of 1945,* Dodd, Mead, 1946
26. ——, *Representative One-Act Plays by American Authors,* rev. ed., Little, Brown, 1937

27. Moses, Montrose J., *Representative British Dramas,* Little, Brown, 1931
28. Nicholson, Kenyon, *The Appleton Book of Short Plays,* Appleton-Century-Crofts, 1926
29. *One-Act Plays for Stage and Study,* Samuel French, Vols. 1–8, 1925–34
30. O'Neill, Eugene, *The Moon of the Caribbees,* Modern Library, 1923
31. *Plays,* The Drama Magazine for Young People, 8 Arlington St., Boston 16, Mass.
32. Shay, Frank, *A Treasury of Plays for Women,* Little, Brown, 1922
33. ——, and Loving, Pierre, *Fifty Contemporary One-Act Plays,* Appleton-Century-Crofts, 1935
34. Smith, Milton M., *Short Plays of Various Types,* Merrill, 1924
35. Thomas, Charles S., *The Atlantic Book of Junior Plays,* Little, Brown, 1924
36. Tucker, Samuel M., *Twelve One-Act Plays for Study and Production,* Ginn, 1929
37. Webber, James P., and Webster, H. H., *One-Act Plays for Secondary Schools,* Houghton Mifflin, 1923
38. ——, *Typical Plays for Secondary Schools,* Houghton Mifflin, 1929
39. Wilder, Thornton, *The Angel That Troubled the Waters,* Coward-McCann, 1928
40. Wylie, Max, *Radio Writing,* Farrar and Rinehart, 1939
41. Catalogue of Walter H. Baker Co., Boston, Mass.
42. Catalogue of Samuel French, Inc., New York, N.Y.
43. Catalogue of Longmans, Green and Co., New York, N.Y.

Q 9
R 0
S 1